CW00536558

# THE SKYLARK

*Sky-Lark* Alauda arvensis: *A detailed account of this well-known songbird, its song and habits, would, I think, be entirely unnecessary here, as there is probably not one of my readers who is not already acquainted with them.*

Lord Lilford, *Notes on the Birds of Northamptonshire and Neighbourhood* (1895)

*For Trevor and Diana Donald, with love and thanks*

# THE
# SKYLARK

## PAUL F. DONALD

Illustrated with line drawings
and colour plates by
ALAN HARRIS

T & A D POYSER
London

Published 2004 by T & AD Poyser, an imprint of A & C Black Publishers Ltd.,
37 Soho Square, London W1D 3QZ

ISBN 0-7136-6568-8

A CIP catalogue record for this book is available from the British Library

A & C Black uses paper produced with elemental chlorine-free pulp, harvested from managed sustainable forests.

www.acblack.com

Typeset by J&L Composition, Filey, North Yorkshire

Printed and bound in China by Leo Paper Products

10 9 8 7 6 5 4 3 2 1

## Reflection

*A brief talk/presentation may be made on the theme of forgiveness and following Jesus even when things are difficult. The scene on the beach might be acted out and people asked to reflect on how they would have felt if they had been Peter.*

## Hymn

You stood there on the shoreline
*or* Hark, my soul, it is the Lord
*or* Follow me

## Prayer

Lord, when we go far from you,
**seek us out and find us.**

Lord, when we feel guilty and cannot face you,
**seek us out and find us.**

Lord, when we are hurt and confused,
**seek us out and find us.**

Lord, when we do not know the way to go,
**seek us out and find us.**
**Call us, Lord, and we will follow you,**
**for you are our risen Lord. Amen.**

## Our Father . . .

## Hymn

Alleluia, alleluia, give thanks to the risen Lord

## Blessing

Go in the love and peace of the risen Lord.
Go with the blessing of the risen Lord.
Go to live and serve in the power of the risen Lord. **Amen.**

# Contents

List of Figures    8
List of Colour plates    11
List of Tables    12
Acknowledgements    13

1  THE LARKS    15
    Distribution, habitats and numbers    16
    Evolution and taxonomy    19
    The different genera    21
        1.  *Mirafra*    22
        2.  *Pinarocorys*    23
        3.  *Heteromirafra*    24
        4.  *Certhilauda*    24
        5.  *Chersomanes*    25
        6.  *Eremopterix*    26
        7.  *Ammomanes*    27
        8.  *Alaemon*    28
        9.  *Rhamphocoris*    29
        10.  *Melanocorypha*    29
        11  *Calandrella*    30
        12.  *Spizocorys*    31
        13.  *Eremalauda*    32
        14.  *Cersophilus*    32
        15.  *Galerida*    33
        16.  *Pseudalaemon*    34
        17.  *Lullula*    35
        18.  *Alauda*    35
        19.  *Eremophila*    37
    Structure of the larks    38
    General ecology and behaviour    40
    Surviving heat and drought    44

2  DISTRIBUTION AND VARIATION    48
    Structure    51
    Subspecific variation    53
    Identification of the *Alauda* larks    55

3   POPULATIONS AND HABITATS                                          58
     Habitats                                                         59
     Other factors affecting Skylark distribution                    64
     Populations and population trends                                67

4   SONG AND SONG FLIGHT                                              72
     Song                                                             73
     The song flight                                                  79
     Duration and timing of song                                     84

5   MATING AND TERRITORIALITY                                         89
     Relationship between the sexes                                   91
     Site fidelity and sex ratios                                     92
     Territoriality and aggression                                    94

6   NESTS AND EGGS                                                    97
     The breeding season                                              98
     Nest building                                                   100
     Eggs and laying                                                 103
     Incubation and hatching                                         109

7   RAISING THE CHICKS                                               113
     Life in the nest                                                114
     Leaving the nest                                                116
     Parental care                                                   117
     Patterns of growth and development                              118
     Feeding the chicks                                              120

8   PRODUCTIVITY                                                     127
     Nest survival and predation                                     128
     Productivity of nests and the number of nesting attempts        133

9   MIGRATION AND OTHER MOVEMENTS                                    137
     Annual migration                                                138
     Mass movements                                                  140
     Movements of British Skylarks                                   143
     Hard weather movements                                          144
     Migratory flight                                                146
     Sex ratios                                                      148

10  WINTER                                                           150
     Habitat use in winter                                           151
     Diet and feeding rates                                          156
     Behaviour in winter                                             159

11  SURVIVAL AND MORTALITY                                           162
     Predators and other causes of mortality                         164
     Predators and population declines                               167
     Hunting today                                                   167

12  SKYLARKS AND MODERN AGRICULTURE                          171
    The politics of agricultural intensification      174
    Declines in biodiversity on farmland              176
    Skylarks and cereals                              178
    Skylarks and set aside                            187
    Skylarks and grassland                            188
    Skylarks, hedgerows and crop diversity            190
    Pesticides and organic farming                    192
    Genetically modified crops                        196
    Skylarks as crop pests                            197
    The conservation of Skylarks on farmland          198

13  POETRY, PERSECUTION AND THE RISE OF POPULAR PROTEST       202
    The Skylark in art and popular culture            204
    Introduced populations                            207
    Hunting through history                           210
    Victorian markets and the rise of protest         216
    Epilogue                                          226

    *Appendices*
    1   The world's larks                           227
    2   Scientific names of plants and animals mentioned in the text   231

Bibliography                                                 234

Index                                                        249

# List of Figures

CHAPTER 1

Figure 1.1.  The distribution of the world's lark species.                    17
Figure 1.2.  The distribution of the world's single-country
             endemic larks.                                                   18
Figure 1.3.  Specialisation in bill structure in two very closely
             related species.                                                 36
Figure 1.4.  Variations in lark bill morphology.                              40
Figure 1.5.  The relationship between population estimates of the
             Raso Lark and rainfall.                                          46

CHAPTER 2

Figure 2.1.  Map of Skylark distribution.                                     50
Figure 2.2.  Male and female wing lengths of Skylarks in the
             Western Palaearctic.                                             52
Figure 2.3.  *Alauda arvensis pekinensis*, eastern Siberia.                   56

CHAPTER 3

Figure 3.1.  Relationship between Skylark territory density and
             extent of cereals as a percentage of total land area in
             ten regions of the UK in 1998.                                   61
Figure 3.2.  The relationship between crop height and Skylark
             territory density on farmland in southern England.               63
Figure 3.3.  The three-dimensional relationship between skylark
             density, boundary index and field area.                         65
Figure 3.4.  Common Birds Census index for the Skylark, 1962–97.              69
Figure 3.5.  Population trend of Skylarks in Latvia, 1995–2002.               70

CHAPTER 4

Figure 4.1.  Spectrographs of a Skylark song, recorded in France.            74
Figure 4.2.  Monthly variation in the song length of Skylarks in
             Denmark in the late 1940s.                                       87

CHAPTER 5

Figure 5.1.   The hopping display.                                          91
Figure 5.2.   Threat posture.                                               96

CHAPTER 6

Figure 6.1.   An unusual nest site in tall oats.                           100
Figure 6.2.   The height of vegetation at Skylark nests in different
              crop types.                                                  101
Figure 6.3.   Nest of 4 particularly pale eggs.                            104
Figure 6.4.   Distribution of clutch sizes in 752 Skylark nests
              on farmland in southern England between 1996 and
              1999.                                                         105
Figure 6.5.   Seasonal changes in the average clutch size in Skylark
              nests in three different agricultural habitats in southern
              England, 1996 to 1999.                                       106

CHAPTER 7

Figure 7.1.   Mean tarsus length and weight of chicks in the
              nest and chicks found after leaving the nest,
              from farms in southern England, 1996–99.                     115
Figure 7.2.   Average body condition index of chicks in broods of
              different size.                                              119
Figure 7.3.   Distribution of forage flight distances (in metres)
              from the nest.                                               121
Figure 7.4.   Skylark bringing food to nest.                               125

CHAPTER 8

Figure 8.1.   The effects of differing levels of predator control on
              nest-survival rates of Skylarks on a Norfolk farm.           132
Figure 8.2.   Gamekeeper's trap, set on the farm in Norfolk where RSPB
              researchers recorded a huge rise in nest success rates.      132
Figure 8.3.   The number of pairs making 1, 2, 3 or 4 nesting
              attempts in a single breeding season in coastal dunes
              during the early 1960s.                                      135

CHAPTER 9

Figure 9.1.   Patterns of abundance of Skylarks in the British Isles,
              November 1981 to February 1982.                              145
Figure 9.2.   Changes in the percentage of females in captures of
              migrating Skylarks in Italy.                                 149

CHAPTER 10

Figure 10.1.  The proportions of different food types in the diet of
Skylarks wintering in six different agricultural habitats
in southern England, 1996–98.                                157
Figure 10.2.  Spectrogram of three calls of a Skylark.                     160
Figure 10.3.  Seasonal changes in the weight of male and female
Skylarks in the Netherlands.                                 161

CHAPTER 12

Figure 12.1.  Skylark distribution and abundance in Germany, 1985.         172
Figure 12.2.  The relationship between population declines
of a range of farmland birds and cereal yield across Europe.  177
Figure 12.3.  Seasonal changes in territory densities of Skylarks
(pairs per hectare) in spring and winter cereals on
lowland farmland in southern England.                        181
Figure 12.4.  The important relationship between Skylark territory
density and crop height in autumn-sown and
spring-sown cereals.                                         182
Figure 12.5.  Harvesting winter wheat in Cambridgeshire, England.          183
Figure 12.6.  Seasonal changes in the position of Skylark nests in
spring and winter cereals in lowland England.                184
Figure 12.7.  Skylark nest built on a tramline in winter cereals in
late June, showing how exposed it is to predators.           185
Figure 12.8.  Survival rates of Skylark nests in cereals that are built
immediately next to a tramline or further into the crop.     185
Figure 12.9.  The remarkable relationship between the area of
spring cereals sown each year in the UK between
1968 and 1996, and the population level of Skylarks.         186
Figure 12.10. Pesticide applications (calculated as spray hectares per
hectare of crop) in three different cereal types in 1996.    193

CHAPTER 13

Figure 13.1.  A portrait of John Clare (1793–1864), by William
Hilton (1786–1893).                                          206
Figure 13.2.  A Skylark hunting scene completed around 1640 by
Wolfgang Birkner.                                            212
Figure 13.3.  A Skylark mirror, or lark glass.                             213
Figure 13.4.  Three late nineteenth- and early twentieth-century
images of hunting with lark mirrors in France.               215
Figure 13.5.  Front cover of the SPB's educational leaflet of 1897.        219

# List of Colour Plates

Plate 1. Races of the Skylark, adults and juveniles. The eggs show the range of variation, most lying between the second and the fourth in the series.

Plate 2. The *Alauda* larks perched and in flight.

Plate 3. *top left and right*: male Raso Lark digging for the bulbs of nutsedges (Sabine Hille) *bottom*: Oriental Skylark (Leo Boon).

Plate 4. *top left*: Skylark of the nominate race, photographed in Sweden. (Henry Lehto) *top right*: A leucistic Skylark (Markus Jenny) *lower left and right*: Skylark in song flight (David Tipling).

Plate 5. *top left*: Skylark eggs hatching in a nest on a grass verge (Paul F. Donald) *top right*: Skylark nest in cereals, adjacent to a tramline (Paul F. Donald) *centre left and right*: Skylark chick pictured at two days old and again at eight days old (Lys B. Muirhead) *lower left*: A Skylark chick that has left the nest (Paul F. Donald) *lower right*: Skylark nest predated by a mammal, probably a Hedgehog (Paul F. Donald).

Plate 6. *top*: Skylark bringing food to chicks in a nest in Switzerland (Markus Jenny) *lower left*: a well camouflaged Skylark nest in set-aside (Markus Jenny) *lower right*: Skylark in juvenile plumage (Henry Lehto).

Plate 7. The perils of nesting on farmland. *top*: Skylark eggs in a nest in grassland crushed during mowing in May (Paul F. Donald) *bottom*: Skylark chick from a nest in cereals killed during harvesting in July (Paul F. Donald).

Plate 8. *top left*: 'Skylark scrapes' on the RSPB's experimental farm in Cambridgeshire (Roger Buisson) *top right*: tramlines in cereals (Paul F. Donald) *centre left*: much modern grassland is and provides insufficient cover for nesting Skylarks (Paul F. Donald) *centre* overgrazed *right*: A cereal monoculture in Oxfordshire (Lys B. Muirhead) *lower left*: set-aside (Paul F. Donald) *lower right*: the effects of agrochemicals on Skylarks are difficult to quantify (Paul F. Donald).

# List of Tables

CHAPTER 3

| | | |
|---|---|---|
| Table 3.1. | Summary of Skylark territory densities in different habitats from a number of European studies. | 59 |
| Table 3.2. | Territory densities of Skylarks in different crop types, the percentage of farmland made up by each crop type and the percentage of the total farmland Skylark population found in each crop type. | 60 |
| Table 3.3. | Population estimates and trends of breeding Skylarks in Europe. | 68 |

CHAPTER 6

| | | |
|---|---|---|
| Table 6.1. | Average clutch sizes of Skylarks estimated for different regions and habitats, from a number of sources. | 108 |

CHAPTER 10

| | | |
|---|---|---|
| Table 10.1. | Summary of studies that demonstrate selection, neutral use or avoidance of various habitats by wintering Skylarks. | 152 |

CHAPTER 13

| | | |
|---|---|---|
| Table 13.1. | Rated prices of Skylarks, 1274–1633. | 211 |

# Acknowledgements

This book is to a considerable extent a product of the RSPB's Skylark Research Project, which ran from 1995 to 1999.[1] I'm extremely grateful to the RSPB for offering me the opportunity and resources to undertake detailed research on this wonderful bird. Andy Evans and Jerry Wilson guided and managed the project, and Dave Buckingham, Lys Muirhead, Will Kirby, Sabine Schmitt and John Middleton were involved throughout. A small army of fieldworkers, volunteers and farmers helped us in many ways during this project and I would like to thank everyone involved. However, I hope that in this book I have not given too much prominence to the RSPB project, which is just one of a large number of detailed studies carried out on this species. I have had the pleasure of discussing Skylarks with just about everyone who has researched the species during the last twenty years, and I would like to thank them all for their insights, help and encouragement. Many people were generous enough to comment on one or more chapters, for which help I would like to thank Rob Robinson, Mike Brooke, Simon Gillings, Natalino Fenech, John Hutchinson, Will Kirby, Markus Jenny, Dave Buckingham, Fiona Roberts, Gillian Gilbert, Tony Morris, Kathryn Murray and Trevor and Diana Donald.

Ian Dawson and Lynn Giddings in the RSPB library were, as always, generous and patient to a fault when it came to tracking down obscure references for me, and Ian's encyclopaedic knowledge of the literature was a huge resource that I tapped on many occasions. Tim Melling and Mark Cocker were kind enough to provide me with all sorts of arcane historical information. I am also grateful to Ian Fisher for preparing the maps, and to Gillian Gilbert for preparing the spectrograms.

I originally started writing this book in collaboration with Juliet Vickery, who unfortunately had to drop out in the early stages. I'm very grateful to Juliet for her help and support throughout.

Jevgeni Shergalin (ZooLit), Simon O'Sullivan, Sabine Schmitt, Ferdinand Rühe and Debbie Pain were kind enough to translate papers for me. For allowing me access to unpublished material and for providing additional information, I would like to thank Peter Ryan, Irene Tieleman, Ainârs Auninš, Joe Williams, Tony Morris, Herman Arentsen, Natalino Fenech, Hilda Keane, Paul Tout, Keith Barnes, Mark Cocker, Stefan Thomsen, Sibylle Stöckli, Knut Jeromin, Colin Wells,

---

[1] However the opinions expressed in this book are mine alone, and do not necessarily reflect those of the RSPB or any other organisation.

Richard Gregory, Piotr Tryjanowski, Francisco Suárez, Manuel Morales, Francisco Moreira, David Conlin, Giorgos Catsadorakis, Clairie Papazoglou and the Lega Abolizione Caccia.

Marianne Taylor and Nigel Redman at A&C Black provided expert support throughout, and I am very grateful to Hugh Brazier for his skilful editorial improvements. Many thanks also to Alan Harris, for enlivening the text and the cover of this book with his wonderful illustrations, and to the photographers whose work adorns these pages.

*Hoopoe-Lark in display flight*

# CHAPTER 1

# The larks

There appears to be no other passerine family that equals the Alaudidae in successful desert occupancy, as regards the numbers of species filling a variety of desert niches. It is tempting to speculate upon the basis for this adaptive success of the larks in the desert environment.

Ernest J. Willoughby (1971)

Larks are the favourites of few birdwatchers. They tend to be dully-plumaged, difficult to find and identify, and reach their greatest variety in austere habitats occupied by relatively few other species. Yet, on closer acquaintance, the larks are an unexpectedly diverse and interesting family. They have successfully conquered some of the most hostile environments on the planet. In a few places, in fact, they are the *only* birds capable of surviving. Their superficial uniformity belies a huge variation between the different species in population, distribution, behaviour, structure and ecology. The songbird species with the largest and the smallest natural geographical ranges in the world may both be larks (the Horned Lark and the Raso Lark respectively). In many respects, the larks are one of the most diverse families of songbird in existence. Yet despite this diversity, there are strong enough similarities between the different lark species to bind them into a very distinct group. This chapter introduces the larks, their variation, distribution and ecology, to identify generalities within the family that will help us better to place the Skylark in the context of its relatives and its environment.


## DISTRIBUTION, HABITATS AND NUMBERS


Larks are found from the Arctic tundra to the South African veldt, and from the prairies of North America to the Australian outback. In virtually any open habitat outside the Americas, the larks form a distinctive and often conspicuous part of the bird community. Yet within this range there is a huge variation in patterns of distribution.

The diversity of lark species is greatest in two relatively restricted arid and semi-arid areas in Africa (Figure 1.1). The northeast arid zone (Somalia and Ethiopia) and the southwest arid zone (Namibia and the Karoo) are both centres of high lark endemism and species richness. In the latter zone, the larks exhibit a higher rate of endemism by area than is found in any other family of birds in Africa (Dean & Hockey 1989), and South Africa hosts more endemic species of lark than any other country (Figure 1.2). Nine species are endemic to Somalia and Ethiopia, and several more are close to being endemic to the Horn of Africa, their ranges just extending into northern Kenya. The high diversity of species in these areas is due to two factors: a long natural history of open habitats, providing the evolutionary time necessary for adaptive radiation, and a high diversity in topography, soil type, vegetation and climate patterns, which create a mosaic of different open habitats within a relatively small area. It is also possible that the paucity of other songbirds in these austere environments has reduced competition and so allowed the larks to radiate into all the available niches. As MacLean (1970) and Willoughby (1971) have pointed out, no family of passerine birds has shown as great an adaptive radiation in the arid regions of the Old World as have the larks.

Perhaps not surprisingly for a family of African origin, larks are poorly represented in the New World by just a single species[1], the Horned (or Shore) Lark, which, in the absence of competition from other larks, occupies a very wide range of habitats across North America and is extremely common. The Horned Lark is also the only lark to have penetrated the tundra zones and many alpine regions. The only Old World regions from which the larks are wholly absent are the forested

---

[1] The Skylark has recently established a breeding foothold in the Pribilof islands of Alaska, apparently naturally, since the subspecies is different to that introduced to Vancouver Island (Baicich *et al.* 1996).

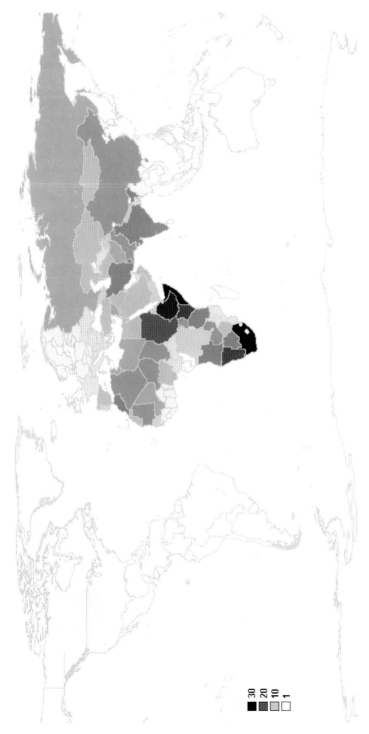

*Figure 1.1.   The distribution of the world's lark species. The depth of shading indicates the number of species breeding in each country.*

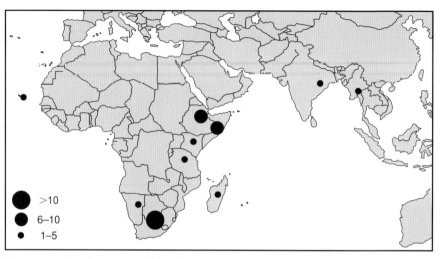

*Figure 1.2.  The distribution of the world's single-country endemic larks.*

boreal zone and uninterrupted expanses of tropical rainforests. With the exception of a small and isolated population of Horned Larks in the Colombian Andes, the larks are absent from Central and South America. The meadowlarks, which in the New World fill a similar niche to larks, are only distantly related. In Australia and Madagascar, the larks are again represented by single species, each of which occupies a very wide range of open habitats. The absence of speciation in Australia, which has very large areas of varied open habitats, might be due to the relatively recent arrival of the family on the continent. No larks occur naturally in New Zealand.

Larks are primarily birds of open habitats, with or without patches of taller vegetation, and most species nest on the ground. There are no true woodland species, although some, such as the Woodlark, inhabit the open spaces between patches of woodland and live in close proximity to trees. The two large, thrush-like *Pinarocorys* larks of the African savannahs frequently perch in the tops of trees, but all species feed almost exclusively on the ground. Other species shun trees and taller vegetation altogether and many reach their highest numbers in habitats totally devoid of trees. A few species, such as the Dune Lark, seem capable of surviving in habitats that are almost devoid of vegetation of any sort.

Within their given habitats, larks often occur at rather low densities. Many natural open and arid habitats, such as deserts, steppes and savannah, are biologically rather unproductive, food is scarce and bird densities therefore low. However, since these habitats can cover huge areas, some of the larks are very numerous. The Horned Lark, which nests across most of the world's tundra regions and throughout much of North America, is one of the most abundant birds on the planet. In certain arid habitats, the larks can make up a large component of the total bird community. In the steppes around Lake Baikal in Siberia, for example, over half of all the individual birds present, and the two commonest species, are larks (Sharaldaeva 1999). In the semi-deserts of the Caspian region, the larks again form the numerically dominant bird group (Shishkin 1982).

Perhaps because they tend to inhabit arid landscapes with low human population density and pressure, the larks as a family contain a lower proportion of endangered species (around 8%) than the average across all bird species (around 14%). There have been no recorded extinctions of larks in the last few hundred years (Fuller 2000). However, some species are extremely rare and have very small ranges, and eight species are now listed by IUCN as Globally Threatened (Birdlife International 2000). Two of these are in the highest Critically Endangered category, placing them amongst those bird species most likely to become extinct within the next few decades. The enigmatic and peculiar Raso Lark (Plate 3) of the Cape Verde Islands has one of the smallest ranges and populations of any bird in the world, with often fewer (and sometimes far fewer) than 100 individuals eking out an existence on a tiny, barren islet of less than 7 km$^2$. In January 2003, the total population of this species was 98 individuals, of which only 30 were females. After long periods of drought, the population of this species may have fallen to fewer than ten pairs (Donald *et al.* 2003). The other Critically Endangered species is Rudd's Lark, a rare and little-known upland grassland specialist from South Africa, where it is threatened by loss of natural grasslands to agriculture (Hockey *et al.* 1988, Barnes 2000). Ash's Lark and Botha's Lark are placed in the second highest threat category, Endangered, and four species are listed as Vulnerable. Each of these eight globally threatened lark species is endemic to a single country.

Some larks remain virtually unknown. Ash's Lark, discovered as recently as 1981 in coastal Somalia, is known only from the original sighting, and the Degodi Lark, discovered in southern Ethiopia in 1971, is not much better known. Equally elusive is Archer's Lark, first found in a strip of grassland in western Somalia in 1920 and subsequently at another site. It has not been seen at the original location since 1922, or at the subsequent site since 1955, although this may better reflect the political situation, and therefore the number of visiting ornithologists, than the species' rarity. The number of threatened species seems set to increase as taxonomic research continues to identify new groups of often rare species within what were previously regarded as single common species.

## EVOLUTION AND TAXONOMY

Despite their superficial uniformity, the larks (which are taxonomically placed in the family Alaudidae) are one of the most distinctive and diverse groups of songbird in existence today. The first ancestors of the songbirds (or passerines) probably evolved on the ancient southern landmass of Gondwanaland, in what is now Australia (Barker *et al.* 2002). From here they spread and radiated throughout the world, and modern songbirds now comprise around half of all the planet's bird species. The larks themselves probably started to diverge from other songbirds in the Ethiopian region of eastern Africa, and the family still reaches its greatest diversity in that continent. The earliest larks are recorded from fossils dating from the middle of the Miocene, around fifteen million years ago, although the earliest fossils that can be attributed to modern genera or species are far more recent, dating from the late Pliocene and early Pleistocene, less than two million years ago. Skylarks or their ancestors were already present in Europe during the Pleistocene (Harrison 1988, Tomek 1990). The major centres of lark radiation in Eurasia were probably the steppes of eastern Europe and southwestern Asia and the semi-deserts of the Mediterranean.

The larks have uncertain affinities with other songbird families, but certainly no close relatives. They differ from all other songbirds in the structure of the syrinx, the bony-ringed resonating chamber at the lower end of the windpipe that is unique to songbirds. The syrinx of larks is distinctive in that it lacks a bony pessulus, a bar that lies across the top of the convergence of the bronchi, and has only five sets of muscles, as opposed to the six to eight of other oscine songbirds. A further distinction is that the back of the tarsus (the longest leg bone) is rounded and covered with small scales (or *scutes*), rather than having the larger, smoother and more sharply edged scales of other songbirds. These apparently trivial anatomical distinctions actually indicate that the larks have been following a lineage separate from that of the other songbirds for a very long time. The moult strategy of larks is unusual (though certainly not unique) among non-tropical songbirds: adults have a complete, rather than a partial, autumn moult, with no spring moult, and juveniles have a complete post-fledging moult. Head-scratching behaviour, previously thought by some taxonomists to be of importance in assessing the relatedness of different bird families, is indirect, the head being scratched over the partially outstretched wing.

Larks have traditionally been regarded as one of the more basal (or 'primitive') groups within the modern passerine assemblage, and thus are generally placed near the start of the passerines in taxonomic lists (and therefore in field guides in which birds are arranged in taxonomic order). However this view is now being challenged. Although they have ten primary feathers, the larks may be taxonomically closer to the nine-primaried songbirds, which include the buntings and finches, because of similarities in bill structure. Recent advances in DNA–DNA hybridisation support this view, and the radical changes in taxonomy brought about by this development include the placing of the Alaudidae in a grouping (the superfamily Passeroidea) that also contains such apparently dissimilar birds as the sunbirds of Africa and Asia, the Old World sparrows, the wagtails, pipits, accentors, finches, buntings, American warblers, New World orioles and the tanagers. Even this placing may, however, be incorrect, and Barker *et al.* (2002) used evidence from conserved nuclear genes to argue that the larks' closest living relatives may, in fact, be the cisticola warblers (a largely African family), another group of birds that reach their greatest abundance in open habitats. Cisticola warblers are also cryptically plumaged, although this may represent a common adaptation to living in open environments with few hiding places rather than any close evolutionary relationship. Within the larks, a growing body of evidence suggests that the basal genus might be the strange (and, intriguingly, the most superficially cisticola-like) *Heteromirafra* larks, whose small and fragmented range might indicate a particularly ancient group (Peter Ryan, pers comm.).

Around 100 species of lark are currently recognised, the exact number depending on whether certain forms are considered as single species or groups of closely related species. Recent studies suggest that several forms that were once thought of as subspecies should now be treated as full species, and the number of generally recognised species is gradually increasing. For example, the long-billed lark complex of South Africa, once thought to comprise a single species with five subspecies, is now recognised as five distinct species (Ryan & Bloomer 1999). Similarly, a new form known as Barlow's Lark has emerged from the Karoo Lark complex of southwest Africa (Ryan *et al.* 1998). The taxonomy of the larks remains far from clear, and most previous attempts at classification, such as that undertaken by the formidable Richard Meinertzhagen (1951), were based upon characteristics such as the length of the outer primary, whether or not the nostrils are exposed, details of nest architecture and the complexity of song and display. The advent of molecular techniques is now revolutionising the way taxonomists view the larks. Ongoing genetic analyses will doubtless identify further new species, particularly in the complex groups of non-migratory larks in southern Africa. It is likely that these analyses will also discover some interesting and unexpected relationships within the larks.

## THE DIFFERENT GENERA

The lark family is variously broken down into between 19 and 23 genera, rather more than were recognised by Meinertzhagen in his review of the family in 1951. This is a large number of genera for the number of species in the family, and many are monospecific (in other words, the genus contains just a single species). It may be that several of these genera are redundant. For example, it is likely it will prove unnecessary to separate the genera *Alauda* (the skylarks), *Galerida* (the crested larks) and *Lullula* (the Woodlark), which recent genetic analyses suggest are extremely close. Nevertheless, the large number of genera relative to the number of species clearly reflects a long history of divergent evolution within the group. The following short tour through the different genera follows the classification of Sibley and Monroe (1990), although more recent suggestions as to how the group should be classified, based largely on recent detailed research carried out in South Africa by Keith Barnes, Peter Ryan and others, are indicated where appropriate. A full list of species is given in Appendix 1.

1. MIRAFRA

*Rufous-naped Lark*

Often called the bushlarks, this is the largest genus in the Alaudidae, comprising 30 or more species of medium to large, short-winged larks of grassland, savannah and arid bush. They are generally solitary or found in pairs, rarely if ever forming flocks, and are usually non-migratory or partially migratory (although a few are nomadic). All are clad in dull browns or greys, but many have a patch of rich russet red in the wing. This genus reaches its greatest diversity in Africa, with around 20 species being endemic to that continent. Most of the remaining species occur in southern Asia, but the genus also contains the only larks to occur naturally in Indonesia, Australasia and Madagascar. The bill varies from short and conical to long and decurved, suggesting a wide range of different feeding methods. Most species seem to be omnivorous, but invertebrates are extremely important in the diet of most birds in this genus, particularly when feeding chicks. The nest is usually covered with a dome of grass, the dome and cup forming a single construction unit. In many species, nest construction takes a 'top-down' approach, the roof of the dome being the first part of the nest to be built, the cup being the last. Larks in this genus appear to drink very infrequently or not at all (Skead 1975). Most species have a characteristic song flight, ranging from short, low-level displays to prolonged flights high above the ground, though a few lack song flights altogether. Songs also vary, from simple repeated notes to complex songs with mimicry. The Red-winged Bushlark is perhaps the most mimetic of all larks: during a 15-minute song a single individual has been heard to mimic the songs of as many as 20 other bird species (Dowsett-Lemaire & Dowsett 1978). Another accomplished mimic in this group is the Melodious (or Latakoo) Lark of southern Africa, which has been heard to mimic birds from a wide range of families, including francolins, guineafowl, plovers, coursers, touracos, cuckoos, bee-eaters, swifts, swallows, sunbirds, warblers, weavers, waxbills and, of course, other larks. The group contains two species (or species groups), the Clapper and Flappet Larks, which, during the display flight, have largely replaced song with short bursts of a loud, rapid clapping, caused by striking the wings together. To do this, the wing-beat rate is doubled, to 24 beats per second, and the wings come together at the top and bottom of their trajectories. Other species in the group also 'flappet' during the song flight, but this is usually accompanied by song. Many *Mirafra* larks have extremely restricted ranges, and the group includes several endangered species.

## 2. PINAROCORYS

*Dusky Lark*

Two species of large, dark and boldly marked lark, endemic to open savannahs in Africa. Both are intra-African migrants, and consequently the wing is adapted for long-distance flight, being long and pointed with a much-reduced first primary. The Rufous-rumped Lark breeds in the savannahs of northern and central Africa, from Ivory Coast to southern Sudan, and spends the non-breeding season in Sahel zones from Senegambia to northern Sudan. In savannahs south of the equator it is replaced by the Dusky Lark, which breeds from Angola to Tanzania and migrates southwards as far as South Africa in the non-breeding season. The flight is undulating, often with the feet dangling. The thrush-like Dusky Lark has a characteristic habit of flicking its wings open when feeding. Both species have aerial song flights of medium or high elevation and duration, at the end of which birds generally descend to perch on top of a tree. The bill is straight and of medium length and strength. Both species are primarily insectivorous, feeding on large insects such as grasshoppers and beetles. Both are attracted to recently burned areas. The nest is a cavity excavated under a clod or tuft, giving it a partial dome, and the area around the nest may be strewn with pieces of bark.

## 3. Heteromirafra

*Rudd's Lark*

   A rather strange genus of three African species, all with extremely restricted ranges. Superficially similar to the *Mirafra* larks, they have very narrow tails, giving them an unusual appearance in flight, and extremely large feet with a long, straight hind claw. The bill is fairly short and small, though quite stout in Rudd's Lark, and larks in this genus probably feed on both seeds and invertebrates. All three species inhabit upland grassland or savannah, with one species each in Somalia (Archer's Lark), Ethiopia (Sidamo Lark) and South Africa (Rudd's Lark). This highly fragmented distribution is likely to be the relic of a previously far larger range across the highlands of eastern Africa. All three species are threatened, Rudd's Lark falling into the highest IUCN risk category of Critically Endangered. The display flight of Rudd's Lark is prolonged, lasting up to 40 minutes, but at fairly low height above the ground, and the song is simple, consisting of a few notes repeated frequently. The Sidamo Lark may have a 'flappeting' display like some of the *Mirafra* larks. Archer's Lark is virtually unknown.

## 4. Certhilauda

   Ten or more species of long-winged, medium to large larks, resident in savannah, arid bush, sparse grassland and almost unvegetated desert dunes in southern Africa. Recent research suggests that this genus could be split to separate the large long-billed larks (*Certhilauda*) from the group of smaller species (*Calendulauda*) previously placed in this genus. All species are resident and apparently never form flocks. All are long-billed, and many species dig for food, invertebrates being particularly important in the diet. Some species feed on termites by entering holes dug by

*Cape Long-billed Lark*

Aardvarks. The nest can be either domed or not domed, a feature varying even within species. Song flights also vary, some species making a short vertical flight to between 5 and 15 m before falling to the ground with a single whistled call, others having a longer aerial display, though generally of short duration and at low levels. Larks in this group closely match the colouration of the substrates they inhabit. This genus includes the Dune Lark, which probably endures greater extremes of heat and aridity than any other bird in the world.

## 5. CHERSOMANES

*Spike-heeled Lark*

Currently regarded as a single species, the Spike-heeled Lark may in fact turn out to comprise a complex of similar, and very interesting, species inhabiting a wide range of open habitats in southern Africa, from grassland to desert. It is a small, short-tailed lark with a characteristically upright stance and conspicuous white corners to the tail. The bill is long and decurved, and much of the diet is comprised of invertebrates collected by digging in the ground. The high proportion of insects in the diet means that this species rarely or never drinks water. Much time is apparently spent feeding around the openings of rodent burrows, either for shade or to collect insects that gather in them. The males take more beetles then the females, which instead take ants and termites. The hind claw, as the name suggests, is long and straight. The nest is a simple cup without a dome, often fairly exposed. The range comprises much of southwestern Africa (Angola, Namibia, Botswana and South Africa), with small isolated populations of what may well turn out to be separate (and probably highly threatened) species in northeastern South Africa and northern Tanzania. The Tanzanian population, confined to a tiny area in the north of the country, has already been separated by some and called Beesley's Lark. A number of subspecies are defined based on their coloration, which varies locally according to rainfall, soil and vegetation. The Spike-heeled Lark is the only lark in which cooperative breeding has been observed, though this may not be normal behaviour (Steyn 1988). Birds co-operate in more than just breeding, as often one bird will perch on a bush or termite mound and act as a sentry while other birds feed. Social organisation appears more complex in this genus than in other lark genera. The song flight consists of a short vertical rise to up to 2 m followed by a sailing descent.

## 6. EREMOPTERIX

*Grey-backed Sparrow-Lark*

Known commonly as the sparrow-larks or finch-larks, this group of seven small larks is unusual in that the males are strikingly marked about the head and body in black, white, brown and grey, whereas the females are plain and rather sparrow-like. Five species are endemic to Africa, one is found in Africa and the Middle East and one species is endemic to southern Asia. Some species are resident, some migratory and some nomadic. All species form flocks of up to several hundred birds outside the breeding season, and some are gregarious even while breeding. Some species drink water regularly, whereas others are wholly reliant on metabolic water. The bill is short and fairly deep. Most species are largely granivorous, though invertebrates can be important, particularly in species that do not drink. The nest is a simple cup built in a depression, sometimes with a rim of small stones. Despite the males' striking plumage, this is one of only two genera within the family (the other is *Spizocorys*) in which the male shares incubation with the female. The song flight is relatively weak, being short and never rising far above the ground.

## 7. AMMOMANES

*Bar-tailed Lark*

Three or four species of rather small, pale, plain larks of the deserts of Africa and southern Asia. Two species (Desert Lark and Bar-tailed Lark) are found in the deserts of North Africa and the Middle East, and another species (Rufous-tailed Lark) is found throughout the Indian plains. A fourth species (Gray's Lark) is confined to the Namib Desert of southwestern Africa, although this may be sufficiently different from the other larks to warrant its own genus, *Ammomanopsis*. The colour of the upperparts varies greatly within species according to the colour of the local substrate. The bill is relatively short, conical and deep at the base. The diet is mixed, and invertebrates are particularly important as a source of water, as these larks rarely drink. All species form wandering groups outside the breeding season, and Gray's Lark appears to live in small groups even during the breeding season. The song flight is deeply undulating and performed at varying heights.

## 8. ALAEMON

*Hoopoe-Lark*

Two rather dissimilar and atypical larks with long, narrow bills and long legs. The larger species, the Hoopoe-Lark, is resident from Cape Verde through North Africa and the Middle East to northwest India, and has the longest bill of any lark. The other, the Lesser Hoopoe-Lark, is far smaller and is endemic to Somalia. Both are very pale larks with a peculiarly lax, soft plumage, and both feed largely by digging for invertebrates, though the larger species has been seen to dig out and kill small geckoes. Snails are broken open by being dropped from a height, rather in the manner of a Lammergeier breaking open bones. The larger species, unusually for a lark, has a very striking black and white wing pattern. Also unusually for a lark, it usually builds its nests in, or even on top of, bushes. The Lesser Hoopoe-Lark, which may actually be closer to *Certhilauda* than *Alaemon*, lacks the striking pied wing pattern of the larger bird and apparently nests only on the ground. Both are birds of sandy desert with sparse vegetation, where they are extremely cursorial, tending to run long distances rather than fly. Birds are capable of sprinting for several hundred metres to escape danger, at speeds of up to 8 km per hour. The song flight of the Hoopoe-Lark is highly variable but always spectacular, despite being of short duration and generally not reaching any great height. Typically, the male flies upwards from the top of a bush or other perch to a height of several metres, then rolls upside down, closes its wings and nose-dives back to the perch, spreading the wings again just before landing. The song flight of the Lesser Hoopoe-Lark is quite different, involving a parachuting descent from a great height.

## 9. RHAMPHOCORIS

*Thick-billed Lark*

A genus probably very closely related to *Melanocorypha*, containing a single atypical species, the Thick-billed Lark of the stony deserts of North Africa and the Middle East. The most striking features are the boldly marked head, breast, wings and tail, and the massive bill. (Also very unusual is the double-barrelled scientific name, *R. clot-bey*) The upper and lower mandibles are contra-curved, so that when the bill is closed there is often a small aperture visible around two thirds of the way along it. Despite the huge size of the bill, the bite of this species is, according to those who have handled it, not very powerful. The species is resident, but forms mobile flocks outside the breeding season. Unlike most other desert-dwelling larks, and probably because of its seed diet, the Thick-billed Lark regularly flies long distances to drink water, taking a single drop at a time. Uniquely for a lark, it usually hops, rather than walks, while feeding. The diet of adults is largely green plant material, but insects and even geckoes are also taken, and the food of chicks is largely made up of invertebrates. The nest is a shallow cup lacking a dome, with a rampart of small stones, built in the shade of a rock or plant, and often facing towards the rising sun to reduce radiation. Like the *Alaemon* larks, the Thick-billed Lark is highly cursorial, running rather than flying from danger. The song flight is poorly known, but has an aerial component.

## 10. MELANOCORYPHA

Six large, bulky, predominantly Eurasian species, often strikingly marked with white in the wing and tail or dark marks on each side of the chest. One of the group, the Black Lark, is strongly sexually dimorphic, the males being largely black and the females grey-brown. Members of this genus breed in a wide range of open habitats, from agricultural land to dry steppes. The bill is heavy, of medium length or long, and most species appear to be omnivores, taking mostly invertebrates in the breeding season and vegetable matter in the non-breeding season. Most species are at least partially migratory, and all form flocks in the non-breeding season. The

*Bimaculated Lark*

nest is a shallow cup on the ground, lacking a dome but often concealed within a tussock of grass. Nests are frequently decorated with rags, paper and even animal dung. The group exhibits a variety of song-flight types. The Calandra Lark has a prolonged, high-level song display, resembling that of the Skylark but possibly reaching even greater heights. The Black Lark has a wide range of bizarre song displays, given both from the ground and in flight, when the song flight somewhat resembles that of a pigeon, the bird clapping its wings together while singing and descending with a stiff-winged glide. The group contains the world's largest lark, the massive Tibetan Lark.

## 11. CALANDRELLA

*Greater Short-toed Lark*

A group of eight or more small, generally indistinctly marked larks of open grassland ranging from Africa and southern Europe to Asia. Most species are rather dull, brownish and 'sparrow-like', the exception being the Red-capped

Lark of Africa, which is strikingly marked with a vivid orange cap and breast patches, perhaps the brightest colour found on any lark. Some species, such as the Greater Short-toed Lark, have large Palaearctic breeding ranges and are migratory, while others, such as the Somali Short-toed Lark, have small ranges and are sedentary. Many species form flocks outside the breeding season, and flocks of up to ten thousand Greater Short-toed Larks, probably the largest flocks formed by any lark, have been recorded in Mali. The bill is short and conical, and the diet is mixed, with invertebrates being particularly important during the breeding season and seeds being the main food at other times. All species drink water regularly. The nest is a simple cup without a dome, but often with a rampart of small stones. The form of the song flight varies between species but is complex, generally involving a steep rise in jerky steps to middle or higher levels and a descent also in steps.

## 12. SPIZOCORYS

*Masked Lark*

Five or six species of small, gregarious lark of African grassland, bush and dry plains. Previously placed in *Calandrella*, they were separated by Dean (1989) on the basis of plumage, nest structure and the simplicity of their song display. All have a well-marked eye-ring and most have a distinct tear-shaped dark mark below the eye, particularly well developed in the Masked Lark, which looks quite different to the other species. Most have extremely small breeding ranges, the Obbia Lark for example being confined to a very thin coastal strip in Somalia. Nomadic groups form outside the breeding season. The bill is short and conical and the diet is mixed and taken exclusively from the surface. These larks seem to require surface water and drink regularly. The nest is a shallow cup without a dome but often with an apron of nesting material extending on the ground beyond the nest. Both sexes incubate the clutch, which tends to be small. The breeding behaviour of these larks is poorly known, but some species at least appear to have simple songs without a song flight.

## 13. EREMALAUDA

*Dunn's Lark*

Two small, plain larks of arid bush and grassland, Dunn's Lark of northern African and the Middle East and Stark's Lark (which may actually be better placed in *Spizocorys*) of southwestern Africa. Both species are nomadic, following local rains to take advantage of short-lived and patchily distributed food supplies. Both have short, deep bills and feed largely on seeds (often collected by digging), and Stark's Lark is unusual in also feeding its chicks largely on seeds. Both species have been observed drinking water, though it is not known if surface water is essential to them. The nest is a shallow cup without a dome or an apron. The song flight is complex, birds often rising vertically to great heights before descending either by diving or parachuting. The song itself, however, is fairly simple.

## 14. CERSOPHILUS

A single unusual species, Dupont's Lark, of uncertain affinities but possibly close to *Mirafra*. It is confined to sandy or stony plains and dry grassland in Spain and along a thin band of coastal North Africa from Morocco to Egypt. The bill is long, slender and decurved, and the diet is composed largely of invertebrates collected by digging. Dupont's Lark has apparently never been observed to drink. It is long-legged, highly cursorial and difficult to flush, running off through vegetation at high speed and then hiding behind a bush. The nest is a deep scrape without a dome, often under a bush or in the shade of a large stone. Unusually

*Dupont's Lark*

for a lark, it often sings at night, usually from the ground. The song flight is very well developed, birds rising to great heights for prolonged periods, often with many bursts of wing claps, descending with a steep and rapid dive.

## 15. GALERIDA

*Thekla Lark*

Five or six species of medium-sized crested larks inhabiting a wide range of open temperate or semi-arid habitats in Africa, Europe and Asia. Two species, the Sun Lark and the Large-billed Lark, are endemic to Africa, and the Tawny Lark and the Malabar Lark (which may or may not be the same species as Thekla Lark) are endemic to India. The range of the Thekla Lark extends from southwestern Europe to East Africa (although there is a large gap in the distribution which may indicate the existence of two species), and the Crested Lark has a wide distribution with many subspecies across Africa and Eurasia, where it occupies a broad band rather to the south of that occupied by the Skylark. Unlike the *Alauda* larks, these species rarely form flocks outside the breeding season and drink frequently. Bills range from heavy and long in the Large-billed Lark of southern Africa to conical or slender in the Crested Lark. All species are omnivores, being primarily insectivorous during the breeding season and granivorous outside it. The slimmer-billed species often dig for food. The nest is a simple cup on the ground, very rarely domed, and sometimes constructed around the base of a bush. All have well developed song flights, during which birds often reach great heights.

## 16. PSEUDALAEMON

*Short-tailed Lark*

A monotypic genus, containing only the poorly known Short-tailed Lark of East Africa. The bill is long, straight and slender, and the diet apparently consists largely of vegetable material. It inhabits short grassland and shrublands, often near human habitation, where it may even enter buildings. Outside the breeding season it forms flocks of up to 50 birds. The song flight, if there is one, is undescribed.

## 17. LULLULA

*Woodlark*

Another genus containing just a single species, the Woodlark of Europe, the Middle East and northwest Africa. It is predominantly migratory in the east of its range and resident in the west, forming flocks outside the breeding season. Its distribution appears to reflect a greater susceptibility to cold weather than other European larks. Of all the larks, the Woodlark shows probably the greatest affinity to woodland, preferring relatively open, sandy habitats with scattered trees. It spends much time perching in trees, and young pine plantations and wooded heaths are an important breeding habitat in parts of its range. The bill is fairly short and fine, and birds feed on a mixture of invertebrates and seeds. The nest is a deep cup without a dome. The song flight is well developed and often prolonged, and the song rich and beautiful.

## 18. ALAUDA

Four species of largely Eurasian larks, including the familiar Skylark and its replacement in southern Asia, the Oriental or Small Skylark (Plate 3). The Japanese Skylark is now generally considered a full species, though it has in the past been treated as a subspecies (*japonica*) of the Skylark. These three species show considerable plumage variation throughout their ranges and can be extremely difficult to separate in the field. The other species in the genus is the critically endangered Raso

*Oriental Skylark*

Lark, which is confined to a tiny (7 km²) island in the Cape Verde Islands off West Africa. This species is smaller and greyer than the other three (Plates 2 & 3). All species have erectile crests, though these are generally less well developed than in *Galerida*. All are omnivores and have an unspecialised conical bill, with the exception of the Raso Lark, in which the male has a long bill used for digging for the bulbs of grasses (Figure 1.3). The Skylark and the Oriental Skylark occupy a wide

*Figure 1.3.    Specialisation in bill structure in two very closely related species. The Skylark (right), which inhabits a wide range of temperate open habitats, has an unspecialised conical bill, whereas the far smaller Raso Lark (left), which inhabits an arid island, has a much longer bill for digging in sand. Both these birds are males. From skins in the British Museum of Natural History, Tring. Photograph: Paul F. Donald.*

range of open temperate or semi-arid habitats and both are closely associated with farmland. Both are migratory over much of their range, and all *Alauda* larks form flocks outside the breeding season. The nest is a simple undomed cup on the ground. These larks drink infrequently or not at all. All species have well developed and prolonged song flights, often reaching great heights.

## 19. EREMOPHILA

*Horned Lark*

Two species, one of which, the Horned or Shore Lark, has a circumpolar distribution and was, until the recent arrival of the Skylark in Alaska, the only lark to occur naturally in the New World. In the absence of competition from other larks, it breeds throughout much of North America in a far wider range of habitats, and in far greater numbers, than in the Old World. It is absent from Central America, but has a small and isolated population in the Colombian Andes, the only larks in South America. In Eurasia, Horned Larks breed on tundra at high latitudes, where they are strongly migratory, and at high altitudes in mountain ranges across southern Eurasia, where they are resident or altitudinal migrants. The other species, Temminck's Horned Lark, is confined to the deserts of North Africa. These larks have a quite different appearance to most others, with strongly marked black and white, or black and yellow, face markings and small 'horns' formed by elongated lateral crown feathers. The bill is small, conical and rather weak. Both species are omnivorous, feeding largely on invertebrates during the breeding season and vegetable material, particularly seeds, at other times. Both species form flocks outside the breeding season. During the breeding season, the diet of invertebrates appears to provide sufficient water, but both species have been recorded drinking around dawn. The nest is a simple cup. The song flight is well developed, birds ascending to great heights before commencing song.

## STRUCTURE OF THE LARKS

The most striking variation in the structure of the larks is in the size and shape of the bill, and the evolutionary plasticity of this feature has allowed the larks to colonise and diversify in some of the most austere habitats on Earth. The intense selection pressures placed on birds inhabiting particularly hostile environments with few food resources has led to the evolution in the larks of a diversity of bill structures matched by few other songbird families (Figure 1.4). The high diversity of bill structures within the larks reflects a wide array of foraging techniques and diets. Even within individual species, there may be considerable variation in bill structure, and several species have large- and small-billed forms in different parts of their range. All larks eat a mixture of seeds and other vegetable matter and invertebrates, though some eat more seeds than invertebrates and others more invertebrates than seeds. Seeds are eaten whole, since larks lack the tooth and notch in the upper mandible that allows birds like the buntings and finches to extract the kernel from the husk. A few species have been recorded feeding on snails, smashing the shells of smaller, softer-shelled species against rocks in the manner of a Song Thrush (Yanes *et al.* 1991). The diet of chicks is made up largely of invertebrates in most or all species, although partly crushed and regurgitated seeds are also present in the chick diets of some species, particularly the sparrow-larks.

There is a close relationship between the size and shape of the bill and the main food items and the way in which they are collected. Species with long, slender bills tend to be largely insectivorous and often collect much of their food by digging in the ground. The longest-billed lark of all, the Hoopoe-Lark, has been seen excavating craters up to 5 cm deep to extract insect larvae. Species with short, conical bills are generally omnivores, and may specialise on invertebrates or vegetable matter at different times of the year. Species with short, deep bills are largely herbivores, feeding mostly on larger seeds. Although there are exceptions, most of the particularly long-billed species of lark occupy very dry and sandy habitats, where the ability to dig for food might be crucial for survival and where the soft substrate permits digging as a method of obtaining food. Temperate species feed mainly by pecking from the surface of the ground: in a study of seven wintering lark species in Russia, over 80% of all feeding actions were simple pecks from the surface of the ground, although other feeding methods observed included plucking vegetation, digging, fly-catching and even kleptoparasitism (Polozov 1989).

There is an interesting range of sexual dimorphism within the larks. In most families, and particularly the most insectivorous groups, the males and females are identical or at least very similar in plumage, although the males are often larger than the females. In the genus *Eremopterix*, however, and in one species of

*Melanocorypha* (the Black Lark), the males are strikingly marked in shades of brown, grey and black, whereas the females are quite different, being largely unmarked and greyish or sandy. Among the larks with no sexual plumage dimorphism, there often exists a difference in size, with the males being larger than the females. The scale of this difference appears to be at least partly related to diet. In primarily insectivorous species, males tend to be considerably larger than females, whereas in granivorous species there is little difference in size between the sexes (Willoughby 1971). This may result from food partitioning between the species. Seeds in arid regions tend to be uniformly small, since most are grass seeds, so both males and females are adapted to eating the same foods and are consequently the same size. Insects, however, come in a wide range of sizes, so if males take larger insects and females take smaller insects, the sexes are not competing for the same resources. This might be very important in species inhabiting arid areas, where food resources might be particularly limited.

In extreme cases, the males and females have such different bill sizes and feeding methods that they effectively behave as separate ecological species. This may occur in several species in the arid zone of southwestern Africa (Willoughby 1971, Dean & Hockey 1989), but perhaps the most striking example is that of the Raso Lark. In this species there is a very great difference in the size of bills of males and females, those of the males averaging around 25% longer, and perhaps 60% greater in volume, than those of the females. Observations of feeding behaviour show that the males spend far more time digging than the females (Plate 3), which instead feed mostly from the surface, and that the males are consequently able to access foods that are unavailable to the females (Donald *et al.* 2003). In particular, males are able to access the water-rich rhizomes of the nutsedge *Cyperus bulbosus*, one of the very few sources of usable water on their tiny island home for much of the year. This might explain the preponderance of males in the dwindling population of this species. Water is clearly an important resource for the Raso Lark, and I have even seen birds drinking seawater from rock pools, though whether they are able to gain much benefit from this is doubtful. There is a strong correlation between the population of Raso Larks in any given year and the amount of rainfall in the previous year.

The length of the first primary feather is extremely variable among larks, ranging from a feather almost as long as the second primary to being almost entirely absent. This variation may have arisen in part from different migratory habits. A long first primary confers a rounded, broad shape to the wing, suitable for reducing energy requirements during short flights, whereas a short first primary leads to a long and pointed wing with a high wing loading, more suitable for fast, prolonged migratory flight. It is likely that migratory species evolved from resident species through the reduction of the outer primary, and within the larks there is a strong correlation between the length of the outer primary and the migratory status of each species. Differences in wing structure differ even within species. Skylarks migrating through Italy, for example, have longer and more pointed wings than resident birds.

*Figure 1.4.    Variations in bill morphology of larks. From top left:* Rhamphocoris clotbey;
Calandrella rufescens; Alaemon hamertoni; Melanocorypha calandra; Ammomanes deserti;
Pseudalaemon fremantii; Spizocorys personata; Melanocorypha maxima; Certhilauda curvi-
rostris; Alauda arvensis; Mirafra sabota; Certhilauda albofasciata.

Another feature that differs greatly between different lark species is the length of
the hind claw. In some species it is strikingly long, either straight or arched, whereas
in others it is shorter. Although there is little information on claw length, it appears
that hind claws are longer in more cursorial species and shorter in species that
habitually perch in trees or bushes, a pattern found also in the pipits. Considerable
differences in claw length between individuals of the same species may arise from
the texture of the substrate. It is unclear whether the considerable seasonal variation
in claw length noted by several observers is due to abrasion or to real changes in
growth.

## GENERAL ECOLOGY AND BEHAVIOUR

Although open, dry habitats may appear to the human eye to be relatively
homogeneous, subtle differences in ecosystems have led to a high degree of specialisation within the larks. Certain larks are highly specialised for particular types
of substrate, and many indeed have evolved to be the same colour as that substrate. The Red Lark of South Africa, for example, inhabits a system of red sand

dunes, and many larks of sandy deserts have a pale, sandy appearance. The Desert Lark occurs in a broad band of arid habitats from northwest Africa to the Middle East. Throughout this range, there is wide variation in the colour of the substrate, from pale yellowish sand to black rocky desert. The Desert Lark adapts to the colour of the substrate it inhabits, and populations of this species will vary greatly in colour even over relatively short distances, according to the colour of the substrate occurring in their area. This same pattern of close colour matching with their preferred substrates divides the larks of southwestern Africa into predominantly grey species in the southern Karoo and predominantly reddish species in the Nama Karoo and Kalahari Sands (Dean & Hockey 1989). Within the Kalahari, the larks are divided into predominantly reddish species in the sand dune areas and predominantly grey species on the grey limestone (MacLean 1970). A usual response by most larks to the presence of predators is to crouch down and keep still, so it is likely that this close matching of plumage coloration to substrate is linked to camouflage. It has been suggested that larks come to match their substrate by dust-bathing in it (e.g. Hoesch 1958), though it is more likely that higher predation rates of birds that do not match their background leads to higher survival and reproduction of those that do, and so to rapid evolutionary changes in plumage pigmentation. The degree of plumage variation on the upperparts of larks appears to support this hypothesis, and there appears to be a strong positive correlation between the degree of streaking on the upperparts of the larks and the amount of vegetation available within their preferred habitats.

The breeding season of larks is either seasonal or, particularly amongst nomadic species, opportunistic, when nesting generally follows irregular rains. In the Kalahari, the onset of breeding in all lark species is initiated by rain, irrespective of whether they are granivores or insectivores. For these species, the length of the breeding season is correlated with the total amount of rainfall, and the gap between the first rains and the onset of breeding, which can be as short as a week, is related to the heaviness of the first rain showers (MacLean 1970). The Dune Lark, on the other hand, has a fixed breeding season that is independent of rain (Boyer 1988), presumably because if it waited for rain in the Namib Desert to commence breeding, it would rapidly go extinct! At the other extreme of temperature, larks can suffer mass nest failure due to extremes of cold. Shevchenko (1989) describes how, in 1988, Horned Larks nesting at altitude in the Altai region produced virtually no chicks due to extremely cold weather, with nocturnal temperature falling to −10°C at night in May. Even in relatively mild conditions in the Caspian semi-desert, Shishkin (1982) estimated that only around a fifth of all larks present nest in any year. This mass non-nesting appears to be unusual for small birds with high reproductive potential and relatively short life spans.

Most larks build their nests on the ground, often in a scraped cup but sometimes, particularly on hard substrates, in a raised cup built on foundations. These can be mechanically very strong: MacLean (1970) describes an incidence of a Land Rover driving right over the nest of a Grey-backed Sparrow-Lark without causing any damage to the nest or the two chicks it contained. Some species nesting in sandy habitats, such as species in the genera *Ammomanes* and *Eremopterix*, build a rampart of small stones up to 4 cm high on the windward side of the nest, and sometimes even completely surrounding it, probably to prevent sand being blown into the nest. Nest ramparts may also help to regulate temperatures in the nest and so facilitate self-incubation, although the effects of ramparts on nest thermoregulation appear inconsistent between species (Afik *et al.* 1991). Nests of the Horned Lark are positioned in such a way that the wind speed over the nest is ten or more times lower than the ambient speed, although, breeding at high latitudes, the nest does not have to be positioned to maximise shade (With & Webb 1993). Some species build nests covered by a dome of vegetation, and desert and steppe species often have the nest entrance facing away from the sun. In the Kalahari, for example, most nests of larks face in a direction between south and east (MacLean 1970), whereas in Iberia the majority of lark nests face in a direction between north and east (Yanes *et al.* 1997), in both cases ensuring the greatest amount of shade during the day. Nests of the Desert Lark are frequently built under an overhanging rock or stone to shade the nest, and often face into the prevailing wind. The positioning of Desert Lark nests ensures that during the heat of the day the temperatures in the nest are much lower than those outside, whereas at night, when temperatures in desert environments can plummet, the nest is warmer than the ambient temperature. Furthermore, the nests receive direct warming from the sun in the period after dawn, when the female has to leave the nest to feed (Orr 1970). The careful positioning of these nests means that they might be self-incubating for several hours each day. Shading of the nest is probably important not just for the incubating female but also for the developing chicks. In Iberia, for example, chicks in nests built facing north or northeast have better growth rates and weights than those in nests facing in other directions (Yanes *et al.* 1996a).

The eggs of larks are generally cryptically spotted or streaked with a white to dull brownish or greyish base colour, often matching the colour of the substrate. In the Kalahari, eggs of larks living in cryptic habitats such as tall grass or tumbled rocks have very dark spots, whereas the eggs of species living in more uniform habitats are paler and plainer (MacLean 1970). Clutch sizes are larger in temperate species (around 4 on average) than in tropical or arid zone species (2–3 on average). In arid-country species, clutches are larger following heavier rains. One African species, Sclater's Lark, appears to be unique amongst the larks in only ever laying a single egg. At the other extreme, clutches of eight eggs have been reported in some of the *Melanocorypha* larks. In tropical Africa, clutches are larger in species inhabiting arid, less wooded habitats. This may be a response to the lower densities of predators in such habitats since it appears that species that suffer higher rates of nest predation have lower clutch sizes. Incubation generally lasts between ten and fourteen days and is usually undertaken by the female alone, though the male shares the incubation in some desert-dwelling species.

Being open nesters, larks suffer very high rates of nest predation (Suárez & Manrique 1992). Even the Dune Lark, which might with good reason expect its parched and waterless home to provide some compensation in the form of reduced predator numbers, suffers from high rates of nest predation (Boyer 1988), presumably carried out by equally parched and drought-stricken creatures. Since larks generally occur at low densities, it is likely that much nest predation is incidental, rather than targeted by predators specialising in taking lark nests. This was neatly illustrated by Yanes & Suarez (1996a), who found that predation of lark nests in Iberia was higher where there were higher populations of rabbits, since these attracted foxes that predated lark nests whenever they happened to stumble across them. The same researchers pointed out the paradox that creating nature reserves for larks and other ground nesting species might actually be unproductive, since nature reserve status protects not only the larks but also the predators of their nests (Suárez *et al.* 1993). Designation of nature reserves in Spain may actually have indirectly reduced lark nest survival rates below the level necessary to maintain their populations (Yanes & Suárez 1996b).

The nests of larks appear to be vulnerable to a bewildering variety of different predators. Although the identity of a nest predator is usually very difficult to establish unless it is caught in the act, lark nests are certainly vulnerable to a wide range of different mammals (cats, canids, insectivores, rodents, mustelids etc.), birds (crows, raptors, storks and a wide range of others), reptiles (snakes, lizards and others) and even invertebrates. A bizarre case of predation of a sparrow-lark nest by a large burrowing spider was described by MacLean (1970). The spider's burrow had emerged in the floor of the nest, and the spider had eaten one of the chicks and badly injured the other by biting it. I once witnessed a 'predation' of a Skylark egg by a large snail, as described in Chapter 8. An interesting case of nest predation is that of the Raso Lark, which suffers high rates of nest predation (maybe as high as 95%) by a reptile, the Cape Verde Giant Gecko (Donald *et al.* 2003). What is interesting about this case is that both species are endemic to the same tiny island. This battle between larks and geckoes has presumably been waged ever since the lark's ancestors first arrived on the island some tens of thousands of years ago, a striking illustration of the fact that even very high rates of nest predation can be sustainable.

Because of these high rates of nest predation, larks have evolved a number of strategies to reduce the risks of predation. Nest sites are selected to give the incubating female good all-round visibility (Götmark *et al.* 1995, Yanes *et al.* 1996a), so she can see predators approaching from a distance and slip away from the nest unnoticed. Lark chicks grow at a rate close to their theoretical maximum, to reduce to a minimum the time they are unable to fly (Shkedy & Safriel 1992). The legs grow particularly rapidly to allow the chicks to run from danger. The legs of lark chicks might be fully developed to adult size in just six or eight days, well before their weight approaches that of an adult. In most species, the chicks leave the nest well before they can fly or feed themselves and scatter over a large area, a strategy to minimise the risk of a predator taking the whole brood in a single visit.

Larks are generally monogamous and territorial in the breeding season and either territorial or congregatory outside the breeding season. Some are only territorial when breeding, and form nomadic flocks in the non-breeding season. Some, such as Gray's Lark, live in small groups throughout the year, and even during the breeding season territoriality is not well developed and mating takes place within the group.

Larks exhibit a wide range of migratory strategies, including residency, nomadism and long-distance migration. In the arid southwestern zone of Africa, certain species are nomadic, forming flocks outside the breeding season that cover large distances in the search for patchily distributed food items (Fahse *et al.* 1998). The movements of larks in this region are closely related to diet: nomadic species are largely or wholly granivorous, resident species largely or wholly insectivorous. These differences themselves might be related to water balance. Insectivores tend not to drink water, instead obtaining all their water from insect prey, whereas granivores need to follow rains either to drink water directly or to obtain water from fresh green seeds (MacLean 1970). These nomads are unpredictable in occurrence, and may appear in large numbers some years in places where they have not been recorded for several years. Other species in this zone, particularly those in the southern and southwestern Karoo, are resident. These two groups differ in size and diet, the resident species being larger than the nomads and largely insectivorous, the nomads being smaller and predominantly granivorous (Dean & Hockey 1989). The ability of the resident species to take ants and termites, a group of insects generally avoided by other birds because of their powerful chemical defences, may explain the ability of certain larks to survive in very austere environments. The residents are more confined to certain habitat types and tend to occur at low densities, while the nomads are more catholic in their choice of habitats. Other larks are migratory, at least in parts of their ranges. Some central Asian species, in particular, undertake very long distance migratory movements.

## SURVIVING HEAT AND DROUGHT

Larks are adapted to some of the world's hottest and driest environments, and have evolved a range of techniques to survive in them. Most species are able to survive without drinking, gaining enough moisture from their food and from dew to survive. Desert Larks may do much of their foraging for seeds in the period shortly after dawn, when seeds have a higher water content than later in the day (Orr 1970). Even those species that drink regularly when water is available are often able to survive without it. The Dune Lark is the only bird that has adapted to living in the Namib Sand Sea, one of the hottest and driest places on the planet. Birds have been observed here walking across sand with a surface temperature in excess of 62°C. Because of these extremes of temperature, the Dune Lark has received a considerable amount of attention from researchers interested in finding out how birds can survive in such dreadful conditions, and it is probably the most studied lark outside Europe. Dune Larks forage largely by excavating small craters in the sand, displacing seed-poor surface sand and bringing to the surface deeper, more seed-laden layers. However, feeding on seeds alone does not provide the birds with sufficient water to survive, so Dune Larks need to spend around a third of their foraging time seeking out invertebrates. To do this they need to move to quite different habitats to those in which they collect seeds (Cox 1983), and they therefore meet their metabolic water needs by exploiting different habitats for different food items. Invertebrates appear to be taken preferentially as temperatures approach 30°C, just before the start of the long midday break in activity. After long periods of drought, Dune Larks appear to move to a diet more dominated by invertebrates as seed densities decline in the absence of rainfall. The Dune Lark has never been observed to drink (possibly because most of them never see a puddle of water in their lives!), and birds apparently survive by having a very low rate of evaporative water loss and by deriving much of their water from the metabolic conversion of food to water (Williams 2001). The evaporative water loss of Dune Larks is up to 40% lower than is normal for a bird of that size (Williams 1999). However, even Dune Larks need to seek shelter from the sun during the hottest part of the day. Then birds spend up to three hours inactive, resting in the shade of clumps of vegetation, where the temperature is up to 20°C cooler (Cox 1983, Safriel 1990).

Many larks use stones or vegetation as perches when the sand gets very hot, and often face into the prevailing wind. Some of the sparrow-larks excavate a small hollow in the shade of bushes or rocks, possibly to expose the cooler sand below. Studies in the deserts of Arabia have shown that many species of lark use the burrows of lizards as refuges from the sun, a habit also noted in southern Africa, where rodent burrows are also used. Temperatures in these burrows can be 20°C cooler than the temperature at the surface, and this difference can reduce water loss by as much as 80% (Williams *et al.* 1999). Other sources of shade are also used, including prostrate gourd plants (Cowan & Brown 2001). Further methods of temperature reduction include panting, ruffling the feathers and dangling the legs in flight. There is also some evidence that as the temperature of the sand increases, so birds take longer and therefore few strides, thereby reducing contact with the ground. Water loss is also reduced by a development of the nasal passages in which exhaled air is passed over cooled membranes, causing the water in it to condense out and so remain within the bird's body. At lower temperatures, this can reduce the total amount of water lost by Dune Larks through evaporation by up to a third (Tieleman *et al.* 1999).

Irene Tieleman and Joe Williams are leading figures in the study of the ways that desert-living birds are able to survive in such arid environments. They have found that the basal metabolic rate (BMR) of larks inhabiting hot desert areas is consistently lower than that of those living in cooler temperate areas, indicating a relatively lower rate of energy expenditure. When comparing the desert-living Hoopoe-Lark and Dunn's Lark with the temperate Skylark and Woodlark, Tieleman *et al.* (2002) showed that the BMR of the desert-dwelling species was over 40% lower than that of the temperate species. Furthermore, they found that the desert species have a rate of evaporative water loss through the skin that is 26%

lower than that in the temperate species. This may be due to differences in the structure or composition of the lipids (fats and oils) in the epidermis. Irene and Joe have also investigated energy use and water flux during nesting, again showing that desert-living species use far less energy and water than their temperate equivalents. Clearly, larks that live in arid habitats rely as much on physiological adaptations as behavioural ones to survive there.

Despite all these adaptations, life is tough for larks living in very arid environments. As aridity increases, so chick growth rates, clutch sizes, the number of clutches laid and nest survival rates all decline (Tieleman 2002). Even the most desert-adapted larks are vulnerable to prolonged droughts. The tiny world population of the critically endangered Raso Lark fluctuates widely in response to rainfall, the total population falling to as few as ten pairs after prolonged droughts but increasing after rain (Figure 1.5). Even the resilient Dune Lark suffers severe population declines when the rains fail for periods of years (Safriel 1990). Nor are desert-living species invulnerable to the effects of global warming. Yoram Yom-Tov (2001) has shown that Crested Larks in Israel showed a decline in body condition (the ratio of body fat to skeletal size) between 1950 and 1999, possibly because of an increase in mean temperature.

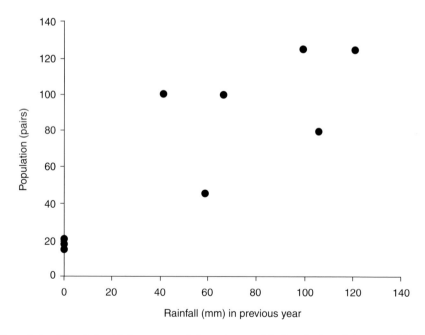

*Figure 1.5. The relationship between population estimates of the Raso Lark made between 1975 and 2001 and rainfall in Tarrafal, São Nicolau, the nearest weather recording station to Raso, some 25 km to the east. The two were significantly correlated ($r_s = 0.824$, $n = 9$, $P < 0.005$), suggesting that rainfall is an important factor determining Raso Lark populations. From Donald et al. (2003).*

Possibly because of their evolution in arid habitats, bathing in water is very rare even in those larks occupying temperate zones with abundant standing water (although bathing has been seen in Skylarks in captivity). Instead, most larks maintain and clean their feathers, and at the same time rid themselves of parasites, by dust bathing. Sunning is another behaviour frequently adopted by larks to maintain their plumage. Although the exact purpose of sunning remains unclear, it is possible that increasing exposure to sunlight can improve feather condition (possibly by increasing the flow of preen oil or by speeding the synthesis of vitamin D) and possibly dislodge parasites from areas the bird cannot reach with its bill. The behaviour of anting is unknown in the larks.

The success of larks in exploiting deserts and other arid areas, where they are often the dominant songbird family, is perhaps due to their ability to adapt to the rapidly changing environmental conditions caused by drought and sporadic rainfall. Their relatively unspecialised ecologies, with most species taking a mixture of invertebrates and vegetable matter, may also contribute to this success (Willoughby 1971). This gives them an advantage not only over other birds, but also certain competing mammals. In the Negev Desert of Israel, for example, Crested Larks have certain advantages over mammalian granivores, like gerbils, in that they are more generalist, taking invertebrates as well as seeds. They are more efficient foragers than small desert mammals in certain habitats, and their diurnal habits give them first access to seeds displaced by the midday winds (Kotler & Brown 1999). The larks generally stop feeding at higher seed densities than the gerbils, suggesting that they have less ability to forage at low seed densities, but they can probably compensate for this by creaming off small patches of high food density (Brown *et al.* 1997, Garb *et al.* 2000).

Certain larks are more specialised than others, and these tend to survive in a narrower range of habitats and have smaller distributions. Where they occur in the same areas, the generalist and specialist species have subtly different ecologies. Comparing the ecology of the generalist Crested Lark in areas where it overlaps with the more specialist Desert Lark, Shkedy & Safriel (1991) found that the Crested Lark takes a wider range of seed sizes than the Desert Lark. However the Crested Lark also carries more fat reserves, an indication that it needs reserves to see it through times of food shortage. The lower fat loading of the Desert Lark suggests that during times of food shortage, the species' specialisation is capable of seeing it through without the need for large and costly fat reserves. In a study of two very closely related species of lark (Greater and Lesser Short-toed Larks) in Iberia, Suárez *et al.* (2002a) found that they were segregated at a number of spatial scales. The geographically widespread Greater Short-toed Lark occupies a wider range of habitats in Spain than does the more restricted Lesser Short-toed Lark, which shows a more clumped distribution in certain habitats. Where both species occur together, they show preferences for different vegetation types.

*Migrant Skylarks and cranes in China*

CHAPTER 2

# Distribution and variation

> If ever proof were wanted that almost unlimited variability
> existed in a group, we have it here, for twenty-seven names have
> at one time or another been given to the various populations of
> Skylarks from Pekin to Spain. If twenty-seven races exist, then
> why not two hundred and seventy or more?
>
> Richard Meinertzhagen (1951)

Three of the four species in the genus *Alauda* are relatively unspecialised and
superficially extremely similar larks that occupy a range of open habitats in
Europe, Asia and North Africa. The most abundant and widespread of the group
is the Skylark (also called the Eurasian Skylark, the Northern Skylark and, pedan-
tically, the Sky Lark). The Skylark is one of the most abundant and widespread of
all the larks, breeding in a broad band across Eurasia, between about 40°N and
65°N, although there are regular breeding populations as far north as 72°N in

Norway, well inside the Arctic Circle (Figure 2.1). In the extreme south of the species' range, birds have been recorded displaying in Qatar (Nation 1996), although Skylarks appear generally to be rare and erratic breeders on the Arabian Peninsula. Vagrants have reached Iceland, Bear Island, the Azores, Madeira, Borneo and California, and Skylarks of one of the Siberian subspecies bred for the first time in Alaska in 1996 (Baicich *et al.* 1996). Vagrant Skylarks are capable of crossing vast expanses of open ocean, as records of the species on Midway Atoll in the mid-Pacific show (Campbell *et al.* 1997a). The taiga presents a barrier to the species' northerly limits across most of its Eurasian range, and the southerly limit is set by deserts and arid steppes, for the Skylark is a temperate species that is replaced in arid habitats by species better adapted to dry conditions. Introduced populations are established in New Zealand, Australia, Hawaii and on Vancouver Island, western Canada.

The breeding range of the second most widespread *Alauda* lark, the Oriental Skylark (also called Eastern, Indian or Small Skylark), lies to the south of that of its larger relative, which it largely replaces over much of central, southern and eastern Asia. Where the breeding ranges of the two species overlap, in southeastern Russia and northern Afghanistan, there is no evidence of interbreeding. It breeds from Iran across Turkestan to Nepal, China and the Philippines, and south through India to Sri Lanka. As with the Skylark, northern populations are migratory, more southerly ones resident. Central Chinese breeding populations winter south to India and Burma (Myanmar). Some breeding populations in central Asia move south in winter to be replaced by wintering Skylarks from further north.

The third member of the genus is the Japanese Skylark, a form that has variously been considered a full species, a subspecies of the Skylark or a subspecies of the Oriental Skylark. Weight of opinion generally favours treating Japanese Skylark as a distinct species, although it is extremely similar to both Skylark and Oriental Skylark and somewhat intermediate between them in many ways. It breeds in extreme eastern Siberia, Korea and Japan, where it is a common resident or short-distance migrant, moving in winter to the Ryukyu Islands. It may also occur in the Kurile Islands (Russia), which lie just to the north of Japan. The Skylark also occurs on several of these islands, though whether the two species interbreed where they occur together is not known.

The fourth *Alauda* lark is an exceptional bird by any standards, and outwardly quite unlike (although closely related to) the others. The Raso Lark of the Cape Verde Islands inhabits a far more arid habitat than any of the other three species and, probably as a direct result, is rather more specialised, particularly with respect to bill structure (Figure 1.3). The Raso Lark probably evolved from Skylarks or Skylark-like ancestors that reached the islands some time between 10,000 and 100,000 years ago, when the Palaearctic fauna was pushed south into northern Africa by the ice sheets that then covered much of Europe. When the ice sheets retreated and the mainland Skylarks moved north again, the ancestors of the Raso Lark were left stranded. Although only known from the island of Raso, this species may well have had a much larger range in the past, when lower sea levels meant that

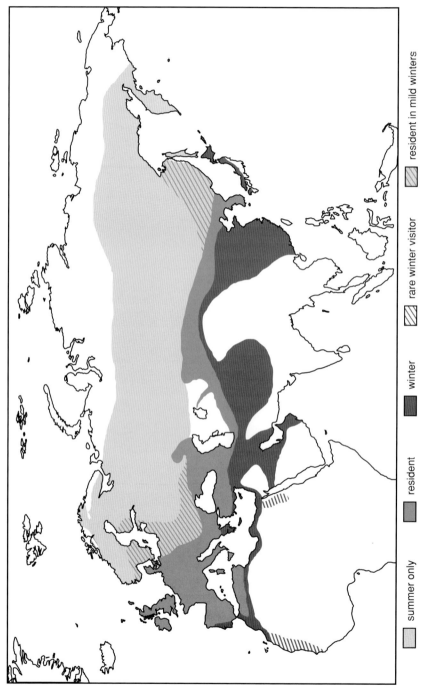

*Figure 2.1. Distribution of the Skylark. Introduced populations exist in New Zealand, Australia, Hawaii and Vancouver Island.*

Raso was joined to what are now three other islands. That the Raso Lark has survived on its tiny island retreat is truly remarkable, as it has had to survive droughts lasting up to 20 years, heavy collecting (Boyd Alexander celebrated his discovery of the species in 1897 by shooting a good part of the population), high nest predation, army artillery practice and the attentions of introduced cats and dogs (Donald *et al.* 2003). The Raso Lark has one of the smallest ranges of any bird in the world: the island itself covers 7 km², but most of the birds are found on the 4 km² of decaying larva that make up the island's low flat plain.

# STRUCTURE

The Skylark is a medium-sized, robust lark, weighing between 25 g and 50 g, depending on sex, subspecies and time of year. Males of the nominate subspecies *arvensis* weigh on average around 42 g during the winter, females around 35 g. Birds that died in southern England during the hard winter of 1962/63 had average weights of just 29 g for males and 24 g for females. Because weight fluctuates so much in relation to time of year, stage of migration, recent feeding conditions and so on, it is a potentially misleading estimate of body size. Wing length is a more constant measurement of a bird's size. The wing lengths of male and female Skylarks from a number of studies are shown in Figure 2.2. The wings of males are around 5–10% longer than those of females and, within Europe at least, there is a general pattern of increase in wing length from southwest to northeast. With experience, it becomes possible to determine the sex of adult birds in the field on the basis of size and subtle differences in wing shape, structure and flight action. Such differences are fairly easy to detect when pairs are seen in flight together.

Identifying the sex of birds on the basis of wing length was a trick well known to the London bird dealers in Victorian England, who needed to know whether to sell the bird as a songster or as meat. In *British Birds with their Nests and Eggs* (1896–98), Arthur Butler described how they:

> take the bird in the left hand with the tail towards them, and with the right hand draw down the wing until the point of the first long primary touches the tip of the outermost tail feather: the wing of the male being distinctly longer than that of the female, the so-called 'shoulder' then appears to be much more angular in the former than in the latter sex. I have seen considerable numbers of birds thus tested, the males being caged and the females being returned to the catchers, and I never knew the test to fail: but females are rarely forwarded by experienced bird-catchers, most of them being killed at the nets and sold to the poulterers.

In his book *The Birds of Norfolk* (1866), Henry Stevenson asserts that some bird trappers did not even have to do this, being able to "tell in the dark the males from

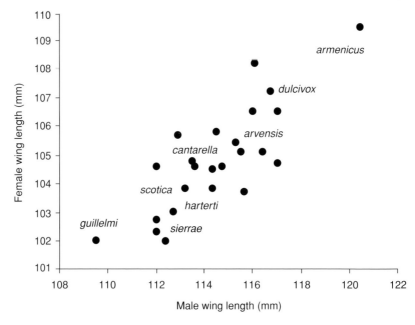

*Figure 2.2.   Male and female wing lengths of Skylarks in the Western Palaearctic, drawn from a number of populations. The approximate central location of each of eight races is indicated.*

the females, as they take the bird from the net, merely by handling them, the former being somewhat the widest across the shoulders".

Skylarks, like most oscine songbirds, have ten primary flight feathers on each wing and twelve tail feathers (rectrices). However, on rare occasions, individuals are found with aberrant numbers of flight feathers. Chernysov (1998) reports a case of a Skylark with thirteen rectrices, six on the left and seven on the right.

The hind claw of Skylarks is long, as is typical for a largely cursorial lark. Although there are few measurements of claw length, it appears that in Skylarks it changes seasonally, being longer in the breeding season and shorter in the winter. Whether this is caused by abrasion, or whether it reflects real seasonal differences in claw growth rates, is at present unknown. Although the long hind claw of Skylarks is almost certainly an adaptation to a cursorial existence, its exact function is uncertain. Writing in 1911, W. P. Pycraft described an altogether more unlikely use of this 'spur':

> It seems to have been widely believed among shepherds, for instance, that the spurs were very effective weapons of offence, since they were capable of blinding sheep. According to tradition, sheep wandering too near the nest of the lark were promptly attacked by the parent birds, which repelled the unconscious trespasser by digging their spurs into the eyes, inflicting a poisonous wound which speedily resulted in blindness. Youatt, however, long since

realised the absurdity of this belief, though he retained the term "lark-spurred" for sheep suffering from a form of ophthalmia which "suddenly occurs without any apparent cause".

## SUBSPECIFIC VARIATION

Throughout its large range, the Skylark occurs in a number of different forms, differing mainly in body and bill size and ground colour (Plate 1). The extent of the pale fringes on the dark-centred tertials is often used as an indicator of the overall darkness of different races. Size appears to increase from western Europe to a maximum in western Siberia, and then to decline again towards the Pacific, although northeastern Siberian birds are relatively large. Many of these different forms are treated as subspecies, although several of the currently accepted subspecies may not warrant full subspecific distinction, instead being extremes of a gradient in plumage and size. Furthermore, the distribution of many of these putative subspecies is practically unknown, largely because many are impossible to separate in the field and because adjacent forms may grade into each other. Colour differences between neighbouring subspecies may be very slight, and smaller than individual variation within subspecies. Within the Western Palaearctic, eight subspecies are generally recognised:

1. *A. a. arvensis* breeds across most of northern and central Europe, from England and southern Scotland east to about 50°E. It is resident in the west and southwest and migratory elsewhere, some migrants wintering as far south as North Africa. The introduced populations on Vancouver Island and Hawaii are of this subspecies.

2. *A. a. scotica* breeds in the Faroes, northern and western Scotland, northwest England and Ireland, where it is largely resident or a short-distance migrant. The introduced New Zealand population is of this subspecies. Generally smaller, darker, more rufous and heavily streaked than *arvensis*.

3. *A. a. cantarella* breeds from northern Spain, across southern France, Italy, the Balkans to as far east as the lower Don and the Caucasus. Generally paler than *arvensis*, with greyer ground colour to the mantle and narrower dark feather-streaks on the upperparts and breast.

4. *A. a. sierrae* breeds in central and southern Portugal and southern Spain, and is either resident or a winter migrant across Gibraltar to northwest Africa. It is darker and browner above than *cantarella*, though not as rufous as *arvensis*, and paler below.

5. *A. a. guillelmi* is apparently resident in northern Portugal and extreme northwestern Spain. It is one of the darkest, smallest and most rufous subspecies, though pale individuals also occur.

6.  *A. a. harterti* breeds in northwest Africa across the Mahgreb and is a rather pale, buff form.
7.  *A. a. armenicus* breeds from eastern Turkey and Armenia to northern Iran. It is very similar to *cantarella*, but larger.
8.  *A. a. dulcivox* breeds from the Urals and lower Volga to northern Kazakhstan, the Altai and northern Iran and Afghanistan, wintering in the eastern Mediterranean and the Middle East. It also occurs in the mountains of southern Russia. It is similar to *cantarella*, though the streaks on the upperparts and underparts are narrower and even more contrasting. It is paler and greyer than *arvensis* and one of the more easily distinguishable forms.

Further east, the picture is even less clear, although a number of forms are generally recognised:

1.  *A. a. pekinensis* breeds in northeast Siberia from the middle Lena to the lower Kolyma, the Okhotsk coast, Kamchatka and the Kurile Islands, wintering in the lower Amur basin, Manchuria and Shantung, Ussuriland, Korea, Sakhalin and Japan. This is a dark race with virtually all-dark tertials (Figure 2.3). Vagrants to Alaska and California are probably of this subspecies.
2.  *A. a. lonnbergi* is a pale race breeding in Sakhalin, Shantar Island and possibly the lower Amur basin, wintering in eastern China, Korea and Japan.
3.  *A. a. kiborti* replaces *dulcivox* across much of central Siberia, from Yenisey to the Lena and Zeya rivers, to the Altai and across eastern Asia to Korea.
4.  *A. a. intermedia* is found in southeast Siberia north to the Amur river.

In addition to all these, Meinertzhagen recognised a number of other forms, including *theresae* (Ireland), *inopinata* (Tibet), *weigoldi* (China) and *blakistoni* (eastern Siberia). Perhaps surprisingly, Meinertzhagen considered the Oriental Skylark to be a subspecies of the Skylark. The greater number of recognised subspecies in the Western Palaearctic than further east might simply reflect a longer history of research and a greater availability of museum specimens there.

The Oriental Skylark also exhibits considerable subspecific variation, with at least ten races being described. The westernmost race is *inconspicua*, of southwest Siberia, the Caspian region and Iran, east to Pakistan and northern India. This is one of the largest, palest races. Birds occasionally wintering in southern Israel are apparently rather darker than *inconspicua*, suggesting they come from further east, possibly the race *lhamarum* of the Pamirs and western Himalayas. This race has more rufous colouration on the ear coverts and on the outer fringes of the primaries than does *inconspicua*. The nominate race *gulgula* is found across most of central and southern India and Sri Lanka east to Burma (Myanmar). A further eight or more races range from southwest India east to the Philippines and north to China and Tibet.

The difficulty in determining the number of subspecies and their distribution was clearly apparent to Richard Meinertzhagen, who wrote in his 1951 review of the larks:

> I have examined specimens from every area cited above [the Western Palaearctic], in all over 1,168 specimens in Leningrad, Berlin, the Tring collection, the British Museum and my own collection. If ever proof were wanted that almost unlimited variability existed in a group, we have it here, for twenty-seven names have at one time or another been given to the various populations of Skylarks from Pekin to Spain. If twenty-seven races exist, then why not two hundred and seventy or more? No two populations, even micro-populations are identical, especially in ground colour and among Skylarks the breeding birds in a single field show more than minor differences.

## IDENTIFICATION OF THE ALAUDA LARKS

Because of the great variation in plumage within species and the close similarity between species, identification of *Alauda* larks in the field can be extremely difficult. All four species are shown in Plate 2. Ageing of birds is impossible after late summer, since juvenile birds undergo a complete moult some two to four weeks after fledging, after which they are indistinguishable from the adults. Sexing *Alauda* larks on plumage is also impossible, as there are no known plumage features that consistently differ even slightly between the sexes.

The Oriental Skylark is around 15% smaller than the Skylark, with distinctly shorter wings and tail. The primaries do not extend beyond the tertials in Oriental Skylark, whereas in the Skylark several primary tips are visible at rest (Figure 2.3). The shorter, broader wings of Oriental Skylark are easily distinguishable in flight, when its broad wings and short tail give it an appearance more like Woodlark. Plumage is similar to Skylark, most resembling the race *dulcivox*, but the breast streaks are generally finer and against a more buff background. The ear coverts are often more rusty in colour and the supercilium whiter and more pronounced than in Skylark. However, subtle plumage details must be treated with caution, as there is a great deal of racial variation in both species. In flight, the most distinguishing plumage features become visible. Oriental Skylarks lack the prominent white trailing edge of the secondaries that shows up as a distinct white line on the wings of Skylarks, although feather wear might give the impression of a pale edge. Also, the outer tail feathers of Oriental Skylark are buff, not bright white as in Skylark. The primaries and secondaries of Oriental Skylark are often edged with rufous, showing up as a rusty panel on the closed wing (Plate 3). The smaller size and slightly longer and thinner bill of Oriental Skylark give it a more pipit-like appearance. According to Kovshar & Berezovikov (1995), this is

*Figure 2.3.*   Alauda arvensis pekinensis, *photographed in eastern Siberia. Note the very long primary projection. In all Skylarks, the primaries extend beyond the tertials, but the projection is particularly long in migratory races, such as* pekinensis. *Photo: Yuri Artukhin.*

enhanced by its gait, which involves more pipit- or wagtail-like head-jerking during walking than is shown by the larger Skylark. It is also a more delicately proportioned bird, with proportionately longer legs, a more upright stance and a habit of occasionally standing bolt upright, rather like a wheatear. The flight calls of Skylark and Oriental Skylark are quite different, the former having a characteristic rich, rolling 'chirrup', the latter a nasal, buzzing 'baz baz', although some Skylark-like calls are also uttered by Oriental Skylark. During the song flight, Oriental Skylark keeps its tail closed, so appears narrower in outline, and rarely parachutes to the ground on the completion of the flight, instead descending in steps. The song is generally less varied and complex than that of the Skylark, and may be delivered more frequently from the ground.

The Japanese Skylark presents a more difficult identification problem, and the species (if such it is) probably overlaps in range with eastern races *pekinensis*, *lonnbergi* and *kibborti* of the Skylark in parts of Russia, China, Japan and Korea, although the degree of overlap is probably small. In many ways, Japanese Skylark falls between Skylark and Oriental Skylark, being intermediate in size and structure, although details of the field identification of this species remain to be elucidated. Compared with the Skylark, Japanese Skylark is smaller, shorter-tailed and has a shorter crest. Like Oriental Skylark, there is a distinctive rufous panel in the wing, formed by the rufous shafts and fringes of the primaries and secondaries. Japanese Skylark shows a rufous wash across the breast within which the neat, well-defined black streaking is confined. Like the Skylark, and unlike Oriental Skylark, Japanese Skylark has a well-defined pale trailing edge to the wing, though this is generally less bright white than in Skylark. The song of Japanese Skylark is delivered from the ground more often than that of Skylark, and is less varied and melodic.

The Raso Lark (Plate 3) presents no identification problems. Even if it were not confined to the tiny island of Raso, many hundreds of kilometres from the next nearest *Alauda* lark, it would still be easy to distinguish, as it is very different in appearance to the other members of the genus. This led early taxonomists to place it in a number of different genera, including its own, *Razocorys*. However, recent genetic analyses and close observations of its behaviour both point conclusively to its being an *Alauda* lark, albeit an aberrant one. It is the smallest *Alauda* lark, around 30% smaller than the Skylark, and far greyer, completely lacking the rufous tones of the other three species (although, in an interesting evolutionary throwback, chicks of the Raso Lark are as rufous as the chicks of the other *Alauda* larks, and look quite different to the adults). As we saw in the previous chapter, the Raso Lark is also the only member of the genus with a bill adapted for digging, and the relatively massive bill and large head give it a strangely front-heavy appearance.

Albinism or partial albinism is not uncommon in Skylarks, and many of the Victorian ornithologists report instances of wholly white birds, though these seem to be rare nowadays (Plate 4). Where partial albinism occurs in Skylarks, it is often symmetrical, the same feathers being white on both sides of the body (Barrett 1966, Harrison 1966). There is considerable individual variation in the extent of dark markings on the undertail-coverts of Skylarks, although the significance of this is unknown (Dougall 1998).

*Skylark singing over coastal marsh*

# CHAPTER 3

# Populations and habitats

> I find that with us the numbers of this bird are, and for some
> years past have been, perceptibly decreasing, and though in the
> winter months, especially after the break-up of a long and severe
> frost, vast flocks may be still occasionally met with on our arable
> lands, I think I may safely say that on our fresh cut stubbles in
> September not a tenth part of the Sky-Larks which used to
> frequent them twenty years ago are now to be met with.
>
> Lord Lilford, *Notes on the Birds of Northamptonshire and
> Neighbourhood* (1895)

Because open habitats generally hold rather fewer food resources than, for example,
woodland or scrub, the birds that inhabit them often occur in rather low densities.
However, open habitats can cover very large areas, so the total populations of some
larks can be very large. The Skylark is numerically the dominant lark species across

much of Europe and central Asia, and is probably the second most abundant lark in the world (after the Horned Lark). In the second Atlas of breeding birds in Britain and Ireland (Gibbons *et al.* 1993), based on fieldwork carried out between 1988 and 1991, the Skylark was present in almost all 10-km grid squares, making it one of the most widespread of all breeding species. Indeed, the Skylark is one of the most widely distributed birds in Europe (Hagemeijer & Blair 1997), being absent as a breeding bird only from Iceland. Within its temperate range, the Skylark can be found in almost all habitats except woodland and wetlands. However, it shows enormous variation in numbers, and in trends in numbers, in different habitats and regions.

## HABITATS

Skylarks breed in a wide range of open habitats, but in greatly differing numbers, since some offer better conditions than others. Table 3.1 summarises Skylark population density estimates of a large number of different studies. Although there is massive variation within individual habitats, much of this arising from differences in fieldwork methods between different studies and differences in their timing, a few patterns emerge. Territory densities are generally lower on farmland, particularly grassland, than on semi-natural habitats such as coastal marshes and heaths. Set-aside is the only farmland habitat to support territory densities comparable to more natural habitats. However, looking simply at density estimates tells us nothing about which are the most important habitats. Those habitats supporting the greatest territory densities are not necessarily those supporting the greatest numbers of individual pairs, since some habitats are far more extensive than others. When

Table 3.1. *Summary of Skylark territory densities in different habitats from a number of European studies.*

| Habitat | Average territory density (pairs per km²) | Range of values | Number of studies |
|---|---|---|---|
| Mixed farmland | 22.8 | 9–58 | 20 |
| Pastoral farmland | 18.4 | 0–60 | 18 |
| Arable farmland | 27.5 | 7–110 | 35 |
| Set-aside | 45.6 | 15–110 | 8 |
| Natural grassland | 40.0 | 11–90 | 10 |
| Moorland | 25.6 | 1–58 | 9 |
| Heath and steppe | 55.8 | 4–300 | 8 |
| Coastal marshes | 75.5 | 14–160 | 16 |
| Woods and scrub | 6.2 | 2–20 | 6 |

looking at habitat use, therefore, it is important to look at where the majority of individual birds occur, as well as where birds occur in their greatest densities. All the evidence for Skylarks suggests that, in fact, the majority of birds are found in habitats, particularly farmland habitats, that support relatively low population densities. This gives rise to an interesting paradox, in that the majority of birds actually occur in habitats that appear to be avoided.

Across Europe, the single most important habitat for Skylarks is undoubtedly farmland, not because it holds particularly high densities of birds (many farmland habitats actually hold rather low densities), but because it covers such a vast area. The total area of farmland in Europe is nearly 5 million km$^2$, around 22% of the continent's total land area. In many countries, farmland makes up a far greater proportion of land area, reaching around 75% in the UK and 80% in Ireland. A recent survey by the BTO (Browne *et al.* 2000) suggests that over 70% of all the UK's Skylarks are found on lowland farmland, and around 50% on arable farmland. A large number of recent studies show clearly that Skylarks do not use different farmland types evenly. Arable land is clearly preferred to grassland (Chamberlain & Gregory 1999), and certain arable crops attract more birds than others. Cereals are an extremely important habitat, and in the UK, wheat and barley hold around 40% of the farmland Skylark population (Table 3.2). In the UK, Skylark territory

*Table 3.2.   Territory densities of Skylarks in different crop types, the percentage of farmland made up by each crop type and the percentage of the total farmland Skylark population found in each crop type. Data for England & Wales and Scotland are presented separately due to differences in the way agricultural statistics are collected. Territory densities are calculated from the 1997 BTO Skylark Survey (Browne* et al. *2000). Table reproduced from Donald & Vickery (2000).*

| Crop | Skylark density (pairs per km$^2$) | % of farmland area | % of farmland Skylark population |
|---|---|---|---|
| **England & Wales** | | | |
| Cereals | 10.8 | 30 | 40 |
| Improved grass | 5.4 | 47 | 31 |
| Set-aside | 29.6 | 3 | 10 |
| Rough grazing | 5.9 | 10 | 7 |
| Root crops | 11.9 | 3 | 5 |
| Brassicas | 9.5 | 4 | 4 |
| Legumes | 12.9 | 2 | 3 |
| **Scotland** | | | |
| Grazed pasture | 8.4 | 45 | 39 |
| Cereals | 11.5 | 28 | 34 |
| Mown grass | 7.6 | 19 | 15 |
| Set-aside | 36.0 | 2 | 9 |
| Brassicas | 5.1 | 4 | 2 |
| Root crops | 5.4 | 2 | 1 |

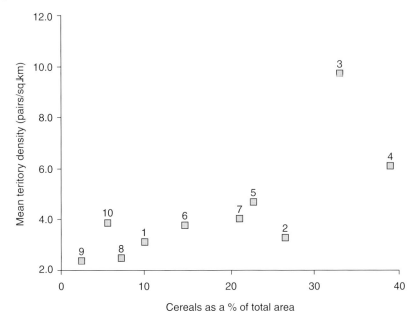

*Figure 3.1. Relationship between Skylark territory density and extent of cereals as a percentage of total land area in ten regions of the UK in 1998. Regions follow the standard regions of the EU (1 North England, 2 Yorkshire/Humberside, 3 East Midlands, 4 East Anglia, 5 Southeast England, 6 Southwest England, 7 West Midlands, 8 Northwest England, 9 Wales, 10 Scotland). The relationship is statistically significant ($r_s = 0.77$, n = 10, P < 0.01). From Donald & Vickery (2000).*

densities arc highest in regions where cereal agriculture predominates (Figure 3.1), and even relatively small areas of arable land within otherwise grass-dominated landscapes are sufficient greatly to increase Skylark numbers (Chamberlain & Gregory 1999, Robinson *et al.* 2001).

Grassland, particularly where it is heavily grazed, holds some of the lowest densities recorded in any habitat. However, some grassland habitats, particularly where they are not managed intensively, can hold very high densities of Skylarks. In the uplands of the UK, Skylarks are found more frequently on grass-dominated moors than in heather moors (Chamberlain 2001). Indeed, upland grassland holds some of the highest densities of Skylarks found in any habitat in the UK (Chamberlain & Gregory 1999). On such moors, grazing levels are a very important determinant of Skylark numbers, as Skylarks occur in higher numbers on grazed moors than on ungrazed moors (Pearce-Higgins & Grant 2002).

A number of minor crops hold high concentrations of Skylarks. In France, sage and lavender fields grown for the perfume industry hold very high densities of breeding birds, particularly where they are not weeded (Eraud *et al.* 2000). Linseed is another crop that can hold high concentrations of birds, as it is a short crop that provides suitable nesting conditions throughout the breeding season. Lucerne also appears to be particularly attractive to Skylarks, and very high numbers have been recorded in lucerne in France during the breeding season (Eraud & Boutin 2002) and in New Zealand during the winter (Thomsen *et al.* 2001). Despite the high densities in such crops, however, their small area means that they do not support more than a tiny proportion of the total population.

Coastal habitats can support some of the highest densities of Skylarks recorded anywhere, but there are huge differences in the territory density estimates of different studies, suggesting considerable variation in the suitability of different coastal habitats. Tim Milsom and his colleagues (2001) have examined differences in Skylark numbers breeding on coastal marshes in relation to differences in habitat. They found that fairly subtle differences in marsh structure had profound effects on the numbers of Skylarks establishing territories there. Numbers are particularly high on marshes with tussocks and rills, and marshes with intermediate levels of surface moisture.

The Skylark may have evolved in Asian steppe habitats, and still reaches high densities in such habitats. In the Siberian steppes around Lake Baikal, the Skylark is the commonest species present, reaching densities of 113 birds per km$^2$ in more vegetated areas, and accounting for between a fifth and a third of all the individual birds present in the region (Sharaldaeva 1999). In the semi-deserts of the Caspian region, Skylarks are again numerically the dominant bird in areas that have been cultivated, especially around cereals, but they are replaced by other lark species in uncultivated areas (Shishkin 1982).

Having seen that different habitats hold different densities of Skylarks, it is important to consider what the mechanism behind this difference is. In other words, are birds responding to differences in habitat *per se*, or to some other factor, such as habitat structure? In fact, the habitat itself, in terms of the species of plants present, is likely to be of secondary importance to the structure. Skylarks occur in low densities in habitats that have very short vegetation, because they do not provide sufficient cover to hide the nest, and also avoid habitats where the vegetation is very tall or dense, because this makes moving around difficult. The effects of livestock grazing in different habitats provide a neat illustration of this. On heather moorland, which supports fairly tall and very dense vegetation, grazing increases the amount of more open habitat and so leads to an increase in Skylark numbers (Pearce-Higgins & Grant 2002). On coastal marshes, however, where the natural vegetation is already short, grazing leads to a decrease in Skylark numbers, and heavily grazed pasture holds some of the lowest densities of breeding Skylarks of any farmland habitat (Browne *et al.* 2000). There are many other examples of the way in which habitat structure can profoundly influence Skylark territory densities. In cereals, Skylark numbers change greatly in response to the height of the sward, but are generally low because cereals develop into one of the tallest arable crops (Chamberlain *et al.* 1999a). Densities in set-aside are often very high, but only where rotation ensures that the vegetation does not become too tall or dense. Conversion of arable land to short downland grass as part of an environmental restoration programme in southern England resulted in a drop in numbers of Skylarks, since the resulting grassland was very short. When the grassland was managed in such a way that sward height increased, numbers of Skylarks increased again to pre-conversion levels (Wakeham-Dawson & Aebischer 2001). Across all farmland habitat types, territory densities peak at vegetation heights of around 60 cm, and decline rapidly as heights increase above 1 m (Figure 3.2). Remarkably similar results, again suggesting an optimum vegetation height of around 60 cm, have been obtained from research in Germany (Toepfer & Stubbe 2001).

We will return to discuss in detail the effects of crop structure on Skylark numbers in Chapter 12, since it has fundamental implications for Skylark population trends, but for now it is enough to appreciate that Skylarks respond at least as much to habitat structure as they do to the actual floral composition of the habitat.

It will become clear in the remaining chapters of this book that most of the scientific information we have on the Skylark derives from studies carried out in a small number of (predominantly European) countries, and also in a small number of habitats. Because of the importance of farmland to this species, most of what we know relates to Skylarks in agricultural habitats. Far less is known of the species in other habitats.

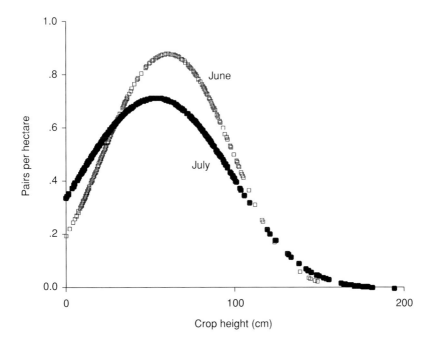

*Figure 3.2.    The relationship between crop height and Skylark territory density on farmland in southern England, all crops combined. The values shown are not actual measurements, but estimates from statistical models. From Donald* et al. *(2001c).*

## OTHER FACTORS AFFECTING SKYLARK DISTRIBUTION

Much of the variation in the numbers of breeding Skylarks is clearly explained by differences in habitat, or more specifically in habitat structure, since different habitats support different numbers and densities of breeding birds. However, the habitat available to birds is not the only factor to influence the distribution of Skylarks, and there can be considerable differences in the abundance of Skylarks even within individual habitats. Some of the causes of this variation are natural; others are due to human modification of the landscape.

Altitude plays an important role in determining Skylark population densities. In Spain, breeding Skylarks are confined to the north of the country where they are found in greatest numbers at higher altitudes, most birds occurring at over 1,000 m (Suárez *et al.* 2002b). Skylarks breed at altitudes up to 2,000 m in Switzerland, up to 2,500 m in Armenia, and at over 3,200 m on alpine meadows in central Asia, but the highest densities are generally on lower ground. In the UK, territory densities decrease with increasing altitude (Brown & Stillman 1993), and very low numbers of birds are found in mountainous regions. This altitudinal effect may be related to climate or simply to the fact that suitable nesting habitat may not be available at higher altitudes. In Spain, it is also likely to be related to competition with other lark species: the Skylark is one of the dominant species in the high, cold shrub steppes, or *páramos*, of northern Spain, but is replaced on lower ground by Crested and Thekla Larks (Tellería *et al.* 1988).

Soil type is another aspect of physical geography that may profoundly influence the distribution of Skylarks. However, trying to separate the effects of soil type from the effects of vegetation is difficult, since soil type clearly influences vegetation. Skylarks appear to prefer sandy soils to clay ones, possibly because they are free-draining and so dry out more quickly after rain, something that might be important to a ground nesting bird. Soil moisture may also be an important determinant of Skylark distribution: in Russia, drainage of wet raised bogs has led to their colonisation by Skylarks (Mal'chevskiy & Pukinskiy 1983). Wet bogs hold some of the lowest densities of Skylarks of any habitat in the UK (Browne *et al.* 2000).

As we saw in Chapter 1, the larks as a family tend to suffer from very high rates of nest predation. The adult birds themselves are also vulnerable to a wide range of avian and mammalian predators (Chapter 11). It might be expected, therefore, that the distribution of Skylarks reflects at least partly the distribution of their predators, and a number of studies have shown this to be the case. In Finland, for example, Skylarks show a strong avoidance of the vicinity of Kestrel nest sites (Suhonen *et al.* 1994). In Poland, Piotr Tryjanowski and his colleagues have examined the distribution of farmland Skylarks in relation to the distribution of their predators, they have found that territory densities of Skylarks are greatly reduced in areas close to dens of the Red Fox, and speculated that the huge increase in fox numbers in Poland has been a significant contributor to population declines of Skylarks in that country (Tryjanowski *et al.* 2002a). A similar avoidance is also shown by Skylarks of areas around the nests of the Great Grey Shrike, an important predator of adult Skylarks and their chicks (Hromada *et al.* 2002). Quite unexpectedly, however, Piotr has found that the presence of Raven nests actually has a positive impact on Skylark numbers, possibly because the number of other predators is lower around Raven nests (Tryjanowski 2001). Skylarks seem to prefer nesting close to Ravens because it might actually decrease nest predation rates.

Studies of the distribution of Skylarks have shown that territory distribution is influenced not only by habitat, but also by the distribution of tall vertical structures that can be used by potential predators. Because of this, Skylarks show a strong selection for larger fields and fields with lower boundaries, because this gives them the opportunity to avoid nesting near tall hedgerows or woodland (Donald *et al.* 2001c). The relationship between Skylark numbers, field boundary structure and field size is shown in Figure 3.3: as field boundary height increases, so Skylark territory densities decline, except where fields are large. Where there are no tall field boundaries, Skylarks instead show a preference for areas where fields are small, since this allows them access to a greater diversity of crop types (Eraud & Boutin 2002). Predator avoidance clearly has such a strong impact on the distribution of Skylarks that it can overrule even the quality of the habitat itself. Even the best habitats may be completely unused by Skylarks if they occur too close to trees. Not only trees, but also man-made structures such as electricity pylons can significantly reduce the numbers of Skylarks present (Milsom *et al.* 2001). Hans Oelke (1968) estimated the distance over which the effect of avoiding tall structures operates to be around 200 m. This means that Skylarks base their decisions about where to set up their territories not just on what is within that territory, but also on what lies a long way

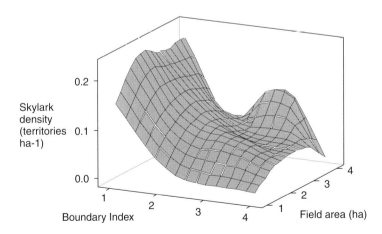

*Figure 3.3.   The three-dimensional relationship between skylark density (pairs per hectare), boundary index (1 = low boundaries, 2 = hedges, 3 = tall hedges with trees, 4 = woodland) and field area (1 = <5 ha, 2 = 5–10 ha, 3 = 10–15 ha, 4 = 15–20 ha), fitted from statistical models. From Whittingham* et al. *(2003).*

beyond it. The distribution of Skylarks is clearly determined both by the quality of individual habitats and by the structure of the landscape they occur in. This has considerable implications for conservation, since farmers wishing to provide good breeding or wintering habitats for Skylarks on their land will achieve little if they place these habitats close to woodland, or in small fields enclosed by tall hedgerows. However, this avoidance of woodland and other tall structures may be limited to farmland habitats. Research carried out in Germany by Thomas Schaefer (2001) has challenged the commonly held view that avoidance by Skylarks of woodland edges is a common behaviour in all habitats. He has shown that in semi-open land-scapes, with patches of open land surrounded by woodland, Skylarks are capable of breeding right up to woodland edges. In such habitats, Skylarks occupy more open habitats than Woodlarks, which require numerous perches. Skylark nests are uncovered and built a long distance from vertical structures, whereas Woodlark nests are covered and built close to woodland edges. All this suggests that perhaps Skylarks evolved as birds of semi-open habitats, like the Woodlark, but unlike that species have been successful at adapting to completely open habitats when these were made available by human clearance of forests. However this does not explain why Skylarks should so clearly avoid woodland edges on farmland.

One of the consequences of increasing affluence in western Europe has been a huge rise in car ownership, and a massive increase in the length of road networks. In England alone, around 400 billion km are driven by motor vehicles each year, a figure around 20% higher than ten years ago. This has brought with it both social and environmental problems, and the construction of major new roads is often greeted with impassioned public protest, particularly where such roads carve through important wildlife habitats. It is becoming increasingly clear, however, that roads create environmental problems that extend far beyond their verges. Important research in the Netherlands has shown that numbers of many breeding birds are greatly reduced in habitats bordering roads, and that these reductions are detectable even hundreds of metres away (Reijnen *et al.* 1996). The degree to which bird numbers are depressed close to roads varies with the amount of traffic, the speed it travels and the species concerned. On quieter roads, with less than 5,000 cars passing per day, numbers of Skylarks are lower within 100 m of the road, but beyond 100 m densities return to normal. Busy roads, carrying 50,000 vehicles or more per day, have a far more serious impact on numbers of Skylarks, which are significantly reduced as far away as 1.5 km from such roads. Similar results have been shown from research on birds of coastal grazing marshes in England (Milsom *et al.* 2001), where Skylark numbers are greatly reduced even around minor roads. This study suggested that territory densities of Skylarks close to roads are only around a third of those 3 km away. This reduction in numbers appears to be due to noise pollution, which may interfere with territoriality and, in certain species, prey location. In countries like the Netherlands and the UK, with dense and busy road networks, increases in noise pollution may have had a serious, though so far unquantified, impact on the numbers of many species.

## POPULATIONS AND POPULATION TRENDS

It is extremely difficult to estimate with any accuracy the populations of wild bird species. Looking at maps of even as small a country as the United Kingdom, one quickly realises the futility of hoping to see and count more than a tiny fraction of the birds that must be present. However, three developments have combined to allow ornithologists in many European countries to make reasonable estimates of the populations of wild birds over far larger areas than would otherwise be possible. The first has been the growth in the popularity of birdwatching as a hobby, with the massive increase in the number of skilled and dedicated observers that this has brought. The second has been the growth of volunteer-based organisations such as the British Trust for Ornithology (BTO), whose professional staff is able to muster large numbers of volunteers to go out and count birds. The third has been the development and adoption of statistical methods to select which areas to count and to analyse the resultant data.

Despite all these advances, the Skylark populations in many European countries remain poorly known, and there are no reliable population estimates at all for most countries outside Europe. The uncertainty of the population in Europe is reflected in the wide range of estimated values, the total European population lying somewhere between 25 and 55 million pairs (Table 3.3). The countries holding the greatest numbers of pairs are Russia, Poland, Spain, Bulgaria, Germany and Belarus. Other European countries with populations of up to or over a million breeding pairs include the Czech Republic, Denmark, France, Italy, Latvia, Lithuania, Portugal, Romania, Sweden, Ukraine and the United Kingdom. There are clearly huge differences in territory density across Europe. For example, the population estimate for the tiny country of Latvia, between 1.1 and 1.8 million pairs, is greater than that for France, with a maximum of 1.3 million pairs, and that for the UK, which in 1997 was estimated at approximately a million pairs (Browne *et al.* 2000). Population densities of Skylarks appear to increase eastwards across Europe, a phenomenon that, as we shall see later, is largely related to differences in agriculture.

The population of Skylarks in the UK is known with a good degree of precision. In 1997, the BTO organised a national survey of breeding Skylarks to try to estimate the population (Browne *et al.* 2000). Some 600 volunteer fieldworkers covered more than 600 km$^2$ of countryside, carefully selected to yield the most representative results. The results of this survey suggested a UK breeding population of between 800,000 and one million pairs. This makes the Skylark one of the most abundant breeding birds in the UK, and might seem to indicate that all is well with the Skylark population. In fact, quite the opposite is true. Although the number of Skylarks remaining is relatively large compared to many other species, the number that has been lost since the 1980s has been even greater. Results of the BTO's Common Birds Census show that populations of Skylarks now are less than half what they were during the early 1980s, a loss of between a million and a million and a half pairs (Figure 3.4). The same monitoring scheme also showed

*Table 3.3. Population estimates and trends of breeding Skylarks in Europe. Updated from BirdLife International/European Bird Census Council (2000).*

| Country | Population (pairs) | Population trend |
|---|---|---|
| Albania | 500–1,000 | ? |
| Austria | 40,000–50,000 | Decline |
| Belarus | 2,300,000–3,000,000 | Stable |
| Belgium | 100,000–140,000 | Decline |
| Bulgaria | 1,000,000–5,000,000 | Stable |
| Croatia | 200,000–250,000 | Stable |
| Czech Republic | 800,000–1,600,000 | Decline |
| Denmark | 1,360,000 | Decline |
| Faeroe Islands | 10 | Decline |
| Estonia | 100,000–200,000 | Decline |
| Finland | 300,000–400,000 | Decline |
| France | 300,000–1,300,000 | Decline |
| Germany | 2,500,000–3,500,000 | Severe decline |
| Greece | 2,000–5,000 | Stable |
| Hungary | 300,000–800,000 | Decline |
| Italy | 500,000–1,000,000 | Decline |
| Latvia | 1,100,000–1,800,000 | Increase |
| Liechtenstein | 35 | Severe decline |
| Lithuania | 800,000–1,400,000 | Stable |
| Luxembourg | 10,000–15,000 | Decline |
| Moldova | 50,000–70,000 | Stable |
| Netherlands | 150,000–175,000 | Severe decline |
| Norway | 100,000–500,000 | Stable |
| Poland | 5,000,000–9,000,000 | Stable |
| Portugal | 100,000–1,000,000 | Decline |
| Republic of Ireland | 490,000 | Decline |
| Romania | 600,000–1,000,000 | Stable |
| Russia | 1,000,000–10,000,000 | Stable |
| Slovakia | 200,000–400,000 | Stable |
| Slovenia | 8,000–12,000 | Severe decline |
| Spain | 2,000,000–6,000,000 | Decline |
| Sweden | 700,000–1,000,000 | Decline |
| Switzerland | 40,000–50,000 | Decline |
| Turkey | 50,000–500,000 | ? |
| Ukraine | 900,000–1,000,000 | Increase |
| UK | 1,000,000 | Severe decline |
| Guernsey | 25–100 | Stable |
| Isle of Man | 100–200 | Decline |
| Jersey | 100–200 | Stable |
| Total (approx) | 25,000,000–55,000,000 | |

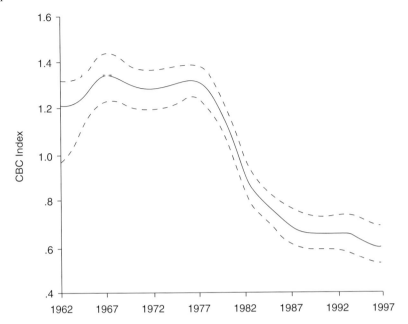

*Figure 3.4.   Population trend of the Skylark in the UK, 1962–1997, from the Common Birds Census. The graph shows the smoothed Mountford index (solid line) with 95% confidence limits (dotted lines). The index is set to an arbitrary value of 1.0 in 1980. From data in Siriwardena* et al. *(1998).*

huge declines in the populations of most other farmland species (Siriwardena *et al.* 1998), suggesting that changes in agriculture have been at least partly to blame. Although the overall percentage declines of some other species have been greater (the Tree Sparrow, for example, declined by more than 80% over the same period), the abundance of Skylarks means that British farmland may have lost more individual Skylarks than individuals of all the other species combined.

Dan Chamberlain and Humphrey Crick (1999) have examined this decline in greater detail, by assessing whether trends have been the same in different habitats. Their results showed that declines have been greatest on intensively managed lowland farmland, with less severe (though still significant) declines in coastal and upland habitats. It is not only on lowland farmland that populations have declined: severe declines have also been reported in upland farmland (Fuller *et al.* 2002). Population declines have also been recorded in some non-agricultural habitats in the UK. For example, massive reductions in numbers have been recorded in populations nesting in peatland habitats and young conifer plantations in Scotland, possibly because these birds winter on farmland, where winter feeding resources may have declined (Hancock & Avery 1998).

This general pattern of massive population decline is not confined to the UK. Severe declines have been recorded in many other countries, including Italy (de Carli *et al.* 1998), Sweden (Robertson & Berg 1992), Germany (Busche 1989,

1994) and western Poland (Tryjanowski 2000b). Across most of western Europe, in fact, populations of Skylarks have dropped dramatically. Table 3.3 shows that Skylark populations are in decline, or severe decline, in well over half of all European countries. A quite different pattern of change is apparent in a number of eastern European countries, where numbers have remained stable, or have even increased greatly. In Latvia, for example, populations showed an increase in numbers between 1990 and 2002 (Figure 3.5), as the collapse of Communism led to a reduction in state support for agriculture, with a consequent reduction in agricultural inputs and the abandonment of some land (Auninš *et al.* 2001). Similar stability or increases in numbers are apparent in most formerly Communist eastern European countries. Preliminary results from a new pan-European common bird monitoring scheme suggest that, across Europe as a whole, Skylark populations fell by 10 to 20% between 1990 and 2002. This was due almost entirely to severe declines in western and northern Europe, as populations in eastern and southern Europe remained virtually unchanged (RSPB/European Bird Census Council/ Birdlife International).

Outside Europe, very little is known of Skylark population trends. However, counts of breeding birds around the Selenga River Delta, which flows into Lake Baikal in eastern Siberia, suggest that here too populations declined greatly between 1984 and 1991, although this might have been influenced by purely local conditions relating to water flow into the lake (Fefelov *et al.* 2001).

The late twentieth century may not have been the first period in which Skylark populations declined greatly. The declines in numbers of Skylarks during the late

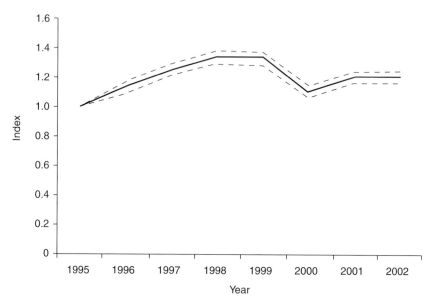

*Figure 3.5.   Population trend of Skylarks in Latvia, 1995–2002. Data supplied by Ainârs Auninš.*

nineteenth century, described by Lord Lilford at the head of this chapter and by many other ornithologists of the period, may well have been due to the general decline in arable agriculture that took place at the time, although most contemporary writers blamed it on the intense hunting pressure on Skylarks then (see Chapter 13). During this period, numbers of another bird of arable agriculture, the Corn Bunting, were also in severe decline through the abandonment of arable land (Donald *et al.* 1994), and it seems likely the population trends of the two species were similar and related.

The reasons for the recent massive population declines across western Europe have been investigated in great detail in a number of countries, and this research has clearly identified the main causes. Before we can begin to understand these declines, however, we need to examine in detail the Skylark's ecology, because, as we shall see in later chapters, a detailed understanding of how the Skylark uses its habitat is fundamental to understanding why it has declined so dramatically. So we shall leave these population collapses behind us for a few chapters and instead examine in detail the life history of the Skylark. Once we have done this, we shall return to the question of why Skylark populations are crashing all over Europe, and will discover that the some of the reasons are really very unexpected indeed.

*Skylark singing from perch*

CHAPTER 4

# Song and song flight

When day's bright banner, first unfurl'd
From darkness, frees the shrouded world,
The skylark, singing as he soars,
On the fresh air his carol pours;
But though to Heaven he wings his flight,
As if he loved those realms of light,
He still returns with weary wing
On earth to end his wandering.

Aspiring bird, in thee I find
An emblem of the youthful mind,
Whose earliest voice, like thine, is given
To notes of joy that mount to heaven;
But fetter'd by the toils of life,
Its sordid cares, its bitter strife,
It feels its noble efforts vain,
And sadly sinks to earth again.

James Northcote, Fable XXXVI, from *Fables, Original and Selected* (1833)

The Skylark has become one of Europe's most familiar and artistically celebrated species by sole virtue of its song flight. Indeed the scientific name of the genus *Alauda*, and by extension the name of the whole family of the Alaudidae, probably comes from a Latin corruption of the Celtic for 'great singer' (*al*, great; *awd*, song). This behaviour has raised it in the public consciousness, and the poetic canon, as no other small, brown bird, with the possible exception of its musical rival, the Nightingale. That two such visually unprepossessing birds should be so famed for their song is not surprising, since throughout the songbird world there is a general inverse relationship between plumage coloration and song development. In simple terms, brightly coloured birds use visual cues to attract mates, dull birds rely more on song. For example, the strikingly coloured and patterned New World warblers have weaker, quieter songs than their drab Old World counterparts (only very distant relatives, in fact), which boast such accomplished songsters as the Marsh Warbler and the Blackcap.

The song flight of the Skylark is not only spiritually uplifting but also represents the peak of development of a poorly understood form of bird behaviour that has received relatively little scientific attention. It consists of two elements, the song itself and the aerial display flight from which it is usually delivered. The latter has undoubtedly contributed more to the species' (literally) elevated status than the former, for the song itself, though long, loud and fairly complex, is unremarkable when considered in isolation. These two elements of the male Skylark's display are discussed here separately, although it is of course the combination of the two that makes a singing Skylark such a conspicuous feature of the countryside.


# SONG


Song in birds serves a number of purposes. It is a device male birds use to attract and then keep a mate, to attract non-mate females, to reduce the chances of being cuckolded and to alert other birds to the fact that the singer is holding a territory. As is being discovered in an increasing number of species, it can also act as a signal to deter potential predators.

It is notoriously difficult to describe the song of birds in words, this being an area in which the poet is superior to the scientist. The song of the Skylark is particularly difficult to describe, as it is fast, complex and highly variable, and I can only hope that most readers are familiar enough with it for me to be spared the task of trying to put it into words. Its complexity, however, is constrained within a fairly narrow frequency range, virtually all sounds falling in the band between 2 and 6 kHz (Figure 4.1). The song typically starts with a series of relatively slow, clear whistles as the male begins his song flight, accelerating in speed and complexity to a seemingly uninterrupted stream of notes. Within this stream, however, it is often possible to hear slower phrases, the most common being a three-note ascending sequence of high vibrato notes.

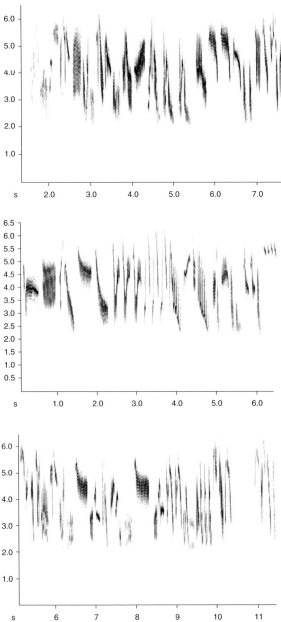

*Figure 4.1.    Spectrograms of a Skylark song, recorded in France. The three separate images relate to sections of the start, middle and end of the song. The spectrograms were produced using the Canary 1.2.4 package, the filter bandwidth was 174.85 Hz and the grid resolution 11.61 ms. The vertical axis represents the frequency of the sounds in kHz, the horizontal axis the time in seconds. Recorded and produced by Gillian Gilbert.*

The meticulously observant Juan Delius (1963), whose pioneering work on Skylarks in the early 1960s remains a vital source of information for modern researchers, recognised three types of song: the song given in flight; the similar but slower, more muted and less ebullient song given from the ground; and the harsh, almost manic, song given by a male pursuing another bird from his territory. Studying Skylarks in Poland, Piotr Tryjanowski (2000a) also found that ground song is more monotonous and quieter than songs given in flight, and suggested that it may serve a different function, perhaps acting as a form of communication between the members of a pair, or between adults and chicks. A further song type was proposed by Lange (1951), who considered that during the descending part of the song flight, the song takes on a minor key and is slower and quieter than during the ascent. According to William Yarrell (1861), "an ear well tuned to his song can even then determine by the notes whether the bird is still ascending, remaining stationary or on the descent." This difference in tone in the ascending and descending flights gave rise to an old country fable that on its ascending flight the Skylark is joyous at the thought of entering Heaven. Having been refused entry by Saint Peter, the lark's song takes on a more melancholy minor key on its descent. An unusual example of coordinated singing is described by D.G. Andrew (1952), who observed an extraordinarily large flock of around a thousand Skylarks that had gathered at a reservoir in Scotland in March 1951, after being forced from their newly occupied moorland breeding territories by late snow. Several hundred of the birds were issuing "a very quietly murmured song on the ground and the combination of so many voices produced a very impressive volume of sound though it bore no resemblance to the bird's normal tuneful song". This probably represents an unusual mass-delivery of the species' subsong, a very specific type of song the purpose of which is poorly understood.

Although the Skylark's song appears to the human ear to be continuous, analyses show it to be made up of a series of discrete phrases or syllables punctuated by short gaps. The analyses by Brackenbury (1978) of slowed-down recordings printed onto paper (called sonograms or spectrograms) showed that the syllables, during which the bird is exhaling, last 350 to 600 milliseconds, and the gaps between, during which the bird is inhaling, last 30 to 100 milliseconds. Within each syllable there are also short gaps, estimated by Csicsáky (1978) to last around 11 milliseconds, far too short for a complete inhalation but possibly enough to partly refill the air sacs from the preceding pulse of sound. Both these types of gap, between- and within-syllable, are apparent in the spectrograms shown in Figure 4.1. As the resting breathing rate of a bird the size of a Skylark is likely to be around one breath per second, these recordings suggest that during song flights, breathing rates are increased as much as fourfold. The frequency of song pulses appears to be dictated by the bird's rate of ventilation but not by the frequency of its wing beats (Csicsáky 1978). Brackenbury (1978) suggested that the rhythm of Skylark song was determined by three separate mechanisms: the underlying respiratory rate, a high frequency respiratory oscillation superimposed upon the underlying respiratory rate, and cyclical contractions of the syringeal muscles. All three rhythmic regulators may be employed in a single syllable. Each phrase is made up of a succession of pulsed sounds, which may be single or in repeated groups. When these are suffi- ciently slow, our ears can detect them as distinct trills, but often they are too fast and the sound appears continuous. However, the complexity of the song is proba bly not lost on other Skylarks, since birds have auditory time discrimination abili- ties that are greatly superior to those of humans.

Song is given mainly by the males, with around 95% of all song being delivered within 100 m of the nest. However, females have a subsong resembling a short and muted version of the male's that is most commonly heard during pair formation, mating and nest building, and as an anxiety call when predators approach the nest. Females appear to be capable of producing a convincingly male-like song. Arthur Butler, writing over a century ago (1896–98), described a Skylark kept in his aviary which "although it was a small bird it sang so well that I felt certain it must be a cock and never examined it; eventually it settled the point by laying an egg." He went on to make the intriguing observation that, in his experience, hand-reared females often sang well, whereas wild-caught females never did. This might have been due at least partly to hormonal changes brought about by unnatural sur- roundings or a change in diet. Skylarks sing well in captivity—the species "bears confinement well, is easily tamed and is an exceptionally free singer in its exile", according to one Victorian naturalist (Dixon 1897)—and the species was a popu- lar cagebird in the eighteenth and nineteenth centuries. Good singers commanded prices of over 15 shillings in the 1850s, a huge cost in today's terms. Caged larks were often blinded, as this was thought to make them sing better.

The repertoire size of individual Skylarks seems to vary, from around 160 to over 460 syllables (Markus Jenny and colleagues, unpublished data), making it a partic- ularly complex song. This complexity is often increased by the insertion into the song of imitations of other bird species. Imitations of the songs or calls of a wide range of birds have been recorded in Skylark song. Particularly common are the calls of waders, and imitations of Greenshank, Redshank, Little Ringed Plover, Oystercatcher, Curlew, Whimbrel and Spotted Redshank have all been recorded (Simms 1992). In Russia, the list also includes Broad-billed Sandpiper and Pacific Golden Plover. On the Gwent Levels, south Wales, where Shelducks are common, the bubbling call of this species is often heard in Skylark song. Other species that have been mimicked include Buzzard, Marsh Warbler, Linnet and Corn Bunting. Song mimicry has been shown in a number of species to confer considerable advan- tages on the singer, since greater song repertoires are more attractive to females. There appears to be considerable regional variation in the incidence of mimicry by Skylarks. Lange (1951) reported it as being very rare in Denmark, whereas other observers report it to be common. The only quantitative study of mimicry in Skylark song appears to be that of Fefelov (1997), who recorded 116 instances of mimicry during a total of 73 minutes of song, with an average of five imitations per song. This mimicry included snatches of the songs or calls of at least 38 different species, again mainly waders, but also Common Tern, Swallow, Richard's Pipit, Goldcrest, Lapland Bunting and Arctic Warbler. Fefelov also recorded snatches of song of several species not found in his Siberian study site, and suggested that birds were learning these on their wintering grounds. Eric Simms (1992) describes a conversation with an Australian ornithologist, in which he learned that the Skylarks introduced into Australia have not been heard to mimic any other species, possibly because their territory density is so low that mimicry does not confer an advantage. The ability of Skylarks to mimic other species was recognised by Victorian owners and dealers of caged birds. In order to prevent their caged birds from losing their original song in favour of imitations of other captive birds, they would often place them in cages next to newly caught birds to keep them, as they called it, 'honest'.

In some species, there are regional or local dialects in song that differ from those of neighbouring groups. These dialects appear to be culturally or behaviourally derived, rather than genetically. One species in which regional dialects appear to be particularly well developed (or, perhaps, just particularly well studied) is the Corn Bunting, which has local dialects so distinctive that, with experience, they can be discerned in the field by the human ear (McGregor *et al.* 1997). Paradoxically, the only published description of local dialects in lark song come from a species that does not even have a song! The Flappet Lark of Africa has a display flight in which the song has been replaced by a loud buzzing caused by clapping the wings together rapidly in flight. Local dialects in these bursts of clapping have been identified, different 'accents' differing in the number of claps per burst of clapping and the interval between bursts (Payne 1978).

This 'microgeographic' variation in song is thought to arise most readily in species with complex songs that imitate other birds, a large geographical range, and strong site tenacity. As the Skylark satisfies all these criteria, it might be expected to show strong regional variation in song. The casual observations of several Skylark researchers suggest that there is indeed considerable regional variation in Skylark song, particularly in the first few phrases of the ascending song flight. However the only formal scientific investigation of this is the work of the seminal Skylark researcher Markus Jenny and his colleagues, as yet unpublished. Their work, carried out in Switzerland, suggests that sub-populations as close as 1.5 km apart differ markedly in their songs. As distances between birds increase, so the similarities of their songs decline. Although the Skylark shows all the characteristics of species likely to exhibit regional song variation, the preliminary findings of Markus Jenny and his colleagues suggest that the species is unusual in the scale of such variation. Previous work on song dialects in other species has shown that microgeographic song variation tends to be located within the phonetic structure of the song, whereas 'macrogeographic' variation (differences in the song of birds separated by large distances or by physical barriers) involves entire syllable repertoires. The findings of Markus Jenny and his colleagues suggest that even over very short distances, Skylark songs differ in basic syllable composition. This is an area of research that would well reward further investigation.

With such a high level of complexity within its own song, with strong variation over short distances and with imitations of many other birds frequently thrown in, how do Skylarks recognise their neighbours' songs as belonging to the same species?

Or, put another way, how can a male be sure that his neighbours recognise his song as being that of a Skylark? Clearly, if they didn't, there would be little point in his defending a territory with song. This interesting question was addressed by Thierry Aubin and Jean-Claude Bremond, working in France in the late 1970s and early 1980s. They found that male Skylarks respond just as readily to a monotonous synthetic electronic 'song' with the same basic structure as real song as they do to the real thing. However, birds habituated more rapidly to the synthetic song than they did to real song, responding less and less to repeated artificial songs the longer they were exposed to them (Aubin 1982). This suggested that having a wide repertoire prevents Skylarks from becoming habituated to the songs of their neighbours. The researchers then addressed the question of which element of the song Skylarks used to recognise their neighbours' songs—was it song length, pitch, timing or size of repertoire? To test this, they used artificially generated 'songs' with different elements of the real song encoded within them. Skylarks responded weakly to very simple songs which mimicked just one of the three elements of Skylark song (the diversity of individual song elements, the pitch of individual song elements, and the ratio of song to silence). However, they reacted strongly to signals that simultaneously imitated all three, suggesting that song recognition depends on the detection of sounds that are complex in many dimensions (Aubin & Bremond 1983).

Skylark song serves not only to advertise for a mate and defend a territory, but also to send a signal to predators. Within a particular species of predator, there is considerable variation between individual birds in their ability to catch prey. Similar variation exists amongst individuals of the prey species: some birds are better at evading predation than others. Individual variation in the ability of a bird to catch or to be caught is likely to be the result of many factors, including age, experience, health and innate genetic competence. When an individual of the prey species is fit and healthy and well able to escape a predator, it benefits itself (and, incidentally, the predator) if it signals this to its attacker, thus avoiding a long chase and high expenditure of energy that benefits neither individual. For such a system to evolve, the signal must be an honest one. Young predators learn to hunt largely through experience and are unlikely to be deterred in the future by behavioural signals that carry no true message. If all individuals of a prey species, irrespective of their ability to escape predation, tried to use the same signal to indicate to predators that they are particularly fit and healthy, the predators would quickly learn to ignore that signal. Honest signals must therefore incur a real cost for the prey individual, thereby demonstrating to the predator that it really does have resources to spare, above and beyond avoiding capture. Fascinating research carried out by Will Cresswell in Scotland during the early 1990s showed that song was used as such a pursuit-deterrent signal by Skylarks. Over three winters, he witnessed nearly 300 attacks by Merlins on Skylarks, recording the duration of the chase, the behavioural response of the Skylark (escape by flight, drop to the ground and hide, or join a flock) and the outcome of the chase (Cresswell 1994). Merlins were found to chase silent or weakly singing birds for longer periods than they chased birds in full song, and to catch them more often. The falcons chased silent Skylarks for an average of

80 seconds, successfully catching over 40% of them. In contrast, the chase time for Skylarks in full song was only 30 seconds, with a success rate for the falcon of just 5%. Birds giving the full territorial song were twice as likely to survive a Merlin attack as birds giving short phrases of subsong, and were chased for far less long. Silent birds stood the best chance of escape if they joined a flock, whereas singing birds did best if they tried to outfly the falcon. As singing during the winter cannot serve to attract a mate or to defend a breeding territory, the song must be a genuine communication from the Skylark to the Merlin, to the benefit of both. It is possible that female Skylarks also sing full male-type song when being chased. In his detailed but as yet unpublished study of Skylarks, John Hutchinson has heard a female in full song just once, and that was when it was being chased by a Peregrine. There is evidence that as they grow older and become more experienced, Merlins learn to avoid singing Skylarks. It would be interesting to know what characteristics predispose a Skylark to escape by singing or by hiding. Further research is necessary to determine whether male and female Skylarks are equally able to sing during an attack, or whether females, which sing less than the males and are physiologically less well adapted to aerial song flights (as discussed in the next section) suffer higher predation by Merlins.

## THE SONG FLIGHT

Aerial song flights are characteristic of several families of birds associated largely with open country. Amongst the songbirds, song flights are well developed in certain species of warbler (such as the aptly named Cloud-scraping Cisticola of Africa), in some pipits, many larks, thrushes, finches and buntings, and in a small number of species in other families. It is a form of behaviour that is irregularly distributed throughout the bird world, and is restricted to a few distinct taxa within some of the more recently evolved orders. It therefore seems to have evolved independently in different families, and to have arisen relatively recently. The habit reaches the peak of its development in the larks, in which a higher proportion of species undertake aerial song flights than in any other terrestrial bird family. Most larks have an aerial song flight, but its height and duration vary greatly between families, between species within families and even between individuals within species.

As we saw in Chapter 1, taxonomists have used the complexity of the song flight as an aid to classifying the larks, and within the family as a whole there is a gradation from the complete absence of a song flight in some species to very complex song flights in others. In the Western Palaearctic, song flights of larks are well developed in the genera *Eremalauda*, *Chersophilus*, *Rhamphocoris*, *Melanocorypha*, *Calandrella*, *Gallerida*, *Lullula*, *Alauda* and *Eremophila*, less well developed in *Eremopterix* and *Ammomanes*, and restricted to a short but elaborate low-level swooping display in *Alaemon*. In some larks, such as the Flappet Lark of Africa, the song element has been dispensed with altogether in the song flight, being replaced by an aerial wing-clapping display, during which the bird doubles its wing-beat rate and claps it wings together to make a loud rattling sound (Norberg 1991).

The song flight is an evolutionary complexity. Given the predominance of song flights in open country species such as the larks, it might seem likely that the song flight is a device to broadcast song more widely in a landscape devoid of tall perches. Alternatively, it might be advantageous to males to survey their own and their neighbours' territories from a height, for evidence of cuckoldry of their own mates or to watch for opportunities to mate with their neighbours' partners. In woodland, male songbirds sing from elevated perches for both these reasons. In open-country species, both are particularly plausible explanations, given the generally low productivity of open-country habitats, which results in lower population densities and hence greater distances between individual birds. However, as so often in the natural world, the obvious explanation is not necessarily the correct one. Many woodland species, such as the familiar Greenfinch, also have elaborate song flights, albeit between arboreal perches, and many open-country species, including some of the larks (see Chapter 1), lack song flights altogether.

A more likely explanation is that the song flight has evolved as a form of sexual advertisement. Like the peacock's tail, song flights have very real costs in terms of energy expenditure and predation risk, and so must confer tangible advantages upon birds that undertake them. Song flights, in fact, probably serve as an honest indicator of the male's fitness, increasing both his attractiveness to females and his ability to defend his territory from other males or other species. A similar situation has been documented in another open-country species, the Lapwing: females' choice of males is based upon the roll angle of their aerial song display flights, which is determined by the width of the male's wing. In that species, broader wings allow males to be aerobatically more manoeuvrable and so to defend nest sites better from predators (Grønstøl 1996), a benefit of obvious value to the female. Whether the ability of a male Skylark to undertake long song flights indicates some specific advantages of that bird as a partner (such as nest protection, as in the case of the Lapwing), or whether it simply indicates a high level of overall fitness, is not known. The song broadcasting, mate watching and sexual selection explanations of song flight are certainly not mutually exclusive, and the evolution of the behaviour is unknown. Perhaps the ancestral larks used simple aerial song flights as substitutes for treetop perches, and this behaviour then developed into the spectacular song flight of the Skylark through the same complex sexual selection that has given us the bizarre displays of the birds of paradise and the unlikely peacock's tail. What seems certain is that the open nature of the habitat inhabited by most species that make elaborate aerial displays has been influential in the evolution of those displays. A woodland species making an aerial display flight is likely to be noticed by fewer of its own species than is a bird inhabiting treeless deserts or steppes.

Any researchers willing to undertake the seemingly impossible task of quantifying the relative costs and benefits of the different elements of song flight behaviour and its evolution would be amply rewarded for their efforts. An interesting start

*Plate 1. Races of the Skylark. Clockwise from top left: adult* arvensis, *juvenile* arvensis, *adult* cantarella, *adult* sierrae, *adult* pekinensis, *adult* harterti, *adult* dulcivox. *All birds are in moderately fresh plumage (November – January) and illustrate extremes in variation compared to the nominate. The eggs show the range of variation, most lying between the second and the fourth in the series.*

*Plate 2.    The Alauda larks perched and in flight. From top to bottom: Skylark (nominate), Japanese Skylark, Oriental Skylark (nominate) and Raso Lark.*

*Plate 3.   top left and right: male Raso Lark digging for the bulbs of nutsedges, one of the few sources of water on its tiny, arid island home (Sabine Hille) bottom: Oriental Skylark, photographed in Israel where it is a rare non-breeding visitor (Leo Boon).*

*Plate 4.    top left: Skylark of the nominate race, photographed in Sweden. The raised crest suggests that this bird is a male (Henry Lehto) top right: a rare photograph of a leucistic Skylark, taken in Switzerland (Markus Jenny) lower left and right: Skylark in song flight showing the broadness of the wing, an adaptation that reduces energy costs during the display (David Tipling).*

*Plate 5.    top left: Skylark eggs hatching in a nest on a grass verge (Paul F. Donald) top right: Skylark nest in cereals, adjacent to a tramline (Paul F. Donald) centre left and right: Skylark chicks develop very rapidly; this chick is pictured at two days old and again at eight days old, when it is ready to leave the nest (Lys B. Muirhead) lower left: a rare photograph of a Skylark chick that has left the nest; fledging is still a week or more away (Paul F. Donald) lower right: Skylark nest predated by a mammal, probably a Hedgehog; the predator was probably interrupted as usually all nest contents are removed (Paul F. Donald).*

*Plate 6.    top: Skylark bringing food to chicks in a nest in Switzerland; these chicks are around 4 days old (Markus Jenny) lower left: a well camouflaged Skylark nest in set-aside; when danger threatens, the chicks flatten themselves in the nest (Markus Jenny) lower right: a Skylark in juvenile plumage; this bird is now fully independent and will shortly moult the juvenile feathers and become indistinguishable from an adult (Henry Lehto).*

*Plate 7.    The perils of nesting on farmland. top: Skylark eggs in a nest in grassland crushed during mowing in May (Paul F. Donald) bottom: Skylark chick from a nest in cereals killed during harvesting in July (Paul F. Donald).*

*Plate 8.    top left: "Skylark scrapes" on the RSPB's experimental farm in Cambridgeshire; these unsown patches within the cereal crop provide considerable advantages for Skylarks in winter cereal landscapes (Roger Buisson) top right: tramlines in cereals offer both opportunities and threats for nesting Skylarks (Paul F. Donald) centre left: much modern grassland is overgrazed and provides insufficient cover for nesting Skylarks (Paul F. Donald) centre right: changes in agricultural econom-ics have produced landscapes lacking in diversity, such as this cereal monoculture in Oxfordshire, which offer few advantages for nesting Skylarks (Lys B. Muirhead) lower left: set-aside offers many advantages, but also several disadvantages, for Skylarks (Paul F. Donald) lower right: the effects of agrochemicals on Skylarks are difficult to quantify, since many other changes have taken place on farmland (Paul F. Donald).*

would be to assess whether male Skylarks making the highest or longest song flights attract the best mates and father more chicks. Certainly, work on an unrelated species that also employs song flights, the Bobolink of North America, has shown that males making longer song flights are in better body condition, attract more females and father more chicks than males making shorter flights. The attractiveness of males to females was reduced when the males' wings were clipped to reduce song flight length (Mather & Robertson 1992). Song flights of Bobolinks therefore appear to be honest sexual signals of a male's quality, and it is likely that this is also the case in other birds that make song flights.

The energetics of Skylark song flights have attracted considerable scientific interest. Song flights are amongst the most energetically demanding results of all the many forms of sexual selection found throughout the animal kingdom. Rising vertically would appear to be very demanding; to do so while singing continuously seems to us an extraordinary feat. Yet research has shown that, during the vertical ascent, the male Skylark is flying well within the limits of his maximum potential energy expenditure. The average power expenditure during the vertical ascent of the Skylarks studied by Hedenström (1995) was less than half the theoretical maximum sustainable capacity. It is therefore likely that the rate of climb of a male during song flight imparts little information to the female on the male's fitness, since poor birds can probably rise as fast as very fit birds. Nevertheless, song flights are energetically very demanding, and the vertical ascent phase of the song flight requires around twice the energy expenditure required for level flight. It is not surprising therefore that Delius (1965) found that longer song flights were followed by longer rest periods (although not necessarily preceded by them).

As song flights are energetically costly, morphological adaptations that reduce energy expenditure should be favoured by natural selection. The prolific Danish ornithologist Anders Møller has investigated the influence of Skylark morphology on the length of song flights. He found that the wings of male Skylarks are both absolutely and, more important, relatively longer and of greater area than those of females, giving males a lower wing loading (the ratio of body weight to wing area) (Møller 1991). With practice, it is possible to use these subtle differences in structure to determine the sex of individual Skylarks in the field, particularly when a pair is flying together. Although males' tarsi are only 2.8% longer than those of females, their wing area is 11% greater and their wing loading 3.9% lower (Plate 4). The sternum (breastbone), the point of anchorage of the main flight muscles, is also relatively larger in males than females (Nussbaumer 1992, Lüps *et al.* 1993). It is not surprising, therefore, that there is a significant relationship between wing loading and the length of song flight in males: males with a lower wing loading make longer song flights than males with higher wing loading. This is likely to be because lower wing loading reduces the energy expenditure of flight. Møller proved his hypothesis by experimentally manipulating wing loading. He artificially increased wing loading by removing the outermost 10 mm of some male Skylarks' wing feathers and found that this resulted in a significant shortening of song flights. It seems, therefore, that males that invest more energy in growing longer flight feathers during moult to increase their wing area, and so to lower wing loading, are rewarded with longer song flights and, presumably, more or better females.

Møller's discovery that male Skylarks are morphologically adapted to reduce energy costs during song flight appears to apply to all birds that make song flights. Pairing closely related species in a number of different families, one that has an aerial song flight and one that does not, Hedenström & Møller (1992) found a general pattern among songbirds that reflects Møller's Skylark results. Those species with song flights have a consistently larger wing span and wing area and a lower wing loading than their less energetic relatives. The exact characteristics found to be associated with species that make song flights suggest that manoeuvrability and flapping-flight performance have been the main selective forces affecting the morphology of males, but not flight speed or rate of climb. The song flight of the Skylark is essentially an endurance-type song flight, aimed primarily at increasing the duration of the level flapping-flight phase. Ascent and descent probably carry less information on the male's fitness, since both are carried out well within the maximum theoretical energetic limits. Females prefer males who can stay up for longer!

The low wing loading of males is therefore a selective response to female mate choice: the selection by females of certain characteristics has brought about changes in the shape of male Skylarks. But to have a lower wing loading requires relatively greater feather growth. The cost to males of growing longer wing feathers to increase song-flight duration is difficult to quantify. Not only does extra feather growth incur a direct cost in the conversion of energy to keratin, but it is possible that low wing loadings, while beneficial for song flights, might be disadvantageous in level flight, for example during migration or when being chased by a predator, when a higher wing loading would facilitate more rapid flight (Hedenström & Alerstam 1996). It may be that male Skylarks have incurred considerable risks in maximising the duration of their song flights.

The altitude and duration of the Skylark's song flight have fascinated people for hundreds of years, although surprisingly few quantitative studies have been undertaken. Victorian naturalists often described birds ascending to immense altitudes, with heights of over 2,000 feet (600 m) being frequently mentioned. These are likely to be gross exaggerations, or at best extremely rare events. Around half of all song flights reach a maximum height of over 50 m, but heights of over 200 m are uncommon. Anders Hedenström and his colleagues, working in Sweden in the early 1990s, carried out detailed research into the energetics and duration of Skylark song flights. Using an optical range finder and a film camera, they were able to calculate the rate of ascent and descent of singing birds and the frequency of their wing beats. They found that in the initial climbing flight, birds rose at around 1 m per second until the final altitude was reached, the wings beating at around 10–12 beats per second (Hedenström 1995). The rate of climb was positively correlated with the final altitude reached, but was always considerably below (and never above 70% of) the theoretical maximum. In their study, Hedenström & Alerstam (1996) recorded the average maximum height reached during the climb at 135 m, with the highest recorded at 223 m. There was a significant positive relationship between the maximum height reached in any song flight and the duration of that song flight: greater heights were reached during longer song flights. After the initial ascent comes a period of level flight, which makes up the greatest part of the song flight. In Hedenström & Alerstam's sample of 63 birds, this took place at an average altitude of 120 m, the lowest recorded at 30 m and the highest at 210 m. Observations made in Japan in the 1950s suggested that the height of song flights may be related to ground temperature: when the surface air temperature was 16°C, birds ascended to 40–70 m, but this altitude increased to 80–100 m when the ground temperature exceeded 24°C (Suzuki *et al.* 1952). Juan Delius estimated that the average height reached by his birds was between 50 and 80 m.

During the level-flying phase of the song flight, birds reduce energy expenditure by flying with an airspeed of around 6 m per second, the so-called 'minimum power speed', or that which uses the minimum energetic cost per unit time of flight. This results in a flap rate of about 7–10 wing beats per second (although Csicsáky, 1978, measured it at nearer 16), a rather higher rate than that of birds in level 'transport' flight. On days with wind speeds above 6 m per second, birds can achieve this relative wind speed simply by facing into the wind and moving little relative to the ground. On days with wind speeds below 6 m per second, however, birds must fly in circles to achieve the necessary minimum power airspeed and still remain over their territory. A consequence of this is that the 'aerial territory', the total area of ground over which the displaying Skylark sings, is greater in lower wind speeds. Thus not only the structure of the bird but also the form of the song flight have become adapted to minimise energy expenditure, and so allow males to maximise the length of their song flights.

At the end of the level flight phase of the song flight, birds descend by one of three methods: a parachuting descent while singing (around 1.5 m per second), a flapping descending flight (1.6 m per second), or diving with folded wings, which results in an average rate of descent of 8.4 m per second (with a maximum rate of 20 m per second). Parachuting is the most common form of descent, comprising 64% of the descents observed by Hedenström, followed by diving (25%) and flapping (11%). A rapid descent by diving with folded wings probably represents an interruption to the song flight rather than a natural termination of it, since it usually precedes an attack on another male or coincides with the incubating female leaving the nest. Descent by all methods was found by Hedenström to be faster than would be predicted if birds were trying to maximise the total length of their song flights. This adds further weight to the idea that the important element of the song flight as far as the female is concerned is the length of the level flapping period, with speed of ascent and descent conveying little information on her mate's fitness.

# DURATION AND TIMING OF SONG

Many ornithologists have examined the duration of song flights, although curiously this has not been given the attention in recent research that one might expect for such well-known and conspicuous behaviour. The song flights recorded in Sweden by Hedenström (1995) lasted an average of four minutes, although flights of over 30 minutes were recorded. Halfdan Lange (1951) recorded similar song flight duration in his study of several thousand song flights in Denmark. The average length of around a thousand song flights recorded in England by Noble Rollin (1943) was considerably shorter, at 2.2 minutes, with song flights longer than 6 minutes being rare. Wolfgang Gerss (1989a) measured the lengths of over 6,000 individual song flights in Germany in the 1980s and, taking account of the time of year, weather and time of day, estimated the average length at just over 2 minutes. Other observers have logged song flights lasting up to or over one hour (e.g. Brown 1986), but these are exceptional. Gerss found that only 5% of the huge number of song flights he timed exceeded 6 minutes, and only 1% exceeded 12 minutes. In his classic 1960s study of the Skylarks on the Ravenglass sand dune system in Cumbria, northwest England, Juan Delius (1965) demonstrated changes in the length of the males' song flight at different stages of the breeding season. During territory establishment and pair formation, song flights averaged 3.4 minutes. This fell to 2.4 minutes while the female was incubating and to 1.3 minutes during the period the first brood were in the nest. Gerss (1989b) also demonstrated peaks in song length during the breeding season corresponding to the timing of successive broods. He also noted that songs were longer when temperatures and solar radiation were higher, and shorter when wind speed and air pressure were high. All the evidence suggests that the duration of song flights is limited largely by energy expenditure: song flights are shorter in high wind, longer flights are followed by longer rest periods, and reducing wing area reduces song flight duration. However the status of the male might also have an effect, and single males might produce consistently longer song flights than paired males. Although the effect of status on song length is not known for the Skylark, it has been shown that in a closely related species, the Raso Lark of the Cape Verde Islands, unpaired males have song flights around five times longer on average than paired males, which spend much time guarding their mates (Donald *et al.* 2003). If the same applies to Skylarks, the rarity of very long songs might indicate a low proportion of unpaired males, and therefore a relatively even sex ratio. Individual song flights of Skylarks appear to vary in length during the course of the day, and there appear to be temporal patterns in song activity during the day. Lange's (1951) observations suggested that song flights in the morning are longer (averaging 5 minutes) than those in the afternoon (3.3 minutes), although no such variation was found by Rollin (1943), and in Gerss's sample of over 6,000 songs, the effects of time of day were very weak.

The song of Skylarks can begin well before dawn. As Henry Stevenson remarked in his 1866 book *The Birds of Norfolk*, "*Up with the lark* is a very common expression amongst early risers, yet in reality the members of the early rising society, with its guaranteed stock of health, wealth and wisdom, are far less likely to hear the first notes of the sky-lark, than those whom pleasure or necessity have caused to be up all night." In April, song begins well before dawn and later in the breeding season may continue until well after dark on suitable evenings. In early June 1951, Eric Simms (1992) organised synchronised recording of the spread of the dawn chorus across Britain. The first song of Skylarks was recorded at 01:30 GMT in the Cairngorms, 01:51 in Northumberland, 02:20 in Kent, 02:27 in Staffordshire, 02:28 in County Antrim, 02:33 in Lancashire and 02:36 in south Wales. The dawn chorus of Skylarks thus rolls across the country in a south-southwesterly direction, anticipating the spread of the dawn itself.

Song-flight activity appears to be fairly constant through the morning but there is a lull around midday followed by a mid-afternoon peak and a further lull in the evening. Noble Rollin (1943) calculated the total daily song output of an individual bird at nearly 70 minutes in April, 47 minutes in May and 181 minutes in July, but this is likely to vary according to weather conditions and the time of the breeding season. A male Skylark on the Inner Farne Islands, with no other Skylarks present, produced a daily total song output of just 5 minutes, whereas a newly arrived bird a few days later produced 46 minutes of song on its first day (Rollin 1956). In Japan, male Skylarks (or Japanese Skylarks) have been found to spend around 15% of daylight hours singing at the height of the breeding season. Song flights become shorter with increasing wind speeds, probably due to increased energetic costs (Gerss 1989b), and in strong winds they cease altogether, often being replaced by ground song. Clark (1947) suggested that fog grounded singing birds and that in mist birds have lower song flights and stay within sight of the ground. The effects of weather on song flight duration were examined by Lange (1951), whose results, perhaps surprisingly, suggested that song flights are longer in overcast conditions and rain than they are in bright sunny weather. This may again have been related to differences in wind speed.

Daily patterns of song flight are determined not only by environmental conditions but also by the behaviour of neighbouring males. Observers familiar with this species, particularly those undertaking the difficult task of trying to count birds accurately, are well aware that if one bird starts a song flight, many or all of its neighbours will also take to the air in song. In extreme cases, a silent and apparently unoccupied field can erupt into song if just one of the birds present starts to sing. This behaviour is in fact typical of a number of species of lark, but the reasons for it are unknown. It is possible that birds simply take to the air when conditions for song flights become suitable, but the suddenness of the eruption of song suggests that the action of one bird triggers the rest. Furthermore, I suspect the behaviour occurs most frequently when temperatures and barometric pressure are high, making conditions unsuitable for lengthy songs. One possible explanation is that if the primary purpose of song at certain times of day or in certain conditions is to indicate the occupancy of territories, it might be advantageous to sing only when neighbours are also singing (thereby saving energy), and disadvantageous not to sing whenever a neighbour starts to sing. However, what it is that triggers the onset of these bursts of singing activity, why a particular individual starts them, or what mechanism brings them to an end are all unknown factors that would reward further research.

There appears to be considerable individual variation in the manner of delivery of song. Clark (1947) suggested that certain birds sing during long but infrequent song flights, whereas others have shorter but more frequent song flights. Furthermore, some birds appear to deliver more of their song from the ground than others. Working in Poland, Piotr Tryjanowski (2000a) examined ground song by Skylarks, finding that less than 3% of the more than 1,000 songs he recorded were delivered from the ground or from a perch, the latter being more common. Singing from overhead wires is generally uncommon, although a few birds habitually use electricity and telephone lines. The incidence of ground song appears to peak later in the breeding season than song delivered in flight, and to peak in the early morning and late afternoon. Whatever its purpose, ground song is not accompanied by any particular posture or behaviour, although the feathers are often ruffled. In Poland, ground song is more frequent in set-aside and allotments, which may represent favourable habitats, and less frequent on arable land. While the influence of weather and the time of the breeding cycle is important, it seems that there is innate individual variation in the method of song delivery and in the balance between few songs given frequently and long songs given infrequently.

Skylark song, whether given from the ground or in flight, can be heard in Britain in all months of the year. However there are considerable seasonal fluctuations in the frequency and quantity of song. These were examined in Denmark by Halfdan Lange (1951), who suggested that the length of individual song flights increases throughout the year, reaching a maximum length in August, when few songs are heard but individual song flights are long (Figure 4.2). He speculated that this might be because the establishment of territories and attracting a mate are accompanied by the vigorous ascent song, so shorter song flights are made more frequently at the start of the breeding season. Later in the season, he suggested, territories and mates could be retained by continuous high-level song alone, so the number of song flights is reduced but each lasts longer. It would be interesting to investigate this assertion in more detail.

Seasonal fluctuations in song output were also examined by R.B. Clark (1947) during the mid 1940s. In a somewhat eccentric study, carried out while the rest of the world was being torn apart by the greatest conflict in human history, Clark busied himself by following a single male Skylark around Middlesex from October 1943 to July 1944 and recording its song frequency. His bird showed two peaks of song activity, one in October and one in March. The bird did not sing at all between mid November and late January, although winter song has been recorded elsewhere (at least partly as a predator-deterrent signal). Although Clark ceased his observations in July (maybe his bird grew tired of all the attention and flew away), it appears that August is also a silent month, as this is when many birds moult and

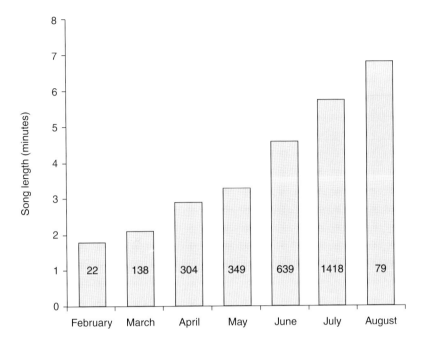

*Figure 4.2.    Monthly variation in the song length of Skylarks in Denmark in the late 1940s, redrawn from data in Lange (1951). The size of the bars represents the average song length in each month; the numbers inside the bars give the number of individual songs from which the average is calculated. As approximately the same amount of time was spent observing birds in each month, these numbers can be used as an indication of the seasonal variation in song output.*

are therefore more vulnerable to predators, although moult may begin with the cessation of nesting as early as June. In Denmark, most birds cease singing in late July (Lange 1951) whereas in England Delius (1965) recorded a cessation of singing in early July. During the breeding season, Clark noticed that individual males periodically ceased all singing for 'quiet periods' of 7 to 23 days. He suggested that these quiet periods coincide with nest building, laying and incubation of eggs by the female, song being resumed when the male starts to help in the feeding of chicks. In fact the opposite is more likely to be true, and these quiet periods probably occur while the males are helping to feed the chicks. Juan Delius suggested that males exhibit a peak of song-flight activity while their mate is incubating. Individual birds that sing long songs continuously throughout the breeding season are probably unpaired, and unpaired males have been seen in Denmark to sing over the territories of all the other birds in the same field.

The complex interactions between the effects on song flights of time of day, time of year, weather, wind speed, status of the male, activity of the female and many other factors clearly require further research. The complex statistical and electronic tools available to today's ornithologists, unknown to Lange, Delius, Rollin or Clark, have yet to be brought to bear on this most evocative of natural phenomena.

*Territorial dispute*

## CHAPTER 5

# Mating and territoriality

We had a new revelation respecting the character of the Sky-Lark when we were recently in a bird-catcher's shop, and in a long cage containing a dozen or more lately captured Larks witnessed a most desperate combat between two young cocks, while others stood round ruffled and bleeding from recent contests.

D'Urban and Mathew, *The Birds of Devon* (1892)

Song is only one of the displays that the male employs to attract and keep a mate and keep other males away. As with most other species, the male Skylark uses postural as well as auditory cues in mating, although this is rarely seen, as it takes place on the ground, often in long vegetation and often at dawn. There are four main types of display, which can be described as 'chasing', 'hopping', 'bowing' and 'wing shivering'. All take place on the ground with the exception of chasing.

Skylarks can be seen chasing each other at all times of the year, and chases can involve the two birds of a pair or two rival males. Chases are even observed in flocks of migrating birds. The chase may therefore be some non-specialised form of behaviour that fulfils several functions. However, it does appear to play some part in courtship display and is observed frequently just before copulation. The behaviour was first described in detail by the same R.B. Clark (1948) who during the height of the Second World War was busy following a single Skylark around Middlesex. His description was published in 1948:

> The essence of this flight, which involves two birds, is a frenzied 'chase' carried out at low altitudes (20 to 30 feet). It begins suddenly and apparently simultaneously in both birds. At the beginning of the chase the distance between the birds is reduced to two or three feet and is then maintained at that; at the same time the speed of flight is very much increased. The birds twist and turn together so sharply and frequently that the whole flight takes place over a small area of ground. It ends as suddenly as it began; as if by mutual consent, the birds return to their normal behaviour.

The male generally sings loudly during the chase.

'Hopping' seems to take place mostly during pair formation, when the female has only recently entered the male's territory, although it may also occur just prior to copulation. In hopping, the male stands in front of the female with the crest raised, body held upright, wing tips held drooping or quivering rapidly. He then performs a bizarre series of five to ten vertical hops or bounces to a height of 1–2 cm, with legs held stiff and head back (Figure 5.1). This display is sometimes accompanied by either full song or a muted but intense subsong. Hopping frequently gives way to bowing, in which the wing tips are again drooped and often shivered but the body is crouched forward and held low and the tail is held up, often fanned slightly to display the white outer feathers. In more intense display, the tail may be held down and the crest and throat and back feathers are puffed out. The male may perform a series of dances, hopping diagonally right and left, bowing the head and quivering the wing tips. Both hopping and bowing sometimes incorporate wing shivering, in which one wing is extended forwards fully and shivered rapidly close to the female, often touching her. This lasts just a second or two but may be repeated several times. Postural display may be preceded or followed by a courtship flight, in which the male pursues the female in a fast, low, erratic and extremely acrobatic flight while singing. A further behaviour that might form part of a display, or might be completely unrelated, is the creation by birds of flattened patches of grass resembling the forms of hares. This behaviour is apparently performed only by males on descending from a song flight. On alighting, the bird rapidly turns round on the same spot, creating the flattened area that it either settles down into or leaves and ignores (Suffern 1951). However, this behaviour must be rare, and after several years of doing little but watching Skylarks I have yet to witness it.

Copulation takes place over the three or four days prior to laying, generally during nest building and in the morning. Although rarely witnessed, it appears to be solicited by the female, who adopts a posture similar to the male's bowing display, with the body held low, the wing tips quivering and the feathers of the back slightly raised. She sometimes also sings quietly. The male hops up to the female and quiv-

*Figure 5.1    The hopping display.*

ers one wing over her back. He then jumps onto her back, beating his wings for balance, as she moves her tail aside to allow cloacal contact. A single copulation appears to be sufficient to fertilise a whole clutch, although several are likely to be made. After copulation, the birds separate, the female to preen and the male to move away and continue territorial behaviour. Such is the sex life of the Skylark.

## RELATIONSHIP BETWEEN THE SEXES

Skylarks are generally monogamous, though rare cases of bigamy have been recorded. In his famous study of a coastal dune population in northwest England, Delius (1965) found that only 2% of relationships involved polygyny, the two females occupying different territories and the male defending both. However, monogamy does not mean that the birds in a pair are entirely faithful to each other. Indeed, the preliminary results of genetic fingerprinting of Skylark chicks suggest that quite a high proportion of the chicks produced by a female in a season are not fathered by her mate (John Hutchinson and Simon Griffiths, pers. comm.).

It is becoming increasingly apparent that this high rate of extra-pair paternity is the norm in birds, at least amongst the majority of species in which birds do not pair for life. The reasons are many and complex, but are largely due to the female's choice about who will father her chicks (Birkhead 2000). An individual male bird stands to lose greatly if his mate's eggs are fertilised by another male, particularly in a species, like the Skylark, in which the male plays a large part in rearing the chicks. Male birds have therefore evolved two basic strategies for reducing this problem. In species such as the birds of prey, when male and female birds are forced by the nature of their feeding methods to spend long periods apart, males copulate very frequently with their mates (typically over 500 times for a single clutch) in an attempt to 'drown out' any sperm from other males. The other major strategy, and the one adopted by male Skylarks, is known as 'mate guarding', where the male spends as much time as possible with the female, to drive away any advances from other males. Males stay very close to their mates during the period immediately preceding nest building and egg laying. At these times of high female receptiveness, males rarely stray more than a few metres from their mates, although Delius's observations in northwest England suggest that the members of a pair can recognise each other at distances of up to 30 m. Even during incubation, males will accompany the female off the nest for her feeding breaks and fly back with her to the nest, often hovering over the nest for a few seconds once she has returned. However at this time the male is free to mate with his neighbours' females, and it is likely that one of the purposes of continued male song during his female's incubation is to attract extra-pair copulations with neighbouring females (Møller 1991). It is likely that pairs stay together throughout the breeding season, and, in Delius's colour-ringed population, all nesting attempts made by a particular female during a breeding season involved the same male. The extent to which pairs remain together between years is poorly understood, but Delius was able to show that, in his coastal dune population, nearly half of all pairs that lived for two or more years stayed together. This tendency was particularly pronounced in pairs that had enjoyed high breeding success during the previous year. One pair remained together for three years and another for four. In non-migratory populations, pairs may remain together throughout the winter.

## SITE FIDELITY AND SEX RATIOS

Skylarks show a strong tendency to return to the same territory and to keep the same mate in successive breeding seasons. More than half of Juan Delius's Skylarks returned to exactly the same territory they had occupied in the previous breeding season, and the rest moved on average only 130 m, usually because the territory they had occupied the previous year was already occupied. The apparent fidelity towards each other of male and female Skylarks between years may simply be due to birds returning to the same territory they occupied in the previous year. They may therefore be exhibiting site fidelity rather than mate fidelity, although the result is the same. Delius recorded very little movement from year to year of pairs that stayed together, particularly if they did well the previous year. Males that moved territories between years, on the other hand, tended to have different females in each year. There was also clear evidence of different levels of site fidelity between the sexes. Females were less likely to return to the same territory as the previous year if the male had already moved elsewhere, but in no cases did the female move to the new territory of her previous year's male. First-year birds also exhibited strong site faithfulness, most returning in the year after hatching to within 1 km of their natal nest. Birds unable to establish their own territory do not move away, but integrate between territories to form a non-breeding population, estimated by Delius to form around 10% of the total population in his study area. He notes that after the severe winter of 1962/63, when many birds died and the Skylark population at his study site was lower than in previous years, there were no non-breeding birds in the population.

Post-natal dispersal is a term used to describe a very specific type of movement, that undertaken by young birds between leaving the nest and establishing their own territories the following year. This is a mechanism which ensures that birds do not compete against, or interbreed with, their parents or siblings, and is a way for species to discover and occupy new sites. Although very little is known about this type of movement in Skylarks, or indeed in any songbird species, the few ringing recoveries available suggest that, at least in the UK, post-natal dispersal occurs over short distances (Dougall 1996). Of the 21 recoveries of birds ringed as a chick and found dead the following breeding season, 19 were within 10 km of the site of ringing. When recoveries at any time of year are included, 82 of 91 birds ringed in their first summer were recovered within 20 km of where they were born. Thus Skylarks show a high degree of what is termed natal philopatry, a tendency to remain in the area in which they were born. As with many other songbirds, this tendency appears to be stronger in males.

Strong site fidelity has been recorded not only in Skylarks that remain in the same area all year round, but also in migratory populations. In Switzerland, for example, Markus Jenny noted high rates of return of males between successive years (62%), but lower rates of return of females (29%). Returning males went back to the same territories they held in the previous year unless they had been of poor quality, in which case they tried to occupy a better territory. Also working in Switzerland, Alex Schläpfer (1988) similarly recorded higher rates of return of males (around 70% on average) than females (42%). Whether this was due to lower site fidelity of females or higher winter mortality is unclear, although studies in Germany suggest that females are likely to move further between successive seasons. Alex Schläpfer calculated that around a third of the birds present on his study site were actually born there. Daunicht (1998) found that 99% of returning males establish a new territory within 0.65 km of their previous year's territory, whereas the comparable distance for returning females was 1.5 km. Furthermore, the emigration rate of young female birds from their natal areas was around twice that of young males. The rates of return of males recorded by all these studies suggest very strong site fidelity, since the proportion not returning equates to the proportion of the population likely to die between successive breeding seasons.

Most bird populations have a sex ratio approximating to one male to one female. This is due to the fact that the sex of an egg is usually randomly fixed during fusion of the sex cells (although adaptive manipulation of sex ratios is being identified in a growing number of species). It is very difficult to manipulate the birth sex ratio of birds and mammals, a fact much lamented by poultry farmers, who would willingly pay large sums of money to increase the proportion of females hatching from eggs. In certain cases in the wild, however, sex ratios of adult birds do vary from 1 : 1. This may be the result of a variation in the ratio of 1 : 1 in the eggs laid, but is more likely to be due to variations in the survival rates of birds, either in the nest or as adults. For example, a close relative of the Skylark, the Raso Lark, has a strongly male-dominated sex ratio, possibly because the females are less able to withstand the droughts that blight the island (Donald *et al.* 2003). A similar phenomenon has been thoroughly documented by Peter and Rosemary Grant in populations of Darwin's finches on the Galapagos Islands: in periods of drought larger-billed birds, which tend to be males, are better able to survive than smaller-billed birds, which tend to be females. In other cases, higher female mortality has been recorded where females incubating eggs suffer high rates of predation while sitting on the nest. During my own research on Skylarks, I occasionally found the remains of females in or near the nest, suggesting that the incubating female's strategy of sitting tight when danger approaches might sometimes have fatal consequences.

Sex ratios in Skylark populations are very poorly understood, but it is likely that in most populations the ratio does not differ greatly from parity. Both Alex Schläpfer and Markus Jenny have noted a relatively small but nevertheless consistent preponderance of males in their Swiss study populations, although this may be at least partly due to the fact that females are more difficult to observe, particularly when incubating. On his German study site, Knut Jeromin (2002) recorded equal numbers of males and females. Other research, however, suggests that, at least in some areas, there may be a massive imbalance in the sex ratio. Working in Schleswig-Holstein, Daunicht (1998) suggested that in some intensive farmland areas the ratio of males to females during the breeding season approaches ten to one, an astonishing deviation from parity. Although the reasons are unclear, and the results need to be verified, it may be that large areas of unsuitable habitat are occupied only by males that have been unsuccessful in attracting a mate. However, this does not explain why, even in the poorest habitats, such a huge disparity has not been recorded elsewhere.

## TERRITORIALITY AND AGGRESSION

During the breeding season, male Skylarks are fiercely territorial. However, it is difficult to define exactly what a Skylark territory actually comprises. Males will aggressively defend the female and the area immediately around the nest, and usually perform most of their song flights over the nest area. Rival males and birds of other species are quickly chased off. Pipits in particular seem to be rarely tolerated within a Skylark territory. However birds spend most of their time feeding and foraging for chicks outside the area that is actively defended, and often do so in close proximity with other Skylarks without conflict. Their visits to feeding areas may take them over several other actively defended territories. It thus appears that a Skylark territory comprises a relatively small, vigorously defended area around the nest, surrounded by a much larger area of 'no man's land' that is not actively defended by any bird and within which other birds are tolerated. I have always mistrusted those maps showing confidently drawn and perfectly tessellating outlines that many researchers have claimed mark the boundaries of individual territories.

It is likely that the size of the actively defended part of the territory differs between different habitats and is dependent on the density of neighbouring rivals, which itself is determined by the quality of the habitat. In his classic study of Skylarks in Switzerland, Alex Schläpfer (1988) demonstrated a clear relationship between the size of the territory and the diversity of different land-use types within it. Smaller territories, of 2–4 ha, contained a greater diversity of crop types than larger ones, which reached a maximum size of around 8 ha. Similar effects of habitat quality on territory size were recorded by Urs Weibel and colleagues (2001), also working in Switzerland, although territories were on average considerably smaller than Alex Schläpfer's, averaging a little over 1 ha. Further work in Switzerland by Sibylle Stöckli (2002) suggested territory sizes of around 1.6 ha, with larger territories in large fields and smaller ones where high-quality habitats such as set-aside were available. The average territory size on Markus Jenny's Swiss study site was around 3.3 ha, and again it was smaller when territories contained a high diversity of different crop types. Similar territory sizes were recorded by Juan Delius in his coastal dune study population, the average size being 5 ha. In spring barley fields in Denmark, detailed radio-tracking of individual Skylarks suggested an average territory size of 2.5–3.5 ha (Odderskær *et al.* 1997a), and in southern France, territories were around 2 ha (Eraud *et al.* 2000). In an area of ecologically-managed farmland in Germany, Jeromin (2002) recorded very small territory sizes of 0.8 to 1.6 hectares. At least some, and probably most, of the differences in estimates of territory size between these studies are likely to arise from the variety of methods used to estimate them, and from differing definitions of exactly what constitutes a territory.

When rival conflicts do occur, they are resolved by a variety of means. Sometimes it is sufficient for the defending male simply to fly towards the intruder, causing him to fly off. At other times, a threat posture may be sufficient. The Skylark has a number of threat postures, of which the most common is a crouched stance, the body held low and tipped forward so the breast is near the ground, the crest and back feathers raised, the tail spread and either held down or raised over the back (Figure 5.2). Sometimes two rival males will adopt this position with their bills almost touching, both singing. After a time, the loser lowers his raised feathers to indicate submission,

*Figure 5.2    Threat posture.*

and generally flies away or engages in displacement activities such as exaggerated feeding or pulling up strands of vegetation.

Often, however, posture is insufficient to see off a rival male and fights are a frequent outcome. Fights between Skylarks can be extraordinarily acrobatic, and are probably the origin of the phrases 'skylarking' and 'larking around'. These graceful confrontations greatly resemble the chasing display during courtship (see above) but are generally more vigorous and violent. Birds may chase each other for considerable distances, as during the courtship chase, but often the two protagonists fly vertically up to a height of several metres, often somersaulting with their claws locked together, and beating each other with their wings. The fights are often accompanied by a very fast, loud song similar to that given during the ascending phase of the song flight. In extreme cases the birds will fall to the ground, their claws interlocked, and continue fighting on the ground or ascend again in another fight flight. Frenzied though these fights appear, they do not seem to cause serious damage, although feathers may fly. The victor might pursue the loser for considerable distances in a fast frenzied flight with many sharp twists and turns. The speed with which the pursuing bird can change direction to follow its antagonist is truly amazing.

A rare form of aggressive display between two males is the 'song duel', where both birds perform song flights in very close proximity, sometimes just a few metres apart. The loser then drifts away while the victor ascends to perform a full song flight. Confrontations between Skylarks can be truly breathtaking, involving complex manoeuvres that appear to defy physics and gravity. It is the low wing loading and broad wings of males, which provide optimal aerofoil surfaces for highly manoeuvrable flight, that make these aerial acrobatics possible.

*Skylark incubating eggs*

CHAPTER 6

# Nests and eggs

From yon black clump of wheat that grows
More rank and higher than the rest,
A lark—I marked her as she rose—
At early morning left her nest.
Her eggs were four of dusky hue,
Blotched brown as is the very ground,
With tinges of a purply hue
The larger ends encircling round.

Behind a clod how snug the nest
Is in a horse's footing fixed!
Of twitch and stubbles roughly dressed,
With roots and horsehair intermixed.
The wheat surrounds it like a bower,
And like to thatch each blowing blade
Throws off the frequent falling shower
– And here's an egg this morning laid!

John Clare, The Lark's Nest

The towering song flight of the male Skylark during the spring and summer is, to human observers, the most obvious manifestation of the species' breeding season. However the aerial display of the male merely diverts our attention upwards and away from a complex and critical series of events taking place largely unseen on the ground below. It is these events that largely determine the likelihood of there being a Skylark singing over the same spot the following year. Skylark populations, like those of all animals, are determined by two driving forces, or population parameters: the number of new birds produced by each adult bird or pair of birds (productivity) and the length of time birds live for (survival). If either increases without a fall in the other, populations increase; if one falls without a compensatory rise in the other, populations decline.

Breeding is a process that involves a number of discrete stages. Birds need to attract and keep a mate, select a suitable nesting site, build a nest, lay eggs and incubate them, care for the chicks and, in multi-brooded species such as the Skylark, repeat the process one or more times during the breeding season. At each stage, birds have to face and try to overcome many problems, such as a lack of suitable nesting habitat, the loss of nests to accidents or predators, and the need to meet increasing demands for food from their growing chicks. Individual birds may face pressures from others of their own species, for example in protecting their mates from the attentions of other birds or competing for food resources with them. In addition, birds may be constrained by environmental conditions that can limit, for example, the number of eggs they are able to lay or the number of nesting attempts they are able to make in the course of a breeding season. Skylarks need to overcome all these problems.

The breeding season of Skylarks has been particularly well studied, since the species remains fairly common in many parts of its range and its nests are, with experience, relatively easy to find. Finding nests allows researchers to follow their progress, assess the diet, growth and condition of chicks and calculate nest survival rates. Because of recent population declines, many ornithologists across Europe have undertaken detailed examinations of this crucial period in the Skylark's year. It will become apparent, however, that while many aspects of the Skylark's breeding season are well known, others remain to be elucidated.

## THE BREEDING SEASON

The length of the breeding season varies considerably across the species' range, and varies annually in each part of the range. Delius recorded nesting from mid April until mid July at his coastal dune study site in northwest England, but found that the earliest nests varied by as much as two weeks in different years. The earliest date of laying of the first egg from more than 1,000 nests found during the 1996–99 RSPB Skylark Research Project in southern England was 3 April. In Switzerland, where Skylarks are largely migratory, the breeding season appears to start slightly later, with the first nests appearing towards the middle of April. In central and northern Europe, most nesting attempts take place in May and June, with few nests being built before the end of April. In southern England, over 70% of the whole summer's nesting attempts are started in these two months, with 11% in April and the remaining 19% in July and early August. This pattern of seasonal distribution in nesting attempts seems to apply equally in France and Germany. However recent research suggests that on intensive modern farmland, and particularly in cereals, the nesting season is ending progressively earlier. Daunicht (1998) goes so far as to suggest that in modern cereal crops some birds may cease all nesting activity as early as May. The implications of this are discussed in further detail in Chapter 12.

Delius's meticulous observations showed that the onset of laying could be explained largely by variation in air temperature, and he suggested that the first eggs are not laid until mean air temperature has risen above 10°C. The onset of egg laying is not dependent solely on temperature, however. Delius observed that breeding started later in females nesting for the first time than it did in birds older than one year. Furthermore, each year certain individual females consistently laid earlier, and others consistently later, irrespective of the average starting date of the population as a whole. As this pattern was observed whether or not the females had different partners in different years, Delius concluded that it was due entirely to characteristics of individual females, rather than their mates. He speculated that the threshold temperature at which nesting was initiated differed among females, birds having lower thresholds nesting consistently earlier than those with higher thresholds. As might be expected, Skylarks introduced into New Zealand and Australia have adapted to the timing of the prevailing seasons there, and nest during the austral summer.

The end of the breeding season is far less synchronous than the start and appears to be unrelated to temperature or weather. Delius found no correlation between individual females in the order in which they started nesting and the order in which they ended it, and no difference in the dates of last clutches between one-year-old females and older birds. At his study site in northwest England, nesting attempts ceased in early to mid July. The latest start date of a nesting attempt in over 1,000 recorded nests found by RSPB researchers on farms in southern England in the late 1990s was 7 August. In certain years with particularly favourable conditions, even more extreme dates have been recorded. A Skylark was flushed from a clutch of three eggs on 17 October 1939 in northwest England, and the bird was still incubating in the last week of October (Hardy 1933). In his book *Birds of Suffolk* (1932), C.B. Ticehurst describes a nest in which the first egg was laid on 15 December 1898, and a nest with two eggs was found in a turnip field in December 1953 (Thorburn 1954). Both these extreme records coincided with abnormally warm periods and with extremely late (or perhaps early) nesting records of a number of other species (Snow 1955). Unfortunately the outcome of neither nest was documented.

## NEST BUILDING

The Skylark is one of the few songbirds in Britain to nest exclusively on the ground in open habitats away from trees or other cover. Many European woodland songbirds, while delivering their song from the canopy, are actually ground nesters, but only a small component of the avifauna shuns arboreal cover altogether. Nests may be built in a wide variety of habitats, but most nests are built in vegetation between about 10 cm and 40 cm in height. During the RSPB Skylark Research Project, the height of the surrounding vegetation was measured at over 800 nests. Nearly 70% of nests were built under vegetation less than 40 cm tall, and all but four were in vegetation less than 1 m tall. The tallest vegetation under which a nest was built was 1.5 m, in a fully grown crop of oats (Figure 6.1), but this is exceptional, and very tall vegetation is generally avoided.

Because of the different structures of different agricultural habitats during the breeding season, there is a tendency for nests in certain crops to be built under vegetation consistently higher or lower than in others. On average, nests in cereal crops are built under vegetation higher than in other types of field, and those in winter cereals are built in higher vegetation than those in spring cereals (Figure 6.2). The preference for nesting in crops between 15 cm and 40 cm tall has been noted by many studies of Skylarks, and explains to a large degree the preferences for certain crops discussed in Chapter 3. Exactly why birds appear to favour vegetation with this structure is uncertain, but it is likely that shorter vegetation might make the

*Figure 6.1.    RSPB Skylark researcher Will Kirby standing at a Skylark nest built in unusually tall vegetation, a mature crop of oats. Photo: Paul F. Donald.*

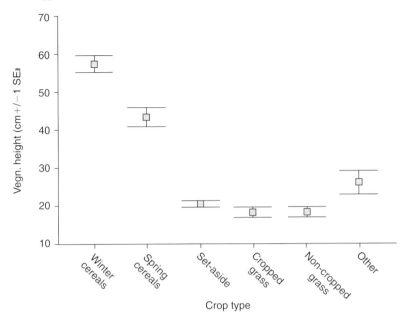

*Figure 6.2.    The height of vegetation at Skylark nests in different crop types. From Donald* et al. *(2002a).*

nest more visible to predators, whereas taller vegetation might impede the birds' progress to and from the nest, or obscure their view of approaching predators. Nest-site selection is likely to be a trade off between concealment and visibility (Gøtmark *et al.* 1995). When crops exceed the preferred height, Skylarks actively seek out nest sites within the crop where plants are more stunted (Schön 1999) or where bare ground is present; the far-reaching implications of this are discussed in more detail in Chapter 12.

The female spends a considerable amount of time selecting a suitable place for building the nest. She may visit and examine up to 20 natural hollows suitable for deepening into nest scrapes, and may start to bring nesting material to several before settling on a single site. Having selected a suitable nesting site, birds begin to construct the nest itself. The nests of Skylarks are built in a depression in the ground, either natural, such as a hoof print (like the nest so accurately described in John Clare's poem at the head of this chapter), or, more frequently, excavated by the birds themselves. Nest-building activity shows a pronounced peak in the morning, with relatively little being seen in the afternoon. The female alone excavates the nest scrape, although the male is usually in close attendance as this is a crucial time to guard his mate from the attentions of other males. The nest scrape is around 7 cm in diameter and can be surprisingly deep, up to 4 cm or more in the centre, although this is not usually apparent when the nest is completed. The depth of the nest scrape is highly variable and on stony or hard soils may be very shallow. John

Walpole-Bond (1938) described unusual cases where the scrape was so deep that the finished nest 'reposes *in toto* several inches below the surface in a regular little well'. In contrast, I have seen nests on hard, flinty soil that appear to have been built directly on the unprepared earth. The scrape is lined with grass or straw, either plucked from living plants or picked up off the ground, so that the lip of the completed nest is generally flush with ground level. Digging a deep scrape to accommodate the nest can prove to be of vital importance later, as some protection is offered against farming operations or trampling. Nests frequently survive cutting or harvesting operations, and may even survive after a tractor wheel has passed directly over them. Several observers have seen nests with 'doorsteps' of flint or chalk nodules, possibly formed by the excavation of the nest scrape. H.E. Woods (1950) found that six out of seven nests he examined at Portsdown Hill, Hampshire, "had these 'doorsteps' consisting in most cases of hard chalky stones and flints, varying in size from a pea to a trouser button." Larks in several other genera, especially those nesting in deserts, habitually construct a rampart or protective parapet of small stones around the windward side of the nest, but it is more likely that these Skylark doorsteps were incidental, rather than being the manifestation of some sort of 'ancestral memory' from a more arid evolutionary past.

During nest building, pairs fly short distances together from the nest site for the female to collect nesting material, closely guarded by the male. Nests are made almost exclusively out of grass, although several accounts mention the use of animal hair and moss. Later in the nesting period, the ability of birds to return at speed to exactly the right spot in what can seem, to human eyes, an entirely featureless habitat is truly remarkable, but at this early stage birds seem to have difficulty in relocating the nest site. It is likely that birds are learning the position of the nest from small irregularities in the vegetation in the immediate vicinity. The female often hovers for extended periods over the general area of the nest, repeatedly dropping down near it, then rising again a few seconds later still carrying the nesting material.

Nest construction takes place in bursts of activity, when the female may return with new material every few minutes, interspersed with bouts of display posturing and occasional mating and by long periods of relative inactivity, when the birds feed nearby and apparently lose interest in the nest. According to Juan Delius, who watched the female with the aid of a strategically placed mirror, the nesting material is integrated into the nest by a rapid backwards-kicking and body-turning action. The bird then uses her bill to weave the tips of the stems together to make a compact and thick mat. Birds are very susceptible to disturbance during nest building, and may abandon a half-finished nest if a person or a predator goes too near. Long periods of rain will also result in the abandonment of nests at very early stages.

Nest construction usually takes three to five days, although it may be several more days before the female starts laying eggs, and new nesting material may be brought to the nest after the onset of egg laying or even incubation. The first nests of the season may take longer to build than subsequent nests, possibly because as temperatures rise there is less need for a thick base to the nest. A new nest is constructed for each nesting attempt, although Walpole-Bond (1938) cites an unusual case of birds laying in the same nest from which the eggs of their previous attempt were predated. Nests of consecutive attempts by the same pair may be built very close to each other in particularly good habitats such as set-aside, in some cases just a few feet apart. In more intensively managed landscapes, however, females move further between consecutive nesting attempts, and may even move to other habitats. Alex Schläpfer (1988) recorded the distances between consecutive nests of individual females in his intensive farmland study site in Switzerland, and found they moved between 30 m and 300 m. On the same study site, neighbouring synchronously active nests were between 50 m and 250 m apart, whereas on set-aside holding very high densities of Skylark territories in Norfolk, neighbouring nests could be as little as 10 m apart.

## EGGS AND LAYING

Eggs are laid at the rate of one per day, usually very early in the morning. Birds usually remain in the vicinity of the nest throughout the laying period, and may visit it periodically and utter alarm calls if the nest is approached while they are close to it, but incubation does not usually start until the clutch is complete. During laying, the first eggs of a clutch, particularly during the early part of the breeding season, may be exposed to temperatures below freezing or to heavy rainfall for several days at a time before the start of incubation, apparently without any adverse effects on their viability. Nests built in northern Russia before the end of April may be covered by snow between the start of laying and the onset of nesting, and in such cases the female apparently remains on the nest (Mal'chevskiy & Pukinskiy 1983).

The eggs vary greatly in colour and patterning between clutches, but are extremely similar within clutches. They are generally mid- to dark brown in ground colour with varying amounts of darker brown or blackish flecking, particularly towards their thicker end (Plate 1, Figure 6.3). Several writers (e.g. Walpole-Bond 1938) record rare instances of pure white eggs. The eggs of Skylarks average around 24 mm long by 17 mm at their widest diameter, giving them an average volume of around 3,350 mm$^3$. The weight of eggs is less easy to determine unless they are measured immediately after laying, since eggs lose weight through evaporation during incubation. However data from the recent RSPB Skylark Research Project suggest an average laying weight of around 3.5 g—rather more than the 3.1 g estimated by Khokhlov (1990) in his very large clutches in the Caucasus. A female laying a clutch of five average-sized eggs is therefore producing around half her own body weight in energetically rich reproductive material, a major investment that has unknown but probably very high costs to the individual.

Eggs in the same clutch are extremely similar in size and shape, although Delius recorded a tendency for successive eggs in the same clutch to be increasingly wider,

*Figure 6.3.    Nest of 4 particularly pale eggs. Photo: Paul F. Donald.*

possibly due to a widening of the shell gland during egg formation. However there is considerable variation in egg size between different clutches. In one recent study that examined egg size in 122 nests on farmland in southern England, the average egg volume of a clutch ranged from 2,440 mm$^3$ to 4,387 mm$^3$: the largest eggs were nearly twice as large as the smallest (Donald *et al.* 2001b). The same study showed that there is no relationship between egg size and the number of eggs in the clutch, the time of year, or the habitat in which the nest is built. This suggests that, while the number of eggs a female may lay in a clutch is variable (as it changes over the course of the breeding season), the size of the eggs themselves is likely to be fixed for a given female, perhaps limited by the size of the bird itself. Indeed, Juan Delius was able to use his colour-ringed population to show that individual females tended to lay eggs of consistently the same size throughout their lives. Occasionally an abnormality occurs, such as that described by Walters (1972) from a nest in the Netherlands. The first egg of this clutch was abnormally large (28.2 mm by 18.3 mm, giving it a volume of around 4,820 mm$^3$), but subsequent eggs were normal. As the other eggs hatched, two small holes appeared in the large egg. When it failed to hatch, Walters opened it and was amazed to find inside it two very small dead embryos, in separate membranes, one at each end of the egg. Double-yolked eggs like this are extremely rare in nature.

Clutch size is an important determinant of productivity at the scale of the individual nest, and is determined at least partly by environmental conditions. Exactly what combination of factors determines the number of eggs laid in a particular clutch is uncertain, although it is likely that for each nesting attempt there is an optimum number of eggs. The clutch size of Skylarks varies from two to six, with four being the most common in Britain (Figure 6.4). As is common for multi-brooded species, clutch sizes start small, rise to a peak in the middle of the breeding season and then fall again (Figure 6.5). This inverted U-shaped relationship between clutch size and time in the breeding season arises as clutch sizes increase towards the best part of the breeding season, when most chicks can be reared, and then decline again as the optimal time for nesting passes (Crick *et al.* 1993). Delius showed that the increase and later the decrease in the average clutch size of Skylarks was due to changes in the clutch size of individual females, rather than to different timing of nesting of birds laying consistent clutch sizes. However, he also found that the variation within individuals was less than the variation between individuals, so that while all birds might show the same inverted U-shaped pattern, some birds lay consistently smaller or larger clutches than others.

The inverted U-shaped relationship between clutch size and time in the breeding season masks another pattern, namely that of consistent differences between clutch sizes of birds nesting in different habitats. Nests in coastal habitats, for example, have larger clutch sizes than nests on farmland (Chamberlain & Crick 1999), and nests on grass moors have higher clutch sizes than those on heather moors

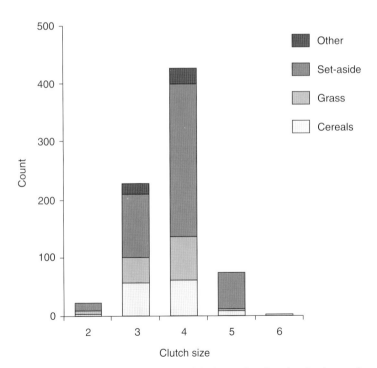

*Figure 6.4. Distribution of clutch sizes in 752 Skylark nests found on farmland in southern England between 1996 and 1999. From Donald* et al. *(2001b).*

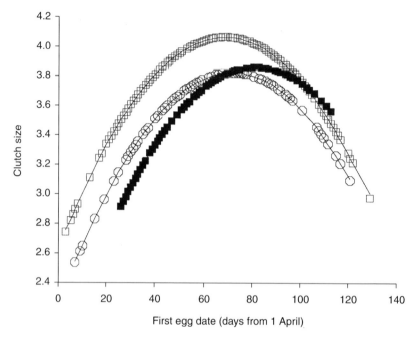

*Figure 6.5. Seasonal changes in the average clutch size in Skylark nests in three different agricultural habitats in southern England, 1996 to 1999. The curves represent the patterns of seasonal change as estimated by statistical modelling. Open squares are nests in set-aside, open circles are nests in grass and filled squares are nests in cereal fields. From Donald* et al. *(2001b).*

(Chamberlain 2001). Nests in set-aside, a farmland habitat that can be regarded as natural in that it is generally not sprayed with chemicals, have higher clutch sizes than do nests in cereal crops, at least during the early part of the breeding season (Weibel 1999, Donald *et al.* 2001b). Furthermore, clutch sizes in nests in set-aside peak several weeks earlier than those in cereals (Figure 6.5). These differences between habitats in patterns of clutch size are likely to be related at least partly to habitat quality and food availability, and therefore the condition of the female and the number of chicks she can raise. The age of females appears to have no effect on clutch size (Delius 1965), suggesting that it is genetically or physiologically controlled. However the extent to which females move between territories in different years apparently does affect clutch sizes. Delius compared the average clutch size of females that occupied the same territories in different years with those of females that moved territories. Although the average clutch size of the two groups was the same, the variation in the latter group was significantly higher. It seems that moving territory can bring large gains or losses in terms of subsequent clutch size.

Recent studies suggest that clutch sizes of five are not unusual, making up nearly 10% of nests found on arable farmland in southern England during the late 1990s, and as many as 14% of all nests in the best habitats (Donald *et al.* 2001b). Earlier observations, such as those Walpole-Bond (1938) in the early decades of the twentieth century and of Delius (1965) in the early 1960s, suggest that clutches of five were less frequent than they are now. Analyses of BTO Nest Record Card data demonstrate a significant rise in average clutch sizes between 1950 and 1994 (Chamberlain & Crick 1999), and more recent data suggest that clutch sizes on certain types of farmland may now be higher than those in any habitat since at least 1950 (Donald *et al.* 2001b). The reasons for this are unclear, but might be connected with recent population declines. It could be that one of the side effects of population decline is that there is less competition between the remaining birds for the available resources, allowing them to rear larger clutches. This may well explain Alex Schläpfer's (1988) observation that when numbers of females were low on his study site in Switzerland, clutch sizes were large. However, this hypothesis assumes, of course, that the declines are not caused by a shortage of food resources during the nesting season in the first place. An alternative explanation is that rising temperatures resulting from climate warming now allow females to hatch more eggs (see below).

Across a number of studies from different countries in Europe, average clutch size appears to increase from west to east (Table 6.1). The highest recorded average clutch sizes were those found by Khokhov (1990) in agricultural areas of the Caucasus region of Russia, where the average clutch size was 4.8, and where nearly 70% of nests contained five or six eggs. Just why clutches in this region are so high is unclear.

Exceptional clutch sizes of six or even seven eggs have been reported from a number of studies elsewhere, including the UK. While many of these are undoubtedly genuine large clutches (at least in the case of clutches of six), in some cases they are likely to be the result of egg dumping, the laying of an egg in the nest of another female. Of the approximately 1,000 nests found by RSPB researchers on lowland farmland between 1996 and 1998, evidence of egg dumping was apparent in just three, the number of eggs rising by one after the onset of incubation. In each case, the number of eggs was later found to have returned to the original clutch size, although whether the female was able to find and remove the correct intruder egg is uncertain. Not all such attempts are doomed to failure, however, and Yanes *et al.* (1996b) have recorded a number of successful instances of egg dumping, both within and between species (there is even a recorded instance of a Quail laying an egg in a Skylark's nest). It is likely that this facultative nest parasitism is a rare form of behaviour that happens mostly in areas where nest predation rates are high and so where females may suddenly find themselves in need of another bird's nest to lay in (Yanes *et al.* 1996b).

Skylarks seem to have some ability to detect and remove eggs that are not their own, which may explain their very low rate of parasitism by Cuckoos, compared with other songbirds with similar nests in similar habitats. In his pioneering work during the 1920s, Edgar Chance recorded 175 nest attacks by six Cuckoos in an area where Skylarks, Tree Pipits and Meadow Pipits were all common. In only two cases were these directed at Skylarks, and subsequent research has not revealed the existence of Cuckoos that specialise in parasitising Skylark nests as they do in parasitising the very similar nests of pipits. Skylarks introduced into British Columbia

*Table 6.1. Average clutch sizes of Skylarks estimated for different regions and habitats, from a number of sources.*

| Clutch size | Standard error | Sample size | Reference | Habitat | Time period | Location |
|---|---|---|---|---|---|---|
| 3.13 | 0.04 | 292 | Chamberlain & Crick (1999) | agricultural | 1950–94 | UK |
| 3.41 | 0.07 | 69 | Chamberlain & Crick (1999) | pastoral | 1950–94 | UK |
| 3.45 | 0.09 | 73 | Chamberlain & Crick (1999) | arable | 1950–94 | UK |
| 3.53 | 0.06 | 109 | Chamberlain & Crick (1999) | agricultural | 1985–94 | UK |
| 3.59 | 0.036 | 304 | Donald et al. (2001b) | agricultural | 1996–98 | UK |
| 3.6 | 0.04 | 396 | Weibel (1999) | agricultural | 1995–98 | Switzerland |
| 3.6 | not given | 117 | Schläpfer (1988) | agricultural | 1983–87 | Switzerland |
| 3.62 | 0.07 | 89 | Chamberlain & Crick (1999) | coastal | 1950–94 | UK |
| 3.69 | not given | 83 | Delius (1963) | coastal | 1960–62 | UK |
| 3.71 | 0.06 | 85 | Daunicht (1998) | agricultural | 1988–91 | Germany |
| 3.75 | not given | 317 | Labitte 1957, in Cramp (1988) | not given | 1950s | France |
| 3.75 | not given | 86 | in Glutz von Blotzheim & Bauer (1985) | not given | 1980s | Germany |
| 3.78 | not given | 208 | in Glutz von Blotzheim & Bauer (1985) | not given | 1980s | Netherlands |
| 3.8 | 0.04 | 448 | Jenny (1990a) | agricultural | 1983–87 | Switzerland |
| 3.85 | 0.032 | 55 | Donald et al. (2001b) | set-aside | 1996–98 | UK |
| 3.87 | not given | 36 | Haun 1931, in Cramp (1988) | not given | 1920s | Germany |
| 3.97 | not given | 60 | Randla 1963, in Cramp (1988) | not given | 1950s | Estonia |
| 4.08 | not given | 35 | in Glutz von Blotzheim & Bauer (1985) | not given | 1960s | Finland |
| 4.8 | not given | | Khokhlov (1990) | agricultural | 1970s | Caucasus |

have not yet joined the extraordinarily long list of bird species that are regularly parasitised by Brown-headed Cowbirds. Indeed, the larks as a family seem to be relatively free from parasitism by the large number of different brood parasites that occur throughout their range (Davies 2000).

## INCUBATION AND HATCHING

Incubation is undertaken by the female alone, and generally begins with the laying of the last egg in the clutch. Although the female may begin incubation activity with the laying of the penultimate egg, this is generally sporadic and does not affect hatching times, possibly because the brood patch does not develop fully until the clutch is complete. It is difficult to estimate the length of incubation, since to do so requires that the nest be found during laying (so the start of incubation is known exactly), that the nest survives throughout the incubation period without being predated or abandoned, and that the nest is visited again at or just after hatching (so the end of incubation is known exactly). Of the more than 1,000 nests my colleagues and I found during the RSPB Skylark Research Project, only 20 fulfilled all these criteria. This small sample showed that the incubation period is actually quite variable, lasting between 10 and 13 days (including the day of laying of the last egg and the day of hatching), with an average of 11.6 days. These estimates are very close to Delius's average of 11.1 days, with extremes of 10 and 12 days. Experiments by Delius involving the replacement of older eggs with younger ones suggested that females abandon a clutch after around 14 days if they have failed to hatch. Unexpectedly, smaller clutches seem to have longer incubation periods. In our sample from southern England, the average for clutches of three eggs was 12.3 days and the average for clutches of four or more eggs was 11.2 days, a statistically significant difference. The likely explanation for this is that smaller clutches tend to be laid at the start and end of the breeding season, when ambient temperatures are lower and embryonic development is therefore slower.

Even the longest recorded incubation period of 13 days is still fairly short for a bird the size of a Skylark. This short incubation period is in fact an adaptation to reduce the likelihood of the nest being predated, since the sooner the eggs hatch, the sooner the chicks can leave the nest. Only the female incubates, although the male will occasionally visit or hover over the nest. Observations by Gibson (1977) of Skylarks breeding in captivity in Canada suggest that the male shares the early incubation, but this has never been observed in wild birds and must be questioned. During incubation the female alternates between periods of dozing, when one eye might close for short periods, and of alertness, when she may preen and peck at surrounding vegetation or passing insects. Occasionally the eggs are turned using the underside of the bill, and Delius describes a form of behaviour he terms 'egg rolling' in which eggs, sometimes all of them, are actually pushed out of the nest to allow repairs to be made to the nest and then rolled back in between the wall of the nest and the female's breast feathers. This may account for the not unusual observation of eggs lying some way outside the nest.

Rarely (I have seen it only a handful of times), the male will bring food to the incubating female (courtship feeding), but the female generally leaves the nest at periodic intervals to feed herself and preen. On cold or wet days, these breaks in incubation occur about once or twice an hour and last only a few minutes, but on warm days the female may leave the nest four or five times an hour for breaks of up to ten minutes or more. Breaks in incubation increase in length with increasing temperatures, being longer during the warmer parts of the day and increasing in length as the breeding season progresses. On hot days, incubating females may spend more time off the nest than on it, although the eggs are probably incubated uninterruptedly at night. As incubation progresses, breaks in incubation become shorter, possibly reflecting the increased thermal requirements of the developing chicks.

When leaving or returning to the nest, the female adopts a characteristic fast, low, silent and furtive flight. On her return to the nest, she drops to the ground with a number of small flitting motions, which, to the experienced nest-finder, are immediately indicative of the presence of a nest. She is usually joined by the male, who, if singing overhead, will abruptly stop and drop down to accompany his mate. Sometimes the female seems to time her incubation breaks to coincide with breaks in singing by her mate, for she often seems to leave the nest as the male concludes his song flight. After she has fed, her mate often follows her as she returns to the nest and may hover over her for a few seconds as she settles back on the eggs.

It is generally the case in birds that if eggs get cold or wet after the onset of incubation, their viability is impaired. However, Skylark eggs seem to be particularly resistant to exposure to wet or cold weather. I have observed a small number of nests that appeared to have been abandoned after the onset of incubation, the eggs being cold and wet, but later visits showed that parents had returned and the eggs had hatched successfully. The apparent ability of Skylarks to interrupt incubation without reducing the viability of the eggs requires further investigation.

During incubation, the female sits very tightly on the nest and will often not break cover until almost trodden on. It is even possible to capture incubating females by hand, as many Victorian collectors discovered. William Yarrell (1861) recounts how "some mowers actually shaved off the upper part of the nest of a Sky Lark without injuring the female, which was sitting on her young; still she did not fly away, and the mowers levelled the grass all round her without her taking further notice of their proceedings." When Yarrell's informant returned to the nest an hour later, he found that "she had actually constructed a dome of dry grass over the nest during the interval, leaving an aperture on one side for ingress and egress, thus endeavouring to secure a continuance of the shelter previously supplied by the long grass". When a sitting female does break cover, she often gives a brief distraction display as she flies from the nest with rapid, shallow wingbeats, batting the vegetation with her wings and keeping very low as if unable to fly properly. In extreme cases she will carry one wing as if broken and move away from the nest in a series of short awkward runs that suggest injury. Having led her pursuers some 10–20 m from the nest, she will fly off and return to the nest once the danger has passed. At other times, she breaks cover with a loud alarm call and flies off directly, hovering around the intruder until the coast is clear.

Although eggs are laid a day apart, incubation starts only with the laying of the last egg. The eggs therefore hatch almost simultaneously, generally within eight hours of each other, often during the middle of the day. There is a weak tendency for the eggs to hatch in the order in which they were laid, suggesting that at least some embryonic development takes place before incubation starts. Hatching takes an hour or two and is unaided by the parents (Plate 5). Large eggshell fragments are removed from the nest by the parents and smaller ones eaten. Experiments by Delius showed that there is clearly a stimulus for parents to remove pale objects, resembling eggshells and chick faecal sacs, from around the vicinity of the nest, whereas dark objects tend to be left alone.

As in all species, a number of eggs fail to hatch, either because they are infertile or because the embryo has died. These two causes of non-hatching appear to occur in approximately equal proportions in Skylark eggs (Odderskær *et al.* 1997a). Research carried out in the UK shows that, of the clutches that survive long enough for at least one egg to hatch, around one in five contains one or two eggs that do not hatch, representing around 5% of all eggs laid (Donald *et al.* 2001b). These figures are virtually identical to those obtained in the studies of both Markus Jenny (1990a) and Urs Weibel (1999) in Switzerland, where again around 5% of all eggs failed to hatch. Eggs in smaller clutches have a higher probability of successfully hatching than eggs in larger clutches, a result demonstrated by research in both Switzerland and the UK (Weibel 1999, Donald *et al.* 2001b).

Recent research has demonstrated that incubation, far from being the passive activity it appears to be, actually places greatly increased energetic demands on the female. In his studies of the energy expenditure of Dune Larks in the Namib Sand Sea, Joe Williams (2001) estimated that the energetic requirements of an incubating female exceeded even those of a female feeding a brood of large chicks. In less parched climates, the energetic demands of incubation must be severe. The female's energy expenditure increases with the number of eggs she has to keep warm (Thomson *et al.* 1998b), and the increased likelihood of hatching failure in larger clutches of Skylarks is probably a result of this. The ability to keep the eggs warm enough to ensure they develop successfully and survive to hatch may be the main factor that limits clutch size. As we have already seen, warm weather seems to shorten the incubation period for Skylarks, suggesting that it reduces the energetic costs to the female. It may be, therefore, that the apparent increase in clutch sizes of Skylarks during the last thirty years is actually a response to rising temperatures. Such a pattern has been observed in the European Swallow, another species that has shown an increase in clutch size during a period of population decline (Møller 2002). The relationship between clutch size, hatching success and climate warming clearly requires further research.

Not only the number but also the size of the eggs has an influence on whether eggs hatch or not, with larger eggs being significantly more likely to hatch than smaller eggs (Donald *et al.* 2001b). The viability of Skylark eggs does not, however, appear to be affected by agrochemicals: a number of studies on farmland in the UK and in Switzerland have shown that there are no differences in hatching rates between eggs in habitats where pesticides are used and those where they are not.

*Adult feeding nestlings*

## CHAPTER 7

# Raising the chicks

But now no time for hovering welkin high
Or downward gliding strain; the young have chipped,
Have burst the brittle cage, and gaping bills
Claim all the labour of the parent pair.

James Grahame, *The Birds of Scotland* (1806)

If the nest survives the attentions of predators for long enough to allow the eggs to hatch, the parents next have to face the challenge of raising the chicks. The chicks of Skylarks hatch blind, almost naked and completely helpless, unable even to stand. Newly hatched chicks are around 3 cm long and weigh about 3 g. They are naked except for a few long, wispy yellowish down feathers, which are longer and thicker on the upperparts than on the underparts and serve to camouflage the chicks in the nest. Although blind, they respond to changes in light and to the sound of their parents, and open their mouths when the adults visit the nest. This can be very useful to researchers trying to find well-hidden nests, since imitating the call of a returning adult causes the chicks to throw up their heads and gape, immediately giving away the location of the nest. As with most songbirds, the gape of Skylark chicks is strikingly patterned. The inside of the mouth is yellowish or orange in colour, and marked with five distinct black spots, one on the front of the tongue, two at the back of the tongue and one on the tip of each mandible. This striking pattern acts as a stimulus for the parent and probably helps the parents locate the chicks' mouths in dark nests. Very young chicks are generally silent, although chicks in poor condition may call when the parents visit the nest with food.


## LIFE IN THE NEST


The female broods the chicks for the first few days after hatching, though brooding of even very small chicks never occupies as much time as did incubation of the eggs. After the fifth day, brooding of chicks is rare and occurs only during poor weather. Development, particularly of the legs, is extremely rapid, a common strategy for a ground-nesting bird which has high nest predation rates (Kirkwood *et al*. 1989, Yanes & Suárez 1997). Indeed, the chicks of at least some larks appear to develop at their maximum theoretical rate (Shkedy & Safriel 1992). Rapid development is of considerable importance in allowing chicks in the nest to survive predation attempts. In another ground-nesting songbird, the Meadow Pipit, 60% of broods in the late nest phase survive predation attempts by fleeing the nest, and the probability that the brood survives a predation attempt increases with higher growth rates (Halupka 1998a).

Both parents start to bring food to the nest in the first few minutes or hours after hatching, and both the rate of provision and size of the food items brought to the nest increase as the brood grow. The eyes open during the second full day, by which time their weight has already more than doubled. After the eyes open, the chicks rapidly move from using auditory to visual stimuli and within a few days are able to focus on and move their heads towards the food in the visiting parents' bills (Plate 6). At the same time, they become more selective in which auditory stimuli they respond to. Prior to the opening of the eyes, chicks respond by gaping to any sound near the nest. After the eyes open, they gape only in response to a specific 'food call' made by approaching parents, and respond to alarm calls by freezing. The pins of the flight feathers begin to erupt on the third day, and by the fourth day the birds are alert, responding to their parents' alarm calls when predators approach by keeping quiet and motionless in the nest. At this stage, the chicks are incredibly well camouflaged against the ground (Plate 6). By the fifth or sixth day of life, the body temperature stabilises at 39°C and the flight feathers begin to emerge from their pins. The legs start to sclerotise (harden) from the fourth day onwards and by the eighth day are fully developed, well before weight or feather growth is complete (Figure 7.1). This rapid development of the legs is typical of a species that leaves the nest before fledging. By the sixth day, chicks are launching themselves vigorously at the parents when they return with food, sometimes leaving the nest for short periods. By the

a.

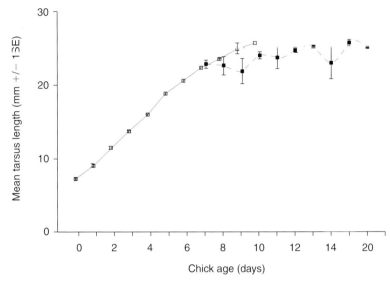

b.

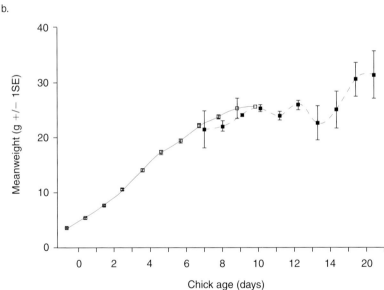

*Figure 7.1. Mean tarsus length (a) and weight (b) of chicks in the nest (solid line) and chicks found after leaving the nest (dotted line), from farms in southern England, 1996–99. The development of the tarsus is complete at around 9 days, but weight continues to increase long after the chicks leave the nest. From Donald (1999).*

seventh day, chicks may spend considerable periods just outside the nest, sometimes moving to surrounding vegetation but always returning to the nest at night. Just eight days after hatching blind and naked, the chicks have increased more than eight-fold in weight, have fully developed legs and have achieved full body thermoregulation (Plate 5). They are now ready to leave the nest, although full fledging and independence are still several weeks away, and the birds cannot fly even weakly for at least another week.

## LEAVING THE NEST

When the time comes for the chicks to leave the nest, the female utters a single call note to entice them out, although in the case of large broods some of the chicks might be just outside the nest already. I once had the good fortune to see this happen, at a nest being filmed for a BBC television programme about the RSPB's work on Skylarks. The short, shrill, penetrating call note used by the female bird to call her chicks from the nest was one I had never heard before, and it may be used solely for this purpose. The chicks all left the nest together immediately, and there had been nothing to suggest before the call was given that they had been preparing to leave.

There seems to be considerable variation in the age at which chicks leave the nest. In southern England, the chicks leave the nest at an average age of 8 days (close to Delius's average of 8.5 days), but they can do so when they are as young as 6 days or as old as 11 days. This means that the period from the laying of the first egg to the chicks leaving the nest is, on average, only around 23 days, a remarkably rapid rate of development. Chicks leave the nests with their legs almost fully developed, but with a weight of only around 70% that of the adults (Figure 7.1). In southern England, the average weight of chicks leaving the nest was 24 g (exactly the same as that of chicks leaving nests in the Pyrenees as measured by Verbeek, 1988) but there was massive variation, ranging from just 14 g to 32 g, due to the variation in the age at which chicks left. Very early vacation of the nest is probably caused by disturbance around the nest or possibly attacks by predators. The chicks rear up onto their adult-sized legs and run from the nest in short bursts of unexpectedly rapid movement. Over the next few days they scatter over considerable distances (Plate 5).

Leaving the nest well before fledging is almost certainly a mechanism to avoid whole-brood predation, though we have little information with which to test this hypothesis. The chances of each individual chick surviving are probably reduced, since parents appear to concentrate their feeding on a small number of chicks, the others presumably starving. The chicks now face a number of new dangers. On clay soils, deep fissures develop as the soil dries out, and my colleagues have found a number of chicks that have fallen down these cracks and starved to death. However the chances of the whole brood being lost to a predator are greatly reduced as the chicks become increasingly spread out. Parents continue to feed the chicks until they are around 16–20 days old, by which time they are capable of short bursts of flight and of feeding themselves. By this time, the parents may already be well embarked upon the next nesting attempt.

## PARENTAL CARE

Having invested so much in producing chicks, the parent Skylarks are extremely assiduous in keeping them fed, and will bring food to the nest no matter how much disturbance there is nearby, so long as the disturbance is not being caused by a potential predator. Human observers too close to the nest will prevent the birds bringing food to it and they can engage in some very convincing distraction displays. Quite often the birds will land some distance from the nest and drop the food on the ground, or eat it themselves, then fly off as if they had just visited a nest, drawing the observer away from the real nest. At other times they will land away from the nest and wait for several minutes before flying up again still carrying the food. But if the disturbance is not perceived as a threat, the birds will keep visiting the nest at the usual rate. Cars (which make excellent bird hides) or portable hides put up near the nest do not prevent the parents from bringing food once they have got used to them.

Sometimes birds will overcome seemingly impossible degrees of disturbance to feed their chicks. Those doyens of Scottish ornithology Evelyn Baxter and Leonora Rintoul (1953) described watching a nest in a field within the city limits of Dundee that became the site of the Royal Highland and Agricultural Society's Show of 1933. They became "interested in watching a pair of Skylarks which had their nest in the central ring, where all the big parades and jumping were going on. A little wire-netting barricade had been put around the nest and the birds went to and fro feeding their young and fluttered twittering over the ring apparently quite unmoved by the crowds and bustle". A similar case was described by H.L. Gee, writing in the 1940s about a nest in a meadow just outside Ipswich:

Then, one day, came an invasion. The gate of the field was lifted from its hinges. Men by the score came tramping in. Lorries bumped over the grass, the sound of their engines terrifying the mother lark and her startled brood. Huge tents were erected. There was much hammering and shouting. No wonder the little mother fluttered anxiously over her nest, expecting every moment that the wheel of a lorry or the heel of a workman would destroy all she loved most. How in the world could she have foreseen that the Royal Show of Ipswich was to be held in that field? Now there was in the field a valuable Jersey cow, and the cow was tended by a kindly herdswoman. She saw the frightened mother lark. She heard her cries. So she either begged, borrowed or stole a bit of sacking and a few sticks, and erected in the middle of the great exhibition the smallest tent of all—a kind of rude wigwam—above the lark's nest. Odd it was to see in the Jersey Ring this flimsy tent; but everyone knew why it was there—the herdswoman saw to that—and though cows and herdsmen and judges and ring-stewards, and I know not who besides, walked within a few inches of the nest, no harm came to the mother bird or her brood. The show lasted a week. Then came men with lorries to carry away the apparatus that had been used. Round the tent were placed protective hurdles; but someone removed the hurdles without knowing why there were there, and a driver backed his lorry so that one of the wheels hung over the nest. This menace so terrified the mother lark that for a time she flew away, but the kindly herdswoman came to the rescue of the baby birds, feeding them with milk. Presently a crowd of men and boys gathered round the lorry, contriving to move it a few inches without the wheel crushing the nest. Next day the herdswoman had to drive her Jersey cow home but before she left, she put up a notice in the field: WARNING: LARK'S NEST. Finally the nest became the responsibility of the local fire brigade. So the Ipswich Royal Show came and went, and one day a man put the gate on its hinges again, and the lark and her fledglings enjoyed sole possession of the field.

## PATTERNS OF GROWTH AND DEVELOPMENT

The patterns of growth and development of chicks in small broods differ from those in larger broods. Chicks in smaller broods tend to have higher body condition (more fat for their skeletal size) than chicks in larger broods (Figure 7.2). Because more of their food goes into the production of fat, chicks in smaller broods have lower skeletal growth rates than chicks in larger broods (Donald *et al.* 2001e). These differences may arise because chicks in nests with few siblings need to accumulate fat reserves to maintain heat and to survive periods of poor weather, since they cool much faster than chicks in larger broods (Verbeek 1988). Alternatively, or maybe additionally, rapid growth rates may occur in large broods due to increased sibling competition: in a large brood, being bigger than your siblings might confer greater advantages when food becomes scarce than it would in a small brood.

An interesting and unexpected recent finding is that female birds about to start laying appear to be able to predict what the food availability will be when the eggs hatch ten or more days later. This was demonstrated by comparing the body condition of chicks in nests where all eggs hatched with those in nests with the same number of chicks where one or more eggs failed to hatch. Body condition was consistently higher in the latter group. Thus a brood of four chicks hatching from a clutch of five eggs tend to be in better condition than a brood of four chicks hatching from a clutch of four eggs. The extra capacity that would have gone to feed the fifth chick in the clutch of five appears to be distributed among the four chicks that

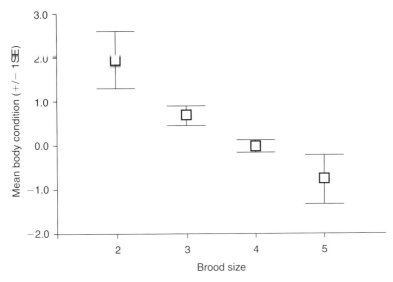

*Figure 7.2. Average body condition index of chicks in broods of different size. The body condition index, which has a mean value of zero across all broods, is calculated in such a way as to control for the effects of chick age. From Donald* et al. *(2001e).*

actually hatched (Donald *et al.* 2001e). So either the female is able to predict at the time of egg laying that there will be sufficient food to raise five chicks, or there is a relationship between female quality and clutch size. It may be that females laying clutches of five eggs are capable of providing more food per chick than birds laying smaller clutches.

The growth rates and body condition of nestlings are affected not only by brood size but also by the weather, particularly rainfall. During periods of heavy rainfall, the female broods the chicks and no feeding is possible. When the female leaves to collect food, the chicks get wet and so use a greater proportion of their energy keeping warm. After very long periods of rainfall, many chicks die of cold and starvation. In Switzerland, Urs Weibel (1999) has shown that temperature also has an effect on chick growth, and that chicks tend to grow faster later in the breeding season. The type of field the nest is in also influences the rate at which chicks develop. Both in the UK and in Switzerland, chicks have been shown to develop most rapidly in farmland habitats that are not used for crop production, and so are not treated with pesticides.

Dead chicks are generally removed from the nest by the parents and dropped from flight some distance away, though larger ones may be left in the nest and partially buried in the nest lining. This behaviour probably explains the belief of some Victorian naturalists that parent birds move their chicks from danger by flying with them in their claws. However, this may actually happen on occasion, and an entry in *Zoologist* in 1865 described how "on the 9th of July four young Larks were found in a rudely-scraped hollow in the ground near a bunch of rushes in which the original nest was placed. It has been flooded by the recent heavy rains, and the young birds must have been removed by their parents, for they were not able to move of themselves". Guy Mountfort (1939) recalled seeing a healthy chick being carried a distance of some 5 m from the nest by the female and dropped, although whether the chick became accidentally entangled with the bird's feet or whether it was a deliberate act by the female to move the chick from danger was not clear.

Starvation appears to be the main cause of partial brood loss during the nestling stage, since virtually all predators take the whole brood rather than just one of them (at least until the age when they can flee the nest when attacked). In southern England, failure of eggs to hatch and the deaths of one or more chicks of cold or starvation accounted for 12% of the potential output of ultimately successful nests (Donald *et al.* 2001b), and virtually the same rate of loss was recorded by Urs Weibel (1999) in Switzerland. Parasites, at least external parasites (ectoparasites) such as fleas, lice and ticks, do not appear to pose the same problems to growing Skylark chicks that they do to the chicks of hole-nesting species. I have closely examined the chicks in several hundred Skylark nests and have not seen an ectoparasite on any of them, or in the lining of the nests. This is probably due to the openness of the nests, which lack the humidity and stable temperature that allows numbers of parasites to build up to levels where chicks suffer or even die in hole-nesting birds.

## FEEDING THE CHICKS

Both parents feed the chicks, the male becoming increasingly involved as the chicks grow larger, and taking over altogether if the female embarks upon another nesting attempt before the young of the previous brood are fully independent. Males provide between a third and half of all the food brought to the nest, although in his detailed unpublished study of Skylarks, John Hutchinson has observed that in a small number of cases the male brings very little food to the nest. Studies on the very similar Japanese Skylark have shown that males provide around 36% of all the food consumed by the nestlings. However, females are capable of rearing chicks on their own. Markus Jenny noted a rare example of a male abandoning his mate while she was incubating to establish another territory some 200 m away with another female. Despite being abandoned by her mate, the original female managed to rear two chicks from her clutch of five eggs. Loss of the female, on the other hand, appears to cause the male to abandon the chicks.

The size of prey items brought to the chicks by their parents is related to the size of the chicks. When newly hatched, chicks are fed very small prey items that are difficult to detect in the bills of the adults, whereas later on large items are brought to the nest that are easily visible to a human observer, even at considerable distances. Adults always fly some distance from the nest to collect food for chicks and fly back with it held in their bills, either dropping straight on to the nest (particularly when the chicks are larger) or landing up to several metres from the nest and walking to it. This behaviour, which probably serves to mislead potential predators, might be behind the common local name Laverock (and variants such as Learock, Laverak etc. as well as the modern Dutch *leeuwerik*), a derivation of the Old English *laferce*, or *lawerce*, meaning one guilty of treason. Despite this cautious approach to the nest, birds invariably leave directly from the nest itself, a behaviour my colleagues and I made use of to find nests during our fieldwork. Often both parents arrive with food together at the nest, the female usually going down to the nest first while the male hovers overhead before moving in when the female flies off. He may even start to sing over the nest, still carrying a beak full of food.

The number of visits made to a nest by the parents to feed the chicks varies with the age and number of the chicks and the distance flown to collect food for them. The average recorded distance flown from the nest by foraging adults during the RSPB Skylark Research Project on farmland in southern England was 75 m. Although the longest recorded foraging flight was 380 m, less than 10% of foraging flights were over 150 m (Figure 7.3). Another study of Skylark foraging flight

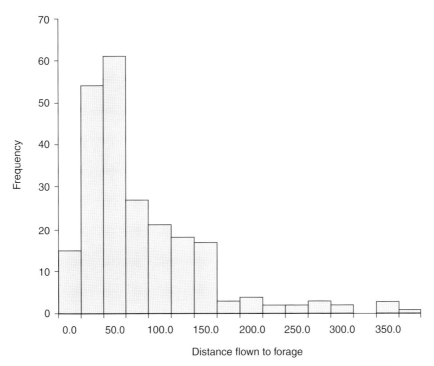

*Figure 7.3. Distribution of forage flight distances (in metres) from the nest. Recorded from Skylark nests in a variety of habitats on lowland farmland in southern England, 1996–98. From Donald (1999).*

distances estimated far longer distances, averaging between 120 m and 230 m according to the type of field the nest was in (Poulsen 1996), while yet a different study estimated the distance travelled to be less than 50 m on average (Murray *et al.* 2002). These differences are likely to arise because the distance flown to forage for chicks depends almost entirely on local conditions, which determine the distribution of food and, most importantly, suitable foraging habitats. However there appears to be a minimum distance travelled, since even birds foraging in the same field as the nest tended to fly 50 m or more from the nest (Figure 7.3). Recent research carried out in Germany by Knut Jeromin (2002) found that parents feeding chicks avoid competing with each other by adopting different feeding strategies. Males fly further from the nest (on average 75m) to collect food than the females (50m). This means that they make fewer visits to the nest than females, but they compensate for this by bringing back larger loads of food, so that the total amount of food provided by both sexes is approximately equal.

A number of studies have looked in detail at the types of habitats selected by parents foraging for food for their chicks. Jeremy Wilson (2001), working on farmland in central England in the mid 1990s, found that birds preferred to collect food for chicks in set-aside, grassy tracks, field margins and organic grass than in arable crops, probably due to a combination of prey availability and an open sward structure with plenty of bare ground to allow easy access. Set-aside, particularly that sown with kale, was also important in another study in central England (Murray *et al.* 2002). In Switzerland, Markus Jenny (1990b) and Urs Weibel (1998) recorded a preference for wild-flower strips, stubbles, tracks and short grassland, with cereals generally being avoided. Once again, the selected habitats were rather open, with low and sparse vegetation. The destination of Skylarks foraging for their chicks appears to be determined not only by the number of potential prey items present, but also by the ease with which they can be collected. In Denmark, for example, Skylarks foraging in cereal crops spend most time in the bare unsown tractor tracks (commonly known as 'tramlines'), rather than in the dense growing crop, although food density is significantly higher in the latter (Odderskær *et al.* 1997a). Even the verges of busy roads are used as a foraging habitat (Laursen 1981). Habitat structure is therefore probably as important as the distribution of food in determining where Skylarks forage for their chicks. Jeromin (2002) has suggested that at the start of the breeding season, when vegetation is low, birds select their foraging destination on the basis of prey numbers, but later in the season, when vegetation has grown up, their decision about where to feed is based on habitat structure.

A wide range of largely invertebrate prey is fed to the chicks. In southern England, the most frequent items are spiders, insect larvae, beetles (particularly carabid ground beetles), grasshoppers, flies, moths and a wide range of other insects. Earthworms, molluscs, mites, aphids, harvestmen and isopods are less frequent food items. Spiders and their egg sacs appear to be particularly important in the diet of very young chicks, as are sawfly larvae (Poulsen *et al.* 1998). The diet of nestling Skylarks has also been examined in Switzerland, where Urs Weibel (1999) identified spiders, flies and beetles as the most important items, making up three quarters of the food items brought by the parents, followed by lepidopterans (moths and butterflies) and hymenopterans (ants, wasps, sawflies and bees). Also working in Switzerland, Markus Jenny found that flies, and particularly the larvae and pupae of craneflies, made up over half the items fed to chicks. Contrary to my own results from southern England, Markus found that very little use was made of beetles, despite their abundance in the field. Of the insect groups with different life stages, approximately half are fed to the chicks as adults and half as larvae, although most of the hymenopterans are fed as larvae. As in England, spiders are particularly important in the diets of very young chicks. Chicks in cereal fields in Denmark are fed very largely on ground beetles, but spiders and insect larvae are again also important (Elmegaard *et al.* 1999).

In the Russian steppes, a similarly wide range of invertebrate food appears in the diet of chicks (Rjabow 1968). As the chicks grow older and approach independence, it is likely that the whole range of adult foods, both invertebrate and vegetable, is provided by the parents. In one study in central England, chicks were regularly fed unripe wheat grain during the later part of the breeding season (Kathryn Murray, pers. comm.), and cereal grain has been recorded in the diet of chicks elsewhere (Mal'chevskiy & Pukinskiy 1983). Cereal grain becomes an important source of chick food during bad weather (Jeromin 2002). A series of short notes published over the years in the journal *British Birds* has described Skylarks feeding large chicks with such unlikely foods as bread, potato salad, black pudding and cheese, all scavenged from picnic sites or gardens.

Most studies of the diet of nestling Skylarks have concluded that it is not particularly specialised, and that the parents bring items to the nest roughly in proportion to their availability. Markus Jenny has suggested that this lack of specialisation lies behind the Skylark's ability to survive even in the most intensively managed farmland, where it is able to efficiently utilise the low numbers and diversity of invertebrates available to it. If the availability of one type of food is reduced, for example through pesticide spraying, foraging Skylarks can simply move to another type of food. The composition of the diet therefore reflects not only the type of habitat parent birds are foraging in, but also the human impact upon that habitat. Birds foraging for chicks in unsprayed set-aside bring back more insect larvae than birds in other agricultural habitats (insect larvae are very vulnerable to pesticides), and birds foraging in intensively managed cereal fields feed more on ground beetles, a group that is fairly tolerant of pesticides. In Denmark, ground beetles make up over 40% of the dry weight of chick food in sprayed cereal fields but far less in unsprayed cereal fields, where the diet of chicks is more varied and possibly of higher nutritive quality (Odderskær *et al.* 1997b). Grasshoppers are rare in the diet of chicks in intensively managed grass fields, which are generally devoid of these insects, but are frequent prey items in unmanaged grassland, where they can be common. In other lark species elsewhere in Europe, grasshoppers comprise the most important single food item in the diet of chicks (e.g. Herranz *et al.* 1994), and their apparent rarity in the diet of Skylark chicks in the UK may be due to the huge declines in grasshopper populations that have been brought about by intensive grassland management.

Occasionally the items brought back to the nest can present problems for the chicks. Research carried out by Kathryn Murray in central England suggests that the parents generally remove the dangerous parts of insect prey, such as the heads of predatory beetles, before feeding them to the chicks. However, one nest I examined in Norfolk contained a chick that was starving because a predatory Devil's Coach Horse beetle, presumably brought still alive to the nest by the parents, had locked its mandibles into the chick's tongue before dying, preventing the chick from swallowing it or anything else. The chick recovered quickly after the beetle was removed. I have also seen several nests in which a chick had swallowed the head of a stem of grass growing next to the nest, which held it like a fish on a line and prevented it from feeding. Once again, freeing these led to rapid recovery, but if left alone the chicks would probably have starved.

The composition of the diet can influence the development of the chicks. In southern England, chicks fed mostly on insect larvae tend to be in better condition than chicks fed on other foods. The variety of food items in the diet also appears to have an effect. In agricultural grass fields, there is very little diversity in the diet and chicks tend to be in relatively poor condition, whereas chicks with more varied diets in other habitats tend to be in better condition (Poulsen *et al.* 1998, Donald *et al.* 2001e).

The rate of delivery of food items by the parents increases as the chicks grow older, reaching up to ten items per chick per hour in one study in Switzerland (Weibel 1999). However the adults can bring back several prey items on each visit. The number of visits by provisioning parents was estimated by Poulsen (1996) at between 3.4 and 7.3 visits per chick per hour, depending on the crop type. In Switzerland, Urs Weibel recorded a rather lower visit rate of between 1.7 and 6.0 visits per chick per hour, with rates again being higher for older broods. The very large numbers of visits to a nest often result in the formation of little tracks or runways of flattened vegetation in the grass leading to and from the nest. These make the nests easier for researchers to find, but probably also for predators.

Parents flying longer distances from the nest to collect food make fewer visits, but compensate for this by bringing larger food loads back to the nest. Clearly the decision the parents make about where to collect food is a trade-off between how far they have to fly and how productive the area is. Nests containing four chicks can receive up to one visit every two minutes, or nearly five hundred during the course of a day. However the rate of feeding is not constant through the day. During periods of rain, the female will stop feeding and brood the chicks, and rain has a significant negative impact on chick growth rates (Donald *et al.* 2001e). When the rain continues for several days, the birds have to combine feeding the chicks with keeping them dry, and prolonged rain leads to very high chick mortality. When conditions are good, during warm dry weather, there is often a lull in feeding during the heat of the day, when parents may leave the chicks unfed for an hour or more at a time.

After feeding the chicks, the parents leave directly from the nest. Faecal sacs produced by very small chicks are eaten by the parents at the nest, but those of larger chicks are removed directly from the cloaca and dropped in flight some distance away. The removal of those bags of waste is made easier for the parents because the cloacae of young chicks are angled upwards, migrating ventrally as the chicks grow and develop. The sacs are bound in a membranous coating which makes it possible for the parents to carry them without them bursting. Faecal sacs are rarely removed from chicks that have already left the nest, small piles of them indicating where the chicks have spent the night.

Because it is very difficult to follow individual Skylarks once they have left the nest, little is known about how far they go or what their survival rates are, although Markus Jenny (1990a) has estimated that on Swiss farmland only around half the chicks leaving the nest survive the next couple of weeks to fledge. The only published study to examine in detail chick dispersal from the nest is that of John Poulsen (1996), who found that chicks move considerable distances away from the nest, and from each other, in the first few days of leaving the nest. Within four days of leaving the nest, many chicks are well over 50 m from the nest, and over 20 m from their nearest sibling. The parents, which are still providing most of the chicks' food at this stage, appear to locate their chicks by call. If chicks are disturbed and move, running quickly as they are still incapable even of short flights, the parents appear to have difficulty in finding them, often hovering with food in

*Figure 7.4.  Skylark (probably a female) bringing food to a nearby nest. The large size of the insect larva suggests the chicks are fairly well grown. This bird is of the subspecies* pekinensis, *photographed in eastern Siberia by Yuri Artukhin.*

their bills for long periods over the general area and uttering a quiet, anxious call. This means that the average number of visits by a parent bringing food to each chick is lower than it is when the chicks are still in the nest. Excessive disturbance at this period in the nesting cycle may cause the parents to lose contact with their chicks permanently, almost certainly leading to the starvation of the chick.

As the chicks grow older and become more self-sufficient, the male parent becomes the main provider as the female starts to accumulate reserves for the next nesting attempt. The parents change from bringing food in to fledglings to walking around with them, collecting food items and feeding them directly to the chicks. Between the twentieth and thirtieth days after hatching, the surviving chicks are largely abandoned to their fate (Plate 6), or even aggressively expelled from their natal territory, as the parents prepare to start the whole process again.

*Skylark nest being predated by a Stoat*

CHAPTER 8

# Productivity

I am not by any means forgetful of the damage done to all
ground-breeding birds by mowing-machines and similar imple-
ments, but as the majority of our Sky-Larks certainly nest on the
arable land, and their young can generally take care of themselves
by the time of the corn-harvest, they are not so much affected by
these inventions as are our game-birds.

Lord Lilford, *Notes on the Birds of Northamptonshire and*
*Neighbourhood* (1895)

Productivity, the total number of chicks produced by each pair in a breeding season, is a measure very different from the number of eggs laid in a nest. A high proportion of nests produce no chicks at all, and pairs may build and lay eggs in more
than one nest over the course of a breeding season. To calculate a reliable measure
of productivity, it is therefore necessary to estimate the number of chicks produced

by an average nesting attempt, then to multiply this figure by the number of nesting attempts made. Neither of these figures is easy to derive, and estimating productivity requires a considerable amount of effort. However, estimating productivity is essential if the population ecology of any species is to be understood. Without doing it, it is impossible to determine the reasons for population trends, and so to suggest measures to halt declines. As we shall see, this apparently academic exercise has in fact revealed much about the causes of the massive population declines of the Skylark described in Chapter 3, causes that have turned out to be unexpected and surprising.

## NEST SURVIVAL AND PREDATION

In the majority of bird species, and in particular in smaller, open-nesting species such as the Skylark, the most important factor determining how many chicks an individual nest produces is the likelihood that the nest survives long enough to produce any chicks at all. Total nest failure can occur for a number of reasons, including starvation or chilling of chicks, death of the parents or accidental crushing. However, across a wide range of bird species, the most common cause of nest failure is predation, which accounts for an average of 80% of all nest failures. Indeed, nest predation has been identified as one of the most important factors determining how many chicks a bird produces during its lifetime. Nest failure rates are extremely important in determining population levels, and an increase or decrease in nest failure rates can cause populations to fall or rise. For example, it is well known by gamekeepers that killing predators of eggs or chicks can increase the populations of gamebirds on their farm. A dramatic illustration of the power of nest predation to affect population sizes is provided by the catastrophic collapses, often to extinction, of island bird species following the introduction of egg predators such as rats or snakes (Fuller 2000). So the failure of nests, though very rarely witnessed by human observers, is a vitally important determinant of the populations of wild birds.

Quantifying the rate of failure of nests, however, is far from straightforward. It is not possible to express nesting success simply as the percentage of all nests that went on to succeed, since nests failing quickly are more likely to be missed by the researcher than those that succeed, leading to an overestimate of success. The statistical method developed by Henry Mayfield (1975), which now bears his name, gets around this bias by calculating nesting success as the probability of failure per day that nests are under observation. The Mayfield method, and more complex extensions of it, allows us to derive accurate and unbiased measurements of nesting success, and to assess what factors influence them.

It has long been known that ground-nesting species, and particularly those that nest in open habitats, suffer from high rates of nest predation. Studies of larks from around the world show that in this family more than four out of every five nests may be destroyed by a predator (e.g. Suárez & Manrique 1992). As a consequence, ground-nesting species like larks tend to have smaller clutch sizes than hole-nesting species (a literal example of the prudence of not putting all one's eggs in one basket), and instead make several nesting attempts during the course of a single breeding season. Other anti-predator strategies include rapid chick development, camouflage, diversionary tactics and the avoidance of areas where there are many predators (see Chapters 3 and 7).

Despite all these strategies, predation accounted for 77% of all failures of Skylark nests during the RSPB Skylark Research Project (Donald *et al.* 2002a), and 71% of the nest failures on Urs Weibel's (1999) farmland study site in Switzerland. On Juan Delius's coastal dune study site, where there were no farming operations to destroy nests, predation accounted for 90% of all nest failures. Although it is difficult to be certain of the identity of Skylark nest predators, since acts of predation are very rarely observed, a wide variety of different animals is likely to be involved. During fieldwork carried out by the RSPB in southern England in the late 1990s, it was thought that nests were predated by, amongst other animals, Hedgehogs, Red Foxes, Badgers, Brown Rats, mustelids, corvids, Kestrels, Marsh and Montagu's Harriers and Grass Snakes. Red Foxes appear to be a particularly important predator of Skylark nests in Poland (Tryjanowski 2000b), and in Germany mammalian predators include Wild Boar, Red Fox, Badger and Racoon Dog (Jeromin 2002). In one bizarre case we recorded, an egg was 'predated' by a large snail which, presumably seeking calcium, rasped a hole through the eggshell, killing the embryo inside. Markus Jenny has also seen slugs destroying eggs by rasping holes in them. In New Zealand, the most important predator of Skylark nests on farmland is the introduced Hedgehog, although the native Australasian Magpie and Australasian Harrier have also been seen predating nests (Thomsen 2002). In most cases of genuine predation, the predator destroys all the eggs or chicks in the nest. If the chicks are predated after their legs have sclerotised (hardened), the legs are often chewed or pulled off and left in the nest by the predator (Plate 5).

Although predation is the most frequent cause of nest failure in Skylarks overall, nests can fail for many other reasons. In modern agricultural grass, for example, where several cuts are taken in a season, destruction of nests through cutting can be a more important cause of nest failure than predation (Plate 7). On his intensive agricultural study site in Switzerland, Markus Jenny (1990) found that mowing accounted for over 80% of all nest losses, compared with less than 10% lost to predation. On one study site, mowing destroyed 95 out of 98 nests. An added danger is that those that do survive the cut become exposed to predators and often fail shortly after. In grazed fields, accidental trampling of nests or chicks by livestock can lead to the failure of many nests, particularly where stocking densities are high. An additional threat to ground nesting birds is irrigation. Flooding of Skylark nests is a major cause of nest failure in irrigated crops in the Caucasus (Khokhlov 1990).

Nest-survival rates of Skylarks on modern farmland are extremely low. In one study in southern England, only a quarter of all nests survived long enough for at least one chick to leave the nest (Donald *et al.* 2002a). The remaining three quarters were predated, abandoned, crushed, trampled or starved. Estimates of nest success from other studies of Skylarks on farmland are similarly low (Chamberlain & Crick 1999, Weibel 1999, Stöckli 2002, Jeromin 2002). Nest success was apparently very high at 46% on Delius's coastal dune study site, but was not calculated using the Mayfield method and so is certainly an overestimate.

Taking an overall average nest-survival rate masks some interesting differences between different types of farmland. When Skylark nest-survival rates are calculated for different crops separately, it becomes clear that the type of farmland a nest is placed in has a profound effect on the likelihood of it being successful. Perhaps surprisingly, given the high level of level of chemical inputs, Skylarks nesting in cereal crops have the highest chance of successful nesting, with a success rate of around 38%, and birds in fallow land (set-aside), where no chemicals are used, a far lower rate of success at just 22% (Donald *et al.* 2002a). Working in Switzerland, Urs Weibel (1999) has obtained strikingly similar results from another large sample of nests. This is, on the face of it, an unexpected result, since fallow land is clearly the preferred habitat in terms of territory density. Yet this difference in territory density might actually be the explanation of the difference in nesting success. As we saw in Chapter 3, set-side attracts large numbers of Skylarks, and so might be expected to attract large numbers of other animals and their predators. Skylarks are one of the few species to nest solely in open habitats, meaning that for the predators there are few other nests to look for away from the food-rich field margins. But when Skylark nests reach high densities, their nests may be sufficiently abundant to tempt predators away from other foods and into the fields to look for them. A Skylark nest containing large chicks is an attractive target for a predator, providing up to 130 g of meat. Urs Weibel's research in Switzerland has shown that the predation rate of Skylark nests increases the closer they are to the edge of the field, suggesting that the most important predators spend most of their time in the food-rich hedgerows and only venture out to take the Skylark nests nearby. So the high numbers of Skylark nests in certain habitats might actually bring about their own destruction through a density dependent process. Where Skylark nests and other food resources for predators are few and far between, such as in modern, intensively managed cereal crops, it is not worth the predators' time to spend a lot of time looking for nests, since the chances of finding a meal are so small, and so fewer nests fail. Despite this, nesting in set-aside has advantages that might outweigh the high nest-predation risk, as birds are able to make more nesting attempts during the course of a breeding season. As we shall see in Chapter 12, the nesting season in modern cereal fields can be a very short one.

It is frequently claimed that high nest predation rates are the result of the increases that have undoubtedly taken place in the numbers of some common predators, particularly Carrion Crows, Magpies and certain mammals. Some have gone further, and suggested that these have been largely or solely responsible for the catastrophic declines in Skylark populations described in Chapter 3. However, all the evidence suggests that this is not the case. Dan Chamberlain and Humphrey Crick (1999) analysed a carefully selected sample of the huge number of BTO Nest Record Cards collected for Skylarks since 1950. Quite unexpectedly, they found that nest survival rates actually increased during the period that Skylarks were declining most rapidly. It seems extremely unlikely, therefore, that Skylark populations have declined because of an increase in nest predation.

However, the numbers of predators do have an effect on Skylark nest survival rates. We were very fortunate during the RSPB Skylark Research Project to have as one of our study sites a farm in Norfolk that probably came as close to the ideal for Skylarks as exists anywhere. Situated on the line of low hills that run parallel to, and a couple of kilometres south of, the beautiful north Norfolk coast, this farm yielded us almost as many nests as the other 20 farms in the Project put together. The main reason for this was the presence of a large number of fields of set-aside that were allowed to establish from stubble and, due to the sandy and flinty nature of the soil, developed a vegetation structure perfect for Skylarks. The densities of Skylarks in these fields were as high as I have seen anywhere in the UK, at over one pair per hectare, and we found several hundred nests over the three years we worked there. The number of birds using these fields, and the fields themselves, did not change during the three years we searched for nests there. So when, quite by chance, predator control was introduced there, we had an ideal opportunity to examine in detail what effects the removal of predators had on Skylark nest survival rates. In the first year of our study, there was no gamekeeper on the farm, in the second year, half the farm was worked by a gamekeeper and half was not, and in the final year the gamekeeper controlled predators (mostly Weasels, Stoats, Grey Squirrels and Hedgehogs) over the whole farm. The effect on Skylark nest success rates was truly dramatic. As the gamekeeper began to control predators, nest survival rates increased hugely (Figure 8.1). Furthermore, predator control appeared to have an effect on the length of the breeding season. Where the gamekeeper set his traps (Figure 8.2), the breeding season finished earlier than where predator numbers were not controlled. This was probably because the birds were not forced to make so many repeat nesting attempts to compensate for predated nests. An analogous situation has been described in Spain, where the designation of some areas as nature reserves has paradoxically had a negative effect on the nesting success of a number of species of lark, since nature reserve designation prevents the killing of predatory mammals (Suárez *et al.* 1993).

But if removing predators increases Skylark nest success locally, as it clearly did in north Norfolk, why then has an increase in the numbers of certain predators coincided with an increase, rather than a decrease, in Skylark nest success rates nationally? And if nest success is so crucial in determining population levels, why have populations declined during a period when nesting success actually increased? Without a full population model, incorporating estimates of all the elements of reproduction and mortality, it is impossible to provide precise answers to these questions. However it is possible to make educated guesses, based upon what we know of this and other species. While it is clear that numbers of certain predators have increased in numbers, particularly avian predators such as members of the crow family, Skylark populations are lower than they were previously, and nests are

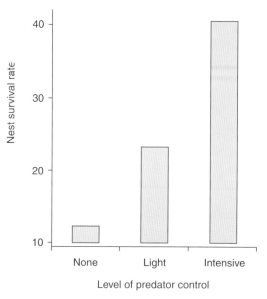

*Figure 8.1.    The effects of differing levels of predator control by a gamekeeper on nest survival rates of Skylarks (expressed as the percentage of nests surviving long enough to produce at least one chick) on a farm in north Norfolk. Data from Donald* et al. *(2002a).*

*Figure 8.2.    Gamekeeper's trap, set on the farm in Norfolk where RSPB researchers recorded a huge rise in nest success rates. Photo: Paul F. Donald.*

consequently more spread out. As we have already seen, when nests are few and far between, predation rates fall as predators spend less effort looking for these rare food resources. It is interesting to note that the spectacular increase in nest survival brought about by the introduction of a gamekeeper at the farm in Norfolk occurred only in fields of set-aside, where territory densities were extremely high. There was no increase in the nesting success of birds in cereal fields on the same farm, where territory densities were far lower. So it appears that the increasing rarity of Skylark nests does at least give them some protection against increasing numbers of predators. But why has the recorded increase in nesting success apparent in the analyses of Chamberlain and Crick not brought about an increase in the British Skylark population? That it has not suggests very strongly that nesting success is not the most important factor determining the population level. A neat demonstration of this comes from work on birds in the moors of Scotland. Moors managed for grouse shooting had far higher numbers of gamekeepers working on them than non-grouse moors, and so presumably far fewer predators, yet Skylark populations were more than twice as high on the non-grouse moors (Tharme *et al.* 2001). Similarly, of all the 20 farms we worked on in southern England during the three years of the RSPB Skylark Research Project, the farm with the smallest numbers of Skylarks was that with the most intensive predator control. Removing predators might therefore increase the survival rates of individual nests, but it clearly does not always result in increased populations (Côté & Sutherland 1997). So, although increased nesting success may have slowed the decline, something else is clearly driving the population on farmland downwards. Some of the other possible candidates will be discussed in Chapter 12.

## PRODUCTIVITY OF NESTS AND THE NUMBER OF NESTING ATTEMPTS

The number of chicks produced by an individual nesting attempt depends on several different factors: the number of eggs laid, the proportion of these that hatch, the number of chicks that die and, most importantly, the likelihood of the nest failing completely, usually through predation. We have already seen that there is considerable variation in all these factors, so all need to be combined if an estimate is to be made of the average number of chicks produced per nesting attempt. Results from the RSPB Skylark Research Project indicate that there is considerable difference in the productivity of nests in different field types. Although clutch sizes are lower in cereals than in other field types, the very high nest success in cereals made these nests the most productive, producing an average of 1.26 chicks per nesting attempt, compared to 0.78 in set-aside and 0.63 in grass. Of course, it is likely that many of these chicks leaving the nest will die before reaching independence, so these figures do not relate to the final productivity of the nest. However the results do suggest that birds nesting in agricultural grass fields and set-aside need to make nearly twice as many nesting attempts in a season to produce as many chicks as a pair nesting in cereals. This might go some way to explaining the very low territory density of Skylarks in grass, but does not explain the very high densities of birds in set-aside (see Chapter 3). This is likely to be due to the long breeding season, and therefore the large number of repeat nesting attempts a pair can make, in set-aside. If successful nests alone are considered, discounting the effects of predation, nests in set-aside become the most productive, due to their larger average clutch size.

The productivity of individual nesting attempts is only part of the equation that determines how many chicks an individual pair of Skylarks produces in a breeding season. Like most songbirds, and probably all larks, Skylarks are multi-brooded. That is, they will make a number of nesting attempts in a single breeding season. Having multiple broods is a common strategy of open-nesting birds with high nest-predation rates, whereas hole-nesting species tend to have a single nesting attempt each year. In this way, the high nest-failure rates described previously can be compensated for. So in order to calculate the number of chicks produced by a pair of birds in a single breeding season, it is necessary to know how many nesting attempts they make. However, estimating the number of nesting attempts is extremely difficult, since it is generally impossible to follow individual pairs for long periods of time, particularly where densities are high. Furthermore, the very high predation rate of Skylark nests means that many will fail quickly and not be found by the researchers. The number of nesting attempts possible in a breeding season is at least partly determined by how quickly birds start to nest again after the loss or success of their previous attempt.

Once again, we must turn to Juan Delius (1965) and his colour-ringed sand dune population for the most meticulous measurements of the interval between the loss of one nesting attempt and the onset of the next. His observations of colour-ringed birds on a coastal dune system suggest that this interval depends on the stage at which the previous nesting attempt was lost. If the previous nesting attempt was lost during egg laying or just after the onset of incubation, the first egg of the next clutch was laid around four days later. This is a remarkably quick recovery when one considers that a new nest has to be built from scratch. If a clutch was lost after the onset of incubation or while the chicks were in the nest, the interval to re-laying rose to around six days. If the nest was not predated and the chicks fledged successfully, re-nesting took place around 18 days after the initial brood hatched, even if the parents were still feeding them. Also working with the benefit of a colour-ringed study population, Alex Schläpfer (1988) was able to examine how well Delius's results from coastal dunes in the 1960s applied to intensive agricultural land in Switzerland in the 1980s. Perhaps not surprisingly, given the more austere environment of modern farmland, Alex found that the interval between replacement clutches on his study site was around twice that recorded from coastal dunes nearly 20 years before. The longest interval between consecutive nesting attempts by an individual pair was 37 days, although the average was closer to 12.

Juan Delius had two major advantages while working on his coastal dune study site. First, many of his birds were colour-ringed, allowing him to follow individual pairs throughout the breeding season. Second, the habitat he was working in was extremely open, allowing him to see not only the rings on the birds' legs but also to obtain extremely clear views of everything his birds were doing. This is to detract nothing from his great perceptiveness and skill as a field ornithologist, and his work on the Skylarks of the Ravenglass dune system remains one of the classic bird population studies. Delius was able to generate empirical figures on the number of nesting attempts made over the course of a breeding season by different pairs of birds. The average number of nesting attempts per pair was 2.7 per year, but this average masks some interesting variation between different pairs (Figure 8.3). The most frequently recorded number of nesting attempts was three, but some birds made only a single attempt while others made four. Of course, not all these were successful, although one pair did manage to raise three broods successfully. Delius could detect no effect of the age of the female on the number of nesting attempts she made, nor was there any consistency between years in the number of nesting attempts made by a single female.

But Delius's data relate to an undisturbed coastal dune system. How do his findings relate to Skylarks on modern, intensively managed farmland? This question has become something of a Holy Grail for modern Skylark researchers. Together with an accurate estimate of annual survival (see Chapter 11), this is the last major obstacle to building a full population model which would allow us to determine once and for all why Skylark populations are declining. One of the main problems

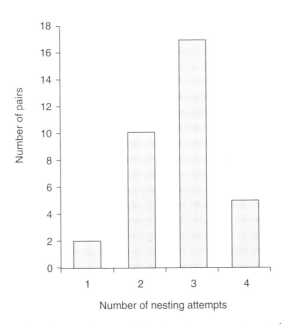

*Figure 8.3.    The number of pairs making 1, 2, 3 or 4 nesting attempts in a single breeding season in coastal dunes during the early 1960s. From data in Delius (1965).*

in determining how many nesting attempts each pair makes in a season is the difficulty of following individual birds around. Even where birds can be colour ringed, it is often very difficult to see their legs sufficiently well on farmland to read the ring combinations. This has not stopped a number of researchers from trying, however. Markus Jenny (1990a) followed a small population of Skylarks around Swiss farmland for several years, and estimated an average of 1.9 to 2.3 nesting attempts per pair per season. The maximum he recorded was six (a total of 22 eggs), but the maximum number of successful attempts was, as in Delius's population, three (although Markus himself influenced this figure by stepping in to prevent one of these nests from being destroyed by grass cutting). These few cases of large numbers of nesting attempts tend to distort the average, and nearly 70% of pairs made only one or two attempts in a season. Markus estimated that, on average, these attempts would produce less than one fledged and independent new bird for each pair over the course of the whole breeding season. Working around the same time, also in Switzerland, Alex Schläpfer similarly found that two nesting attempts per year were about average. On average, the pairs in Alex's population would produce 2.5 fledglings per season, but many of these would die before reaching independence. Working on intensive farmland in Germany during the late 1980s, Daunicht (1998) estimated that females managed an average of just 1.8 broods per year, and that some, particularly those settling in winter cereals, actually made no nesting attempts at all. However, because the survival rates of individual nests in Daunicht's study were high, he estimated a fairly high seasonal productivity of three chicks leaving the nest per female per year.

All these studies from farmland suggest that, on average, Skylarks make less than the three nesting attempts that are probably required to maintain populations (Wilson *et al.* 1997, Wolfenden & Peach 2001). It is becoming increasingly clear that this is one of the main reasons why populations have declined. The causes of this reduction in the number of nesting attempts will be discussed in further detail in Chapter 12.

*Flock of migrants arriving over coast*

CHAPTER 9

# Migration and other movements

Speaking of the complaints respecting the diminution of birds, Herr Gätke says:- "To a witness, however, of the enormous passage of migrants, of the myriads of individuals which on autumn nights pass this island [Heligoland], like the flakes of a snow-storm, not only within the area of the lighthouse, but for miles north and south out to sea, these complaints seem quite incomprehensible. It is surely impossible that the hand of man can exercise any perceptible influence on such enormous migration streams"; and he adds that the number of 15,000 Larks caught in one autumn night does not approximately express a proportion of one for each 10,000 individuals of such a migrant stream.

Arthur G. Butler, *British Birds with their Nests and Eggs*
(1896–98)

In Britain the Skylark can be found throughout the year, but in many parts of its breeding range it is solely a summer visitor. In northern, central and eastern Europe, the song of the first returning Skylark is as much a sign of spring as the first Cuckoo or Swallow. Each autumn and spring there are mass movements of tens of millions of Skylarks between breeding grounds in northern, central and eastern Europe and wintering grounds in southern and western Europe and in the Caucasus. A century ago, when European populations were far higher, and winters far colder than they are now, these migrations produced one of the most spectacular mass movements of birds ever recorded, rivalling the famous nineteenth-century accounts of sky-darkening flocks of the now extinct Passenger Pigeon in North America, and locust-like flocks of Red-billed Queleas in Africa today.


## ANNUAL MIGRATION


The movements of western European Skylarks have been examined through analysing recoveries of ringed birds (Hemery *et al.* 1991, Spaepen 1995a). Only around one in every 700 Skylarks that are caught and ringed is ever reported again, either through being found dead or by being caught by another ringer. However, the vast numbers of Skylarks ringed in Europe (well over 600,000 by 1995), particularly in Belgium and the Netherlands, allow us to piece together some picture of movements.

It is clear from ringing recoveries that some Skylark populations undergo very long autumn and spring migrations. Several birds have been recovered over 3,000 km from where they were ringed, the longest movement on record being 3,613 km, a nestling from Finnish Lapland that was later recovered in Spain (Spaepen 1995a). Central, northern and eastern European populations spend the winter mainly in the UK, France (especially in the southwest of the country and the Rhône Valley), Italy and, particularly, Iberia. These areas correspond to those with the least snowfall. Some birds winter as far south as northwest Africa. There are regular movements of birds across the Straits of Gibraltar, where birds ringed in France, Belgium, Holland, Germany, Denmark, Sweden, Finland, Switzerland and the Czech Republic have all been recovered (Finlayson 1992). Exceptionally, birds wander as far south as Senegal and Mauritania, probably the only records of the species in the Afrotropical zone. Vagrants have also been recorded as far west as Madeira and the Azores.

But it is to southern France and Spain that the majority of Europe's migrating Skylarks head in winter. The mass of recorded autumn movement is therefore in a westerly or southwesterly direction (e.g. Stolt 1980). Over 95% of all recorded autumn migration movements take place at a bearing between 195° and 254°, in other words from just west of south to just south of west. Birds breeding as far east as western Russia and as far north as Finland migrate westwards or southwards each autumn to France and Spain, and many are caught and ringed in long-running studies of migration in Belgium and the Netherlands. Crude estimates based on ringing recoveries suggest that between 25 and 100 million Skylarks migrate to, or through, France each year (Spaepen 1995b). Ringing recoveries suggest that birds migrating to or through Italy have their origins from southern central Europe to as far east as the Urals in Russia. Birds breeding in central Russia apparently winter in very large numbers in the Middle East, with vagrants as far south as Kuwait. Further eastwards, it seems that Skylarks breeding in eastern Russian and Mongolia winter in a broad band from northern India to eastern China, although the wintering range is poorly known. Introduced populations in Australia, Tasmania and New Zealand are wholly sedentary, probably because their founder populations were non-migratory British birds.

The autumn migration of European Skylarks is a prolonged one, lasting from early September well into November, but the main migratory movements through the Low Countries and further south in Italy take place in mid to late October. In France and Italy there exist a large number of old hunting proverbs relating Skylark migration to saints' days falling around October. Autumn passage across the Straits of Gibraltar peaks during the second half of October, with return northerly passage peaking at the end of February. Further east, migration away from the St Petersburg (Leningrad) region starts at the beginning of September. Walpole-Bond (1938) records the onset of return migration eastwards along the English south coast starting in February but taking place mainly in March and early April.

However, the timing of migration is not fixed, and some central European birds are back on their breeding grounds as early as the end of January. The Skylark is one of the earliest migrants to return to central and eastern Europe. In southern Sweden and in Finland returning birds may arrive as early as the start of February, but arrivals before April are unusual in the north of Scandinavia. The average first arrival date of returning birds in Poland is 20 February (Tryjanowski *et al.* 2002b). Further east, return of the first spring migrants to the St Petersburg area can occur any time between the beginning of March and the first week of April, depending on weather conditions and the severity of the previous winter (Mal'chevskiy & Pukinskiy 1983). After the first arrival, migrants continue to pass through, and nocturnal and diurnal migration continues for at least a further month as birds head north for breeding grounds in Finland and northern Russia. Further east still, Skylarks breeding at Lake Baikal in Siberia return to their breeding grounds around the middle of April (Fefelov *et al.* 2001), so there appears to be a pattern of increasingly late return to the breeding grounds the further east one goes. Throughout northern and central Europe, arrival dates can vary by as much as a month between years, depending on weather conditions. In all areas, it is the males that arrive back on the breeding grounds first, sometimes as much as a month before the females. This may in part be due to their shorter return journey (see below).

Climate warming is starting to profoundly influence the phenology (the timing of life history events) of many species, including the timing of migration. Analysis of the 132-year-old data set recording the spring arrival dates of Skylarks in Estonia, for example, shows that arrival dates have advanced markedly as temperatures have risen (Ahas 1999). A similar trend towards earlier arrivals has also been recorded in Poland (Tryjanowski *et al.* 2002b). In Norway, the arrival dates of Skylarks in spring are closely correlated with fluxes in the North Atlantic Oscillation (NAO). In high NAO years, warm and wet winter weather is brought to Europe by frequent and strong westerly winds across the Atlantic, whereas in low NAO winters the warm and wet weather remains over the western Atlantic, leaving Europe cold and dry. Following high NAO winters, Skylarks arrive back on their Norwegian breeding grounds significantly earlier than they do after low NAO winters (Forchhammer *et al.* 1998).

## MASS MOVEMENTS

As populations of Skylarks across Europe have declined, so have their migratory movements, and to most European birdwatchers today there is nothing particularly special about the migration of Skylarks. A century or more ago, however, Skylark migration must have ranked amongst the most spectacular mass movements of birds ever seen. Many Victorian accounts of the mass migration of Skylarks describe truly extraordinary events, such as that witnessed by Henry Seebohm at Heligoland, a small island off the coast of Germany in the North Sea, one October night in 1876. It is worth quoting his account in full (contemporary spellings like 'potatoe' included). Originally published in his book *A History of British Birds* (1882–85), it is a beautifully observed description of an extraordinary natural spectacle that will probably never be witnessed again:

> At half-past twelve I was awakened with the news that the migration had already begun. Hastily dressing myself, I at once made for the lighthouse. The night was almost pitch dark, but the town was all astir. In every street men with large lanterns and a sort of angler's landing net were making for the lighthouse. As I crossed the potatoe-fields birds were continually getting up at my feet. When I arrived at the lighthouse, an intensely interesting sight presented itself. The whole of the zone of light within range of the mirrors was alive with birds coming and going. Nothing else was visible in the darkness of the night but the lantern of the lighthouse vignetted in a drifting sea of birds. From the darkness in the east, clouds of birds were continually emerging in an uninterrupted stream; a few swerved from their course, fluttered for a moment as if dazzled by the light, and then gradually vanished with the rest in the western gloom. Occasionally a bird wheeled around the lighthouse and then passed on, and sometimes one fluttered against the glass like a moth against a lamp, tried to perch on the wire netting, and was caught by the lighthouse man. I should be afraid to hazard a guess at the hundreds of thousands that must have passed in a couple of hours; but the stray birds which the lighthouse man succeeded in securing amounted to nearly 300. The scene from the balcony of the lighthouse was equally interesting; in every direction birds could be seen flying like a swarm of bees, and

every few seconds one flew against the glass. All the birds seemed to be flying up wind, and it was only on the lee side of the light that any birds were caught. They were nearly all Sky-Larks; but in the heap captured there was one Redstart and one Reed-Bunting. The air was filled with the warbling cry of the Larks, now and then a thrush was heard; and once a Heron screamed as it passed by. The night was starless and the town invisible, but the island looked like the suburbs of a gas-lit city, being sprinkled over with brilliant lanterns. Many of the Sky-Larks alighted on the ground and allowed the Heligolanders to pass their nets over them. About three o'clock in the morning a heavy thunderstorm came on, with deluges of rain; a few breaks in the cloud revealed stars, and the migration came to an end, or continued above the range of our vision.

Equally impressive autumn movements of migrating Skylarks were recorded crossing into Britain. These movements, or 'rushes', were likely to include both birds passing through southern Britain on their way to wintering quarters in south-western Europe and birds whose final wintering destination was the British Isles. Once again, it is worth quoting at length a dramatic passage from Seebohm:

Equally interesting is the arrival of the Larks on our shores, not only on the east coast of England, but also on the same coast of Scotland. The 'Migration Report' for 1882 mentions a *rush* of Sky-Larks at Sumburgh Head, on the Shetlands, from the 11th to the 18th of September. On the Isle of May, in the Firth of Forth, a 'vast rush' of Larks and other birds passed westwards in October; whilst hundreds are described as being drowned in the sea or killed on the balcony of the lighthouse at Bell Rock, on the coast of the mainland, on the night of the 12th of October. Enormous numbers are reported as arriving at twenty-nine stations in various parts of the east coast of England in October and up to the end of the year.

Dixon thus writes of the autumn movement of this bird:—"Perhaps no locality in the British Islands is more suitable or better adapted to observe the incoming stream of Sky-Larks than the low-lying coast of Lincolnshire, on the northern shores of the Wash. The rush of Sky-Larks that land on our eastern coasts in autumn is almost past belief. Towards the end of October, or during the first week of November, the number that pass over these marshes is enormous. When the migration is on, you may see the great army of birds passing at a moderate height for days together; and you may know that the grand flight is still continuing during the night, by constantly hearing the little travellers calling to each other as they pass on, coming from over the sea, to the inland pastures. In the daytime many of the birds break out into song the moment they are over dry land, as if full of joy at making the passage safely. Comparatively few of the birds alight here, the great majority pass down the coast at once."

It was not just the east coast of England that recorded impressive movements of birds. On the Isles of Scilly mass movements were described in October 1903, when "from twelve to three on the second day the flocks must have averaged about a hundred, and followed each other so closely that in the distance they looked like a dusky band rising out of the sea" (Penhallurick 1978). In his book *Our Favourite Song Birds* (1897), Charles Dixon writes that

> each autumn it pours into Western Europe and across the North Sea into our islands in numbers that can be described only as amazing. During October and November millions of this bird must enter our eastern counties or sweep along the British coasts of the North Sea on their way to winter quarters further south. Day after day, and night after night, this stupendous migration of Sky-Larks goes on, the birds appearing in never-ending flocks.

Writing some time later of worries about the effects on the population of taking large numbers of migrating Skylarks for food, Henry Seebohm's companion on Heligoland, Herr Gätke, is cited by Arthur Butler (1896–98) as saying "To a witness of the enormous passage of migrants, of the myriads of individuals which on autumn nights travel past this island, like the flakes of a snow-storm, not only within the area of the lighthouse, but for miles north and south out to sea, these complaints seem quite incomprehensible. It is surely impossible that the hand of man can exercise any perceptible influence on such enormous migration streams". He went on to suggest that the 15,000 birds caught in one autumn night on Heligoland did "not approximately express a proportion of one for each 10,000 individuals of such a migrant stream".

Herr Gätke's belief in the Skylark's invulnerability at the hands of man proved sadly mistaken, and the vast movements of birds such as those described by Henry Seebohm are seen no longer. It is interesting to speculate on why the massive and impressive movements recorded by Victorian naturalists are now a thing of the past. The population declines recorded all over Europe (and described in Chapter 3) are generally thought to be a relatively recent phenomenon, yet the great migratory flights of this species are long gone. It may be that the population declines recorded in the UK during the 1980s by the Common Birds Census represent merely the tail end of a long-term decline that has been taking place right across Europe for far longer than the life of that scheme. Unfortunately there is precious little evidence either to support or to disprove this, particularly from northern and eastern Europe, where these great migrations had their origin. Another possibility is that due to a general warming of the climate a far lower proportion of central and eastern European birds now undertake regular migratory flights. In mild winters, wintering birds have been recorded as far north as southern Finland and as far east as Romania and Ukraine. Certainly, many more birds now winter in countries like Germany than a few decades ago, but whether this number of birds is sufficient to account for Seebohm's vast hordes is questionable.

## MOVEMENTS OF BRITISH SKYLARKS

In the UK, the breeding population appears to be largely resident, although at least part of the population of the Northern Isles migrates to southern England (Wernham *et al.* 2002). In his analysis of British ringing recoveries (birds ringed and later found dead), Tom Dougall (1996) found that over two thirds of recoveries were within 10 km of the site of ringing. However, individual birds are capable of travelling great distances. The greatest distance recorded by a British-ringed Skylark was of a bird caught in February 1954 in Hampshire, which was found alive and released on a ship in the Gulf of Bothnia (the stretch of water between Sweden and Finland) in May of the same year, a distance of 1,788 km. This was likely to have been a bird born in northern Europe and ringed as a winter visitor in southern England. But British-bred birds can also move considerable distances. A Skylark ringed as a nestling on 27 May 1980 in Lothian was found dead in Portugal five months later. The longest distance travelled within the British Isles was 1,199 km, by a bird ringed at the Eddystone Lighthouse, Devon, in November 1964 that was killed by a cat on Unst, Shetland, in August 1965. Only nine of the more than 200 British-ringed recoveries have been recovered outside the UK (one each in the Baltic, Norway, Denmark, Netherlands, Channel Islands and Portugal, and three in France).

Although British Skylarks are fairly sedentary, there is evidence of local movements in many areas. Skylarks occupied only 70% of the 2,695 10-km grid squares in Britain and Ireland during the Winter Atlas (Lack 1986) compared with 98% during the first Breeding Atlas (Sharrock 1976). Many upland habitats become abandoned and there is evidence of a movement in many regions to warmer coastal areas. Simon Gillings (2001) has calculated that in winter the number of Skylarks per hectare approximately halves for every 140 m increase in altitude. Certain coastal populations also abandon their breeding grounds in winter, and the coastal-dune study populations of Juan Delius in Cumbria and Ian Wolfenden in Merseyside are absent in winter.

Migrant birds arriving on the eastern shores of Britain in autumn comprise a mixture of birds arriving to winter and birds passing through to France and Iberia. Birds arrive and pass through the whole of the British Isles (including even western Ireland) on a broad front, and are apparently not deterred from their course even by cities. During the autumn of 1956, a broad band of migration, estimated at over 360,000 birds, passed over London during the course of four days. Although migration is generally across a broad front, Eric Simms (1992) has suggested that there are certain concentrated channels of migration across the country caused by birds following river valleys, passes and scarps. In particular, he has drawn attention to the existence of a thoroughfare of migration, not only of Skylarks but of several other songbirds and gulls, in a narrow band of around 1 km across southern England between the Wash and the Bristol Channel. This 'Cotswold Corridor', following the valleys of the Rivers Welland and Avon, minimises the distance travelled over land when crossing from the east to west costs of southern Britain, although how birds know this is difficult to explain.

## HARD WEATHER MOVEMENTS

Due to the increased risks of hard weather, particularly prolonged snow-lie, on a bird that can feed only on the ground, Skylarks regularly undertake nomadic movements within winters in response to weather patterns. This facultative partial migration, which is functionally quite different from regular seasonal migration, is regularly observed in western Europe in plovers, certain thrushes and Skylarks (all ground-feeding birds of open country) and usually occurs in a southerly or westerly direction after snow. These movements could, when the species was more abundant, be as spectacular as the regular migration flights described by Henry Seebohm. Walpole-Bond (1938) recounts mass movements of Skylarks in winter in Sussex on the southeast coast of England:

> At almost any time during winter sudden 'flushes' of Sky-Larks are apt to occur, whilst under really arctic conditions almost incredible multitudes of these birds from all the sources mentioned move along our sea-board, generally travelling west, though occasionally east or south-east, and very exceptionally northwards. For instance, Mr G.D. Rowley put the number of Sky-Larks that passed his house in Brighton on December 16th, 1874, at over a million!

Citing the notes of another observer, Walpole-Bond describes a hard-weather movement that took place during heavy snow in January 1887, when "the movement was more or less against the wind (as is usual) and from west to east. An immense number of birds of a good many kinds passed over that day, but the number of Larks was astounding. Hundreds of them were passing along the shore every minute from early morning until late afternoon." Walpole-Bond goes on to describe that during such movements huge numbers of birds were caught for food using clap-nets. During one hard-weather movement in January 1897, over 12,000 Skylarks were caught around Brighton in a single morning. It was presumably a movement like this that brought huge numbers of Skylarks, "for multitude like Quails in the wildernesse", to the besieged city of Exeter during the English Civil War (D'Urban and Mathew 1892). The Royalist defenders were able to survive the bitterly cold winter of 1645–46 by catching and eating vast numbers of these birds. Hard-weather movements also posed other threats to the birds. Huge numbers used to be killed by flying into lighthouses, and at the Bell Rock Lighthouse in December 1882 "they were striking hard for a couple of hours like a shower of hail". Writing in their book *The Birds of Devon* (1892), D'Urban and Mathew describe how:

In the winter of 1860 we were Woodcock-shooting on Lundy Island, when there was a heavy fall of snow, with a large continuance of hard black frost. After three or four days of this weather Sky-Larks began to arrive on the island, and every day the frost lasted there were fresh accessions. While we were trying the top of the island we could see flock after flock drop in, until the Larks became so thick upon the ground that often several would be shot unavoidably when a Woodcock or Snipe rose before the guns. Numbers perished from cold and hunger, and had their bones picked by the hungry rats, which swarm upon the island.

One particular hard weather movement fortuitously coincided with fieldwork being carried out nationally in the UK for *The Atlas of Wintering Birds in Britain and Ireland* (Lack 1986), providing a rare opportunity to plot movements of birds

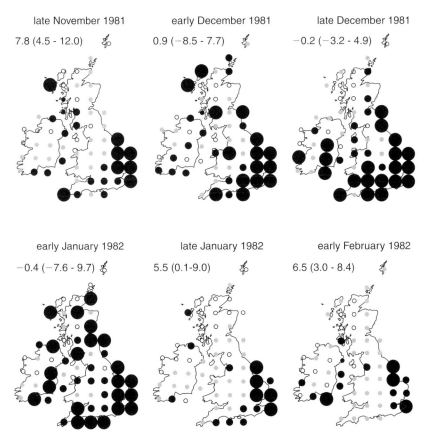

*Figure 9.1.    Patterns of abundance of Skylarks in the British Isles, November 1981 to February 1982. The size of the dots represents relative abundance. Mean air temperatures are given by each map, with the range of temperatures in parentheses. From Gillings (2001).*

in relation to temperature. Simon Gillings (2001) used data collected in the hard winter of 1981/82, during which a very large number of resident birds died (Wolfenden & Peach 2001), to chart the hard weather movement of birds from continental Europe into many parts of the British Isles (Figure 9.1). This was particularly apparent during December and early January, when temperatures were at their lowest in Europe. Large numbers of Skylarks were recorded throughout Britain, particularly in warmer coastal areas. By late January, when temperatures had risen above freezing, much of northern and western Britain was abandoned by Skylarks as birds returned to mainland Europe. The origin of these birds is probably the Low Countries, since populations further north and east are already on the wintering grounds of France and Iberia. Vast hard weather movements are rarely recorded these days, due to a combination of warmer winters and greatly reduced populations across Europe.

## MIGRATORY FLIGHT

Direct migratory flight is a very different phenomenon to short-distance foraging flights, and migratory populations are adapted to cope with prolonged, long-distance movements. The wings of the migratory Skylarks passing through Italy, which include birds from as far away as Ukraine and Russia, are longer and more pointed than those measured in sedentary birds in Scotland, representing an adaptation for longer migration. Longer, more pointed wings lead to an increased wing loading, which, although disadvantageous for short flights, allows birds to fly faster in long-distance level flights. During migration, Skylarks achieve an average level flight speed of around 15 m per second (around 54 km per hour), although birds migrating in larger flocks tend to have lower airspeeds, probably because of the effects of drag and uplift from other birds (Hedenström & Alerstam 1996). This is considerably faster than that predicted from flight mechanical theory for a bird the size and shape of a Skylark, for reasons that are unclear.

The diurnal migration flights recorded by Hedenström & Alerstam took place at an average altitude of 285 m, with some birds being recorded as high as 740 m. Birds migrating at higher altitudes had faster airspeeds than those at lower altitudes, due at least partly to reduced air density at higher altitudes. This might explain why migration takes place at significantly higher altitudes than the summer song flight. The height at which migration takes place is also influenced by wind speed and direction, birds appearing to reach greater altitudes with strong tail winds. When migrating over the sea, Skylarks often fly very close to the surface, possibly using the updrafts from waves to reduce energy expenditure, and observations of birds arriving off the sea on the east coast of Britain suggest that birds fly within a metre or two of the waves. Once over the land again, the birds rapidly regain height. Observations from Denmark suggest that prior to migration over the sea, birds may accumulate at regular 'jumping-off' points. When a critical number of birds is reached, they take off in large numbers, before breaking up into smaller flocks within a few hundred metres (Rabøl & Noer 1973).

Nocturnal migration by Skylarks appears to be influenced at least partly by the phases of the moon. Studies of nocturnal autumn migration in France suggest that, while migration can occur during all phases of the moon, the largest movements of birds occur while the moon is in its waxing gibbous phase (when over half the disc is illuminated and the area illuminated is increasing). This phase of the moon produces the best conditions for migration since, from the onset of darkness, it provides the necessary horizon for birds to navigate by and it illuminates topographic features. Furthermore, it allows birds to benefit from optimal light conditions for over a week (James *et al.* 2000). The same light conditions were favoured during the Second World War by bomber crews, and hundreds of migrating Skylarks used to be observed in the beams of anti-aircraft searchlights during the migration season.

Working on Skylarks in sensor-equipped cages, Guyomarch & Guillet (1996) found that birds started to exhibit migratory restlessness around two hours after nightfall, the activity falling off before rising again to another peak around two hours before dawn. However migration is not only nocturnal, and it seems that migrating birds complete their migration in a single journey, staying on the move both day and night if conditions are favourable. Ringing recoveries suggest that migrating birds can cover at least 810 km per day (Spaepen 1995a). Combined with the average flight speed of 54 km per hour recorded by Hedenström & Alerstam, this suggests that migrating Skylarks might fly for up to 15 hours per day. There seems to be great variation in the flow of migration, however, with huge movements on some days followed by very little the next. Furthermore, diurnal migration appears to be most concentrated at certain times of day. In Ireland in the late 1940s most autumn migration took place between 07:30 and 12:00 (Goodbody 1950), and in Belgium very little migration is recorded after 14:00 (Spaepen & van Cauteren 1962).

The flock size of migrating birds appears to vary, though much of the variation in the literature is likely to be due to the massive declines in population and greatly reduced migratory movements that have taken place over the last century. The vast streams of birds witnessed by Henry Seebohm during the nineteenth century are no longer recorded, and migratory movements now seem largely to consist of small, loosely connected flocks. Those observed in Sweden by Anders Hedenström during his investigations into the species' flight mechanics averaged just 10 birds, the largest holding 35 birds. In Ireland in the 1950s, flocks of migrants were also small, between 2 and 50 birds, with some singles (Goodbody 1950). Studying the spring migration of Skylarks in Denmark, Rabøl & Noer (1973) found that flock sizes of greater than 10 birds were unstable, and soon broke up into smaller loose units, the distance between birds being generally over 5 m. The same authors found that flock size can be influenced by weather, being larger in cloudy conditions or conditions of poor visibility. A flock of 600 migrants entering Cornwall in October 1965 was exceptionally large

(Penhallurick 1978). However, some migrant flocks still number in the thousands, particularly on return spring passage and in eastern populations. For example, a flock of 4,000 was seen in Turkey in mid March during the1970s (Simms 1992). Flock sizes of migrants involved in hard weather movements appear to be considerably larger than flocks of birds undertaking their usual seasonal migration (Rabøl & Noer 1973). Most migrating flocks are composed solely of Skylarks, but mixed-species flocks have been noted, often including Corn Buntings. A number of observers have noticed a characteristic and unusual behaviour during migratory flight. Quite often, two birds will break away from the main flock and perform a fast, acrobatic pursuit, one bird chasing the other, often singing, for several seconds before both birds rejoin the flock. It is not known why birds do this.


## SEX RATIOS


In certain groups of birds, males and females spend the winter in different areas. In some duck species in which males and females have readily separable plumage, these differences are obvious, with one sex predominating in one particular region and the other in another. In the case of many ducks, males winter further north than females. Although there are few data, it appears that Skylarks show a similar pattern, with males migrating less far and wintering further north than females. Evidence from Germany, for example, suggests that the small proportion of birds that does not migrate away in the autumn consists largely of males. On the German island of Heligoland, wintering male Skylarks outnumber females by nearly ten to one (Vauk 1972), and of the Skylarks caught in the Netherlands during hard weather movements in December to February, over 80% are males (Schekkerman 1999).

Although some of the observed sex bias during migration may be due to the use by ringers of tape recordings of song, which might attract more males to the nets than females, similar patterns are observed from studies where no tape recordings are used (e.g. Herremans 1984). Amongst resident birds in Scotland, Tom Dougall (1997) found no disparity in the sex ratio except in one severe winter, when females, some of which could have been migrants from elsewhere, predominated. His results suggested that nomadic flocks in Britain during hard weather may be comprised largely of females. Perhaps the most convincing evidence that female Skylarks predominate in the more southerly parts of southern Europe is the work of Sergio Scebba (2001), who measured over 3,000 Skylarks on autumn migration along Italy's Tyrrhenian coastline near Naples. Nearly 60% of the birds that could be sexed were females, a statistically significant deviation from equality. Furthermore, females pass through this part of Italy earlier in the autumn than do males, perhaps suggesting that theirs is a longer migratory route (Figure 9.2). An earlier passage of female birds has also been noted in the Netherlands, where during the first three weeks of migration (in the last week of September and the first

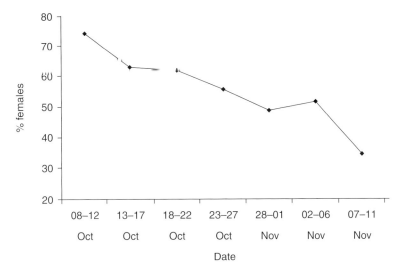

*Figure 9.2. Changes in the percentage of females in captures of migrating Skylarks in Italy. From data in Scebba (2001).*

half of October) the majority of birds passing through are females. After the middle of October, males begin to predominate and by November nearly all migrant Skylarks are males (Schekkerman 1999).

The reasons why male and female Skylarks show different migration patterns and appear to be at least partly separated geographically in winter are unclear. A number of theories have been put forward to explain similar patterns of sexual segregation in ducks. It may be that larger males are better able to withstand lower temperatures, since larger birds have a lower ratio of surface area (through which heat is lost) to body mass. Alternatively, males and females may use different resources during the winter, resulting in their spatial separation. The distribution of different predators might also be a factor. There may be an advantage for males to winter as close to their breeding grounds as they can, since the earliest arriving males would be able to occupy the best territories. In the case of the Skylark, any or all of these could be true. Another possibility is that the lower wing loading of males, which makes fast level flight less efficient, might make migration more energetically demanding and, in a trade-off between costs and benefits, might result in males migrating less far. The reasons are unknown, but it would be interesting to assess whether males and females occupy different habitats in winter, or use different resources. Assessing the winter ranges of males and females might be particularly important if the effects of severe hunting pressure on some parts of the winter population (see Chapter 11) are to be assessed.

*Skylark flock in snow*

CHAPTER 10

# Winter

> In deep snow Sky-Larks crowd into kitchen-gardens to feed upon
> the various greens. We have watched them standing round a plant
> picking off the green flesh from the leaves on all sides, until noth-
> ing is left but the bare ribs, and the snow is trampled hard with
> their bare feet. But in the severe winter of 1890–91 many died in
> our garden, becoming too weak or frost-bitten even to feed upon
> the tops of the greens which stood out above the snow.
>
> D'Urban and Mathew, *The Birds of Devon* (1892)

Winter is a critical time in the lives of birds in the world's temperate regions. The
populations of many species are determined to a large extent by their ability to survive the winter, as was vividly demonstrated by the collapse of many species' populations following the severe winter of 1962/63 (Dobinson & Richards 1964). In
order to meet the combined challenges of low temperatures (and therefore higher
metabolic requirements), scarcity of food and short daylight hours, many smaller
species abandon their summer territories to form mobile flocks, often comprising

several species, to locate dispersed food sources and to share the duty of vigilance against predators. In order to maximise their potential food supply, many species use a greater range of habitats during the winter than they do during the breeding season. Species that feed chiefly on invertebrates during the summer often take advantage of seasonal fluctuations in food availability by switching in winter to a partly or wholly vegetarian diet. Many species attempt to escape harsh conditions altogether by undertaking long-distance movements, as we saw in the last chapter. There are thus a number of survival techniques available to birds to survive the temperate winter. Being a ground-feeder, and so particularly susceptible to ground frosts and prolonged snow-lie, the Skylark is vulnerable to harsh winter weather, and the species employs all these different techniques to help birds survive the winter. However, even this range of survival tactics is unable to prevent the deaths of large numbers of birds each winter.

## HABITAT USE IN WINTER

Skylarks are not evenly distributed within their European wintering range. During the winter, as during the breeding season, Skylarks show clear preferences for certain habitats and landscape types, and an equally clear avoidance of others.

The habitat associations of Skylarks in winter have been studied in considerable detail, particularly in Britain, since one of the hypotheses put forward to explain the massive population declines described in Chapter 3 is that their food sources in winter have been reduced. Across most of central and northern Europe, the Skylark in winter becomes a bird of arable farmland, and virtually all grassland areas and other open habitats are abandoned. As grassland landscapes are generally at higher altitudes in the UK than arable areas, this abandonment of grassland might simply reflect the movement of birds to lower altitudes. However, analyses carried out by Simon Gillings (2001) of data collected in the British Isles during the early 1980s clearly demonstrate that the abandonment of grassland areas is a separate phenomenon to the abandonment of higher altitudes, since even at low altitudes birds move out of grassland areas.

These landscape-scale effects are replicated at a more local scale by a number of analyses looking in detail at habitat use on individual farms. Once again, this shows that arable habitats are selected and grassland areas generally avoided, even when they occur next to each other on the same farm. However, not all arable habitats are used equally. A number of different studies have demonstrated a clear preference by Skylarks for certain crop types and an avoidance of others (Table 10.1). Assessing habitat selection by birds is not as straightforward as it may seem, since birds do not always have all the options available to them. A flock of birds may be present in a certain habitat simply because better habitats are not available, but their presence does not necessarily indicate that the habitat they are in is particularly good. Recently developed statistical techniques now allow us to interpret our

*Table 10.1.   Summary of studies that demonstrate selection, neutral use or avoidance of various habitats by wintering Skylarks.*

| Habitat | Positively selected | Neither selected nor avoided | Avoided |
|---|---|---|---|
| Coastal marshes | UK–Gillings & Fuller 2001<br>UK–Brown & Atkinson 1996 | | |
| Cereal stubbles | UK–Donald et al. 2001a<br>UK–Gillings & Fuller 2001<br>UK–Wilson et al. 1996<br>UK–Robinson 2001<br>UK–Buckingham et al. 1999<br>UK–Wakeham-Dawson<br>  & Aebischer 1998<br>UK–Mason &<br>  Macdonald 1999<br>UK–Hart et al. 2002<br>UK–Moorcroft et al. 2002<br>Spain–Díaz & Tellería 1994<br>Germany–Bauer &<br>  Ranftl 1996 | | |
| Winter cereals | | UK–Gillings & Fuller 2001<br>UK–Donald et al. 2001a<br>UK–Buckingham et al. 1999 | UK–Wilson et al. 1996<br>UK–Robinson 2001<br>UK–Wakeham-Dawson &<br>  Aebischer 1998<br>UK–Mason &<br>  Macdonald 1999 |
| Oilseed rape | UK–Gillings & Fuller 2001<br>UK–Donald et al. 2001a | UK–Buckingham et al. 1999 | |
| Other stubbles | UK–Gillings & Fuller 2001<br>UK–Donald et al. 2001a<br>UK–Robinson 2001<br>UK–Buckingham et al. 1999 | | |
| Bare till | | UK–Gillings & Fuller 2001<br>UK–Wilson et al. 1996<br>UK–Donald et al. 2001a<br>UK–Buckingham et al. 1999 | |
| Grazed grass | | | UK–Gillings & Fuller 2001<br>UK–Wilson et al. 1996<br>UK–Donald et al. 2001a<br>UK–Buckingham et al. 1999 |
| Ungrazed grass | | UK–Gillings & Fuller 2001<br>UK–Wilson et al. 1996<br>UK–Donald et al. 2001a | UK–Robinson 2001 |

observations more carefully and piece together a clearer insight into where birds choose to distribute themselves. For wintering Skylarks, the results of a number of studies in the UK are unanimous, in that all demonstrate a very strong selection of cereal stubbles and an avoidance of grazed grass (Table 10.1). In Iberia, where a high proportion of central and eastern European breeding Skylarks spend the winter, birds again show a strong preference for arable land. Although a scarce bird during the breeding season, the Skylark becomes the most abundant bird of Iberian cereal steppes during the winter, favouring fallows (including stubbles from the previous year) and growing cereals (Díaz & Tellería 1994, Delgado & Moreira 2000), although the highest densities are found in dry pasture (Suárez *et al.* 2002b). Not all growing cereals are used equally, with higher densities occurring on fields of oats, probably because the availability of seeds is higher in such crops (Delgado & Moreira 2002). In Japan, Skylarks favour the stubbles of another cereal crop, rice (Maeda 2001). Although they are strongly favoured where they occur, cereal stubbles are not necessarily essential to the maintenance of high populations. On the Canterbury Plains of New Zealand, where introduced Skylarks occur at extremely high densities, cereal stubbles are virtually absent. Instead, birds congregate in large numbers in winter on lucerne pasture, ryegrass pasture and growing cereals (Thomsen *et al.* 2001).

The preference for stubbles is clearly not a recent development, since many nineteenth-century observers also noted a marked preference by Skylarks for this type of field. Stubbles are the cut stems of the cereal crop harvested from the field the previous autumn. As they are not ploughed after harvest, stubble fields hold large quantities of grain spilled from the cereal crop before and during harvest. So large were these quantities of grain that, before mechanisation greatly reduced spillage, the collection by hand of spilled grain after harvest, a practice known as 'gleaning', formed an important source of food or income for farm labourers' families. While the amount of grain lost by the farmer is now far less than it was a century ago, it appears from the diet of Skylarks in stubble fields (see below) that sufficient grain is still present to make stubbles a favourite habitat for wintering birds.

But as far as Skylarks are concerned, all stubbles are certainly not the same. Where management practices have reduced the availability of food, even stubbles can become unsuitable. For example, Rob Robinson (2001) showed that stubbles that have been sprayed with herbicides are strongly avoided by foraging Skylarks, since they hold far fewer seeds than unsprayed stubbles. There is also strong evidence that the type of cereal has an effect on the suitability of that stubble. The stubbles of barley appear to be far more attractive to Skylarks than the stubbles of wheat, possibly because barley sheds more grain during harvest than does wheat (Donald *et al.* 2001a). Non-cereal stubbles are also important, and high numbers of Skylarks are found in linseed, sugar beet and oil seed stubbles.

The amount of grain present in a stubble field is important not only because it determines how many Skylarks can be fed, but also because birds feed more efficiently when grain densities are high. Skylarks require something in the region of

135 kJ of energy each day, the equivalent of around 200 grains of wheat. When the density of grain on the soil surface falls below 20 seeds per m², Skylarks need to forage through the whole day to gain sufficient food, whereas at densities of over 75 grains per m², the daily food requirement can be met in just a few hours (Robinson 2001). High surface densities of grain and other seeds not only give Skylarks a safety margin if the weather turns bad, but also allow them more time for vigilance for predators. In October and November, when food availability in stubbles is high, birds may spend up to 80% of daylight hours resting and preening.

However, it may be more than food availability that attracts Skylarks to stubbles, and it may be that food availability may not even be higher in stubbles than in other field types. In a study in Lincolnshire, Hart *et al.* (2002) found that, while Skylarks were, predictably, most common on stubbles, the highest seed densities were actually found on recently tilled fields. Furthermore, Skylarks were not more common in stubbles with high numbers of seeds than they were in stubbles with few seeds, and adding extra seeds to fields did not affect the distribution of Skylarks. The decisions made by Skylarks on which fields to feed in are clearly based on a number of different and interacting factors.

Grassland habitats are generally avoided by British Skylarks in winter (Table 10.1), but there is considerable variation in use between different grassland types. While Skylarks generally avoid permanent pasture, large numbers of birds can be found in fields of temporary grass, or leys, especially where the sward is not completely closed and bare areas are available for foraging in. Skylarks particularly select grass leys with high numbers of seeding grasses, presumably because the seeds provide a good source of food (Perkins *et al.* 2000). Large numbers of Skylarks are also found on grassland that has been converted from arable land, especially where there is a well-developed sward structure above 10 cm in height (Wakeham-Dawson & Aebischer 1998). In Iberia, dry pastures hold far higher densities of wintering Skylarks than any other habitat, and these habitats might be vital in supporting through the winter the huge number of migrants arriving each autumn from central and northern Europe (Suárez *et al.* 2002b).

Although the majority of wintering Skylarks are found on arable land, and particularly cereal stubble, the highest densities of wintering birds in the UK are found not on farmland but on coastal marshes. Even today, after decades of population decline, large flocks of 100 or more birds are not a rare sight on saltmarshes. A national survey of wintering Skylarks, undertaken by the British Trust for Ornithology in the winter of 1997/98, showed that of all the habitats examined across the country, coastal saltmarshes hold by far the highest densities of birds (Gillings & Fuller 2001). On the coastal marshes of the Wash and north Norfolk, Skylarks are one of the most abundant songbirds. In such habitats, most Skylarks are found in the middle-level saltmarshes, those with occasional inundation. In her study of wintering Skylarks on the saltmarshes of Cardiff Bay, now sadly submerged beneath the waters of an artificial lake, Bozena Kalejta-Summers (1997) found that in the first half of the winter Skylarks were confined largely to *Asteretum* plant communities, where birds fed largely on the seeds of *Aster*, *Sueda* and *Atriplex*. As the availability of these seeds declined over the course of the winter, so Skylarks were forced to move increasingly to marshes dominated by *Spartinetum*, a habitat strongly avoided earlier in the winter. In north Norfolk, Skylarks appear to avoid *Aster* altogether, and occur instead largely on vegetated shingle and dunes (Brown & Atkinson 1996), habitats that were not available to the birds studied in Cardiff Bay. Where birds do occur on saltmarshes in Norfolk, they appear to favour *Sueda* and *Limonium* vegetation. Just why Skylarks find these coastal marshes so attractive is unclear. It may be that the warming effects of the sea and the defrosting action of saline environments reduce the chances of freezing, or there may be a particularly rich food supply available. The continuing loss of saltmarshes, likely to be accelerated in the future by climate change and sea-level rise, may pose a severe threat to wintering Skylarks in the UK.

Skylarks clearly have very strong preferences for certain habitats, and on farmland certain fields are far more likely to be selected than others. But once a bird or a flock of birds have chosen a particular field, they are faced with the choice of where in that field to settle. Results from a number of studies suggest that the distribution of birds in a particular field is not simply random, but is determined by a number of factors. Working on wintering Skylarks in Dorset, Dave Buckingham (2001) examined their distribution at the scale of individual fields. He found that Skylarks forage further from the edge of the field than would be expected if they were randomly distributed. In other words, they avoid field margins, particularly in smaller fields. Birds choose to settle in the centre of wide open fields, and exposed hilltops are particularly preferred. This gives birds a better view of approaching predators, which might otherwise use field boundaries to approach feeding flocks unseen. Such is the requirement for good all-round visibility that, as in the breeding season, Skylarks will completely avoid small, enclosed fields, even if those fields contain their most favoured habitats. Field size is a very important determinant of Skylark distribution in winter that is quite separate from the decisions birds make about habitat (Donald *et al.* 2001a). Fields have to be of the right habitat *and* the right size. The absolute minimum size necessary to attract Skylarks to a field of stubble appears to be around 2–3 ha, but even larger fields will not attract birds if they are surrounded by tall hedgerows or trees. At the start of the winter, Skylarks tend to congregate in the middle of field. As the winter progresses, however, Skylarks feed increasingly close to the edges of the field, as their food supplies in the centre of the field are used up (Robinson & Sutherland 1999). Once the decisions relating to crop type and field size have been made, a further determinant of the distribution of Skylarks within a particular field is the structure of the vegetation. Skylarks prefer areas where bare ground and taller vegetation occur together, possibly because bare ground allows easy routes of access between patches of taller vegetation that may offer food or shelter.

In particularly hard weather, Skylarks may feed in some very atypical places, the need for food drawing them into areas where they would otherwise never venture.

Gilbert White (1789) wrote to Daines Barrington that during the very severe winter of 1776/77, "tamed by the season the skylarks settled in the streets of towns, because they saw the ground was clear [of snow]", and in the famously hard winter of 1962/63, Skylarks were recorded feeding from bird tables in urban gardens in central London and other cities. During a period of very severe weather in January 1979, Skylarks were seen to feed on near-vertical cliff faces in Sussex, as these were the only areas free of snow at the time (Alder 1982).

## DIET AND FEEDING RATES

The strong preferences in winter for certain habitats, and the avoidance of others, are likely to arise largely through the distribution of food, rather than through some other quality of the habitat. Diet is therefore likely to be important in determining where birds choose to spend the winter and their chances of survival. As with many other birds, the diet of Skylarks differs between summer and winter to take advantage of seasonal variations in food availability. During the summer, invertebrates make up a high proportion of the diet of adult birds, and virtually the entire diet of chicks. In winter, however, Skylarks switch to a largely or wholly vegetarian diet. Cereal grain is very easy to detect in the droppings of Skylarks because, unlike finches and buntings, Skylarks do not remove the husks of seeds before eating them and these pass through undigested. This is probably because they lack the notch in the base of the bill of other seed-eaters that allows them to hold the seed for husking. To help them break down vegetable matter, and particularly tough seed cases, Skylarks ingest large numbers of small stones, called gastroliths (Tryjanowski 1995b).

In winter, Skylarks adopt a number of feeding methods. By far the most frequent is simple pecking from the surface, which in a study in Russia (Polozov 1989) made up over 97% of feeding actions. However birds will also pluck vegetation from growing plants, uproot seedlings to get at the seed, chase invertebrates and even steal food from other Skylarks. A number of detailed investigations have been carried out into the diet of Skylarks in winter to determine whether food availability determines the distribution of birds in different habitats. In one study of winter diet on a wide range of different types of farm across southern England (Donald *et al.* 2001a), clear differences were noted in the composition of the diet in different field types (Figure 10.1). The most important items in the diet broadly reflect the type of field the birds are feeding in. Birds in fields of newly emerged winter cereals feed largely on those cereals, birds in grass fields consume large amounts of grass leaf, and birds in stubbles feed more on cereal grain than birds in other fields. However the study also threw up some interesting anomalies. In both winter cereals and fields of agricultural grass, a significant proportion of the diet of wintering Skylarks is made up of broadleaved weed leaves. As these were extremely scarce in these types of fields (making up less than 1% of green cover in cereals and less than

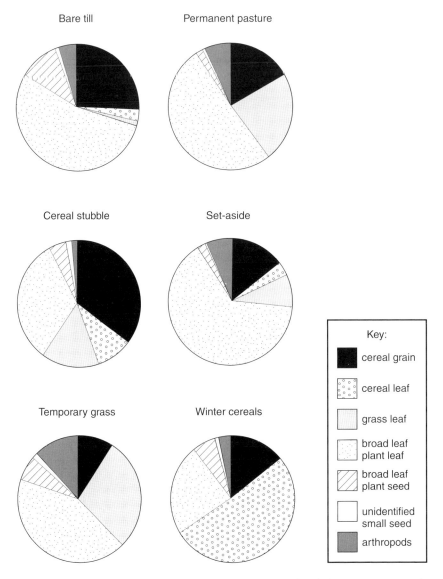

*Figure 10.1. The proportions of different food types in the diet of Skylarks wintering (November to January) in six different agricultural habitats in southern England, 1996–98. These are calculated from a microscopic analysis of faecal samples and are corrected to represent the dry weight of each food type ingested. Data redrawn from Donald et al. (2001a).*

3% in grass), Skylarks were clearly targeting these food items. The appearance of cereal grain in the diet of birds in fields of grass seems odd, but was actually due to birds congregating around piles of oats put out as winter feed for horses and other stock. The cereal grain present in the diet of birds feeding in winter cereal fields probably originates from the growing crop itself, as Rhys Green (1978) has seen birds uprooting the newly emerged shoots and nipping off the grain. Strangely, the seeds of broadleaved weeds were not present in large amounts in any of the agricultural habitats examined in this study, although the seeds of a wide range of plant species have been recorded in the winter diet in the past (Wilson *et al.* 1999). A different study of the winter diet of Skylarks in southern England, based upon an analysis of the remains of birds in Hen Harrier pellets, found a higher rate of seed intake, with the seeds of Fat-hen, Knotgrass and Black-bindweed being particularly important (Clarke *et al.* 2003). It could be that, in some areas, improvements in weed control have made these seeds so rare that they have ceased to be a major food source for Skylarks in winter.

Differences in the composition of the diet of birds feeding in different farmland habitats, such as those illustrated in Figure 10.1, do not reflect differences in feeding rates, or the total amount of time birds need to forage each day to obtain sufficient food to survive. These are likely to differ between different crops depending on the calorific value and amount of the food available. In a detailed study of the diet of Skylarks, Rhys Green (1978) found that in winter cereal fields, intake rates are extremely high, with an average of almost one peck per second. In stubbles, on the other hand, birds had far lower rates of food intake, averaging one peck every twenty seconds. Nevertheless, the calorific intake rate was higher in the stubbles, since each peck in stubbles yielded a larger food item than in cereals, and the calorific value of each item was higher. In growing cereal crops, therefore, birds have to consume very large amounts of material to get the energy they need. Rhys calculated that birds in stubble fields consumed nearly ten times more metabolisable energy per hour than birds feeding in cereals. This is readily apparent in the field, since it is easy to find large numbers of droppings littering the ground where Skylarks have been in cereal fields, whereas droppings in stubble fields are very hard to find, even where large numbers of birds have been present. In growing winter cereals, therefore, Skylarks adopt a grazing strategy a little like that of geese, consuming and excreting very large amounts of food with low nutritive value. Indeed, Skylark droppings in cereal fields look very much like miniature goose droppings, being relatively large, cylindrical and green. There may be other similarities: like geese, Skylarks appear to favour fields that have received applications of chemical fertilisers that might increase the intake of soluble nitrogen (Halse & Trevenen 1986, David Buckingham, pers comm.). A high rate of consumption is necessary because Skylarks have a short intestine and lack the large caecum of specialist herbivores, rendering them unable to extract nutriment from grass efficiently.

## BEHAVIOUR IN WINTER

Many species of bird, including the Skylark, gather together in flocks during the non-breeding season. Flocking confers a number of advantages, including the sharing of vigilance, predator avoidance and more effective searching for food. Large flocks of wintering Skylarks were a favoured target of bird catchers during the eighteenth and nineteenth centuries, since the clustering of large numbers in small areas allowed huge numbers to be taken with relatively little effort. Victorian accounts describe flocks of hundreds or thousands of Skylarks, particularly during hard weather movements. During the very hard winter of 1962/63, flocks of one or two thousand birds were recorded in many areas. However, flocks of this size are now rare in the UK, particularly on farmland. Of the nearly 2,000 flocks encountered by RSPB fieldworkers over two winters in southern England in the late 1990s, only three were larger than 100 birds (the largest being 150), and only 5% of flocks held more than 20 birds. In fact, many Skylarks in southern England appear to spend the winter mainly alone or in pairs, as over 60% of encounters were of single birds or pairs. Nevertheless, the clumping of large numbers of birds in flocks actually means that over 60% of individual Skylarks spend the winter in groups of ten or more birds. Flocks of Skylarks in winter have a characteristic appearance, being loose-knit, restless and flighty. In flight, the flocks keep low and fly fast, and birds have a distinctive undulating flight, often fluttering or hovering before alighting. The contact call, frequently given, is an evocative liquid 'chirrup' with a number of variants (Figure 10.2).

So why do some birds spend the winter alone or in pairs, whereas others join up into large flocks? It may be that the flocking behaviour of birds is affected by the weather, with singles and pairs gathering into flocks in hard weather, a pattern that has been seen on farmland in eastern England. However this does not explain why it is possible to see a mixture of pairs and large flocks on a single farm on the same day. The explanation may hinge on the origin of the birds involved. It has been suggested by a number of researchers that the singles and pairs, or very small groups, are resident birds, whereas the larger flocks are nomadic migrants from central and northern Europe or from the uplands of Britain. Without detailed observations of ringed birds it is difficult to be sure, but on the farms the RSPB worked on during the late 1990s, the distribution of single birds and pairs closely matched the distribution of birds breeding there the previous summer. Larger flocks, on the other hand, tended to occur on fields that held few or no birds the summer before. Furthermore, the distribution of single birds and small groups remained relatively unchanged over the course of the winter, whereas larger flocks were rarely recorded from the same field twice. In southern France, the first flocks of the winter coincide with the arrival of migrants from northern and central Europe. Skylark flocks rarely contain other species, and Skylarks only ever congregate with other species where a particularly rich source of food brings large numbers of birds together.

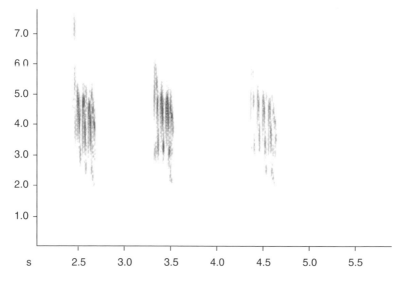

*Figure 10.2   Spectrogram of three calls of a Skylark. The spectrogram was produced using the Canary 1.2.4 package, the filter bandwidth was 174.85 Hz and the grid resolution 11.61 ms. The vertical axis represents the frequency of the sounds in kHz, the horizontal axis the time in seconds. Recorded and produced by Gillian Gilbert.*

At night, roosting takes place on the ground in the open fields where Skylarks have spent the day feeding. Roosting often takes place in a natural hollow or, occasionally, a hollow excavated by the birds themselves during dust bathing. During extremely cold weather, Skylarks have been seen to excavate hollows up to 15 cm deep for roosting. There is no evidence that birds move to specific roosting sites, seeming instead simply to roost where they happen to stop feeding. During the day it is fairly easy to find where birds roosted the night before simply by looking for their distinctive pyramidal piles of droppings. These are particularly obvious on cereal fields, as birds consume and excrete huge quantities of cereal leaves. Birds appear to roost some distance apart from each other, even those feeding in flocks, and, judging by the size of the piles of droppings, they appear to move little during the night. When the ground is covered by snow, birds may roost in tunnels dug into the snow. Those described by Gladwin (1985) were up to 30 cm long and angled downwards into the snow at between 30° and 45°. In this particular case, the Skylarks were sharing the roost tunnels with Yellowhammers, although mixed species roosting does not appear to be common.

William Yarrell (1861) describes how in winter Skylarks "are in excellent condition, even during frost . . .; but should a fall of snow cover the ground, their condition is altered for the worse in a few days". Skylarks killed by prolonged snow weigh only around two thirds as much as healthy birds, but most birds

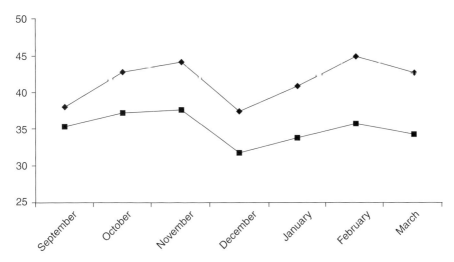

*Figure 10.3.    Seasonal changes in the weight (grams) of male (upper line) and female (lower line) Skylarks killed by flying into lighthouses in the Netherlands. Drawn from data in Cramp (1988).*

make it through the winter with no apparent decline in body weight (Figure 10.3). During particularly severe weather, and especially snow-lie, Skylarks need to ensure they maintain an adequate supply of fat. Working over several winters in the early 1990s in southern Scotland, Tom Dougall (1999) found that both male and female Skylarks actually increase in weight over the course of the winter, peaking around the end of January. What was particularly interesting about Tom's results was that, while both sexes carry more fat during winters with more snow, females consistently carry more fat than males in proportion to their body size. This may be because females could be more nomadic in winter than males and so need to carry fuel for more migratory flights and as insurance against not finding a reliable food source.

*Merlin with Skylark prey*

CHAPTER 11

# Survival and mortality

We happened, in the beginning of November 1856, to be sailing from Cagliari to Palermo, against fresh southerly breezes, and during the voyage, which occupied the best part of three days, we were constantly surrounded by myriads of tired Sky-Larks, many of which came on board. On our arrival at our port we found the greater part of the male population up in arms, not, as usual, against the government, but for the slaughter of these poor birds, which were dropping about, worn out by their journey, not only along the sea-beach, but on the quays, wharves, public gardens, and even in the streets of the town; many were caught by hand or knocked over by sticks and stones, but along the 'Marina,' or marine promenade, a constant discharge of small-arms was kept up from daylight to dark during the few days of our stay.

Lord Lilford, *Notes on the Birds of Northamptonshire and Neighbourhood* (1895)

It is notoriously difficult to measure the average life span of wild birds. To measure life span (or, more technically, annual survival rates, which are generally expressed as the probability of a bird surviving from one year to the next), it is generally necessary to follow the fortunes of individual birds marked in a way that distinguishes them from all others, usually using leg rings. Even if birds can be caught and ringed, and subsequently followed for long periods, their disappearance might not indicate that they have died, merely that they no longer live at that particular site. Complex statistical techniques have been developed to allow researchers to control to some extent the effects of emigration and immigration, but long-term data-sets of marked birds that are sufficiently complete to allow accurate calculations of survival rates are rare.

There are very few studies of Skylark sufficiently intensive to derive anything like an accurate estimate of annual survival rates. However those studies that have produced estimates of survival show reasonable consistency. Using ringing recovery data, Spaepen (1991) estimated the annual survival rate of Skylarks migrating through Belgium at 59–62%. In his classic study of colour-ringed Skylarks in a dune system, Juan Delius (1965) estimated a similar annual survival rate of 67%. This is rather higher than the 56% estimated by Alex Schläpfer (1988) on farmland in Switzerland in the mid 1980s. Working in Germany, Daunicht (1998) suggested that males have higher annual survival rates (78%) than females (68%), but both these estimates appear rather high. The most reliable estimates of Skylark annual survival rates come from the only study that has run for long enough to examine trends over time in survival. This is the remarkable research carried out by Ian Wolfenden at the Crosby–Hightown coastal dunes near Liverpool, northwest England (Wolfenden & Peach 2001), an outstanding example of what can be achieved by a skilled and dedicated amateur carrying out research in his spare time. For over 20 years, Ian has been colour-ringing and observing Skylarks on a 150 ha study site in an attempt to estimate survival rates. Complex statistical analysis of his data by Will Peach has shown that during the early 1980s, when populations in the UK started to collapse, annual survival rates (the probability of a bird surviving for a year) at this site were very low, at around 39%. However these increased during the study, and by the late 1980s they averaged 66%, or two in three birds surviving more than a year. Survival rates of first-year birds are likely to be far lower than those of adults, probably something in the region of 20–30%, although direct estimates are difficult to calculate, since young birds are likely to move away from the area of their birth. Daunicht's estimate of 48% first winter survival again appears rather high. The rate of recruitment of chicks into Ian Wolfenden's dune population was 14%, the remaining 86% either dying during their first winter or moving out of the study area. In Germany, Daunicht (1998) calculated a far lower recruitment rate of just 4%. Based on estimates of nesting productivity and first-year survival from other studies, it seems likely that annual adult survival rates of 50–60% or more are necessary to maintain a stable population (Wolfenden & Peach 2001).

With annual survival rates of around 60% for adults, and far lower for first year birds, it is likely that most Skylarks that survive long enough to fledge do not live more than a few years in the wild. The average age of the birds in Delius's coastal dune population was just over three years, and that of Markus Jenny's (1990c) population on Swiss farmland around the same, although females were on average considerably younger, suggesting lower rates of survival. However, ringing recoveries suggest that some birds live considerably longer. Of the 20 Skylarks ringed in Britain as first-year birds that were later recovered, six were older than five years, and one bird was ten years old (Dougall 1996). The oldest birds recorded so far in Ian Wolfenden's study population are a male aged seven years and a female aged eight and a half years. These must be exceptionally lucky individuals, since the chances of a Skylark living to this age can be calculated to be approximately a third of one per cent. In other words, only one Skylark in three hundred is likely to reach this age. Birds in captivity, protected from predators, food shortage and severe weather, are capable of surviving far longer than their wild congeners. William Yarrell, in his *History of British Birds* (1861), recounts an instance of a caged Skylark living nineteen and a half years, and Cecil Smith, in his *Birds of Somersetshire* (1869), recalls a caged Skylark reaching twenty years, "and its song continued almost to the last".

## PREDATORS AND OTHER CAUSES OF MORTALITY

Most birds, and particularly most small birds, do not die of old age. The reason most Skylarks do not survive more than a year or two is that there are huge numbers of threats facing birds every minute of every day. Sooner or later, all birds will succumb to one or a combination of them. Survival rates are extremely difficult to assess in the field, but it is even more difficult to determine the most important causes of death, since our observations of bird deaths are few and inevitably biased. We are far more likely to see a bird being killed by a cat than we are to see a bird starving to death in the middle of a field in winter, though the latter is likely to be a very much more common cause of death than the former. Most estimates of the causes of mortality come from ringing recoveries, birds that have been ringed that are later found dead. This method suffers heavily from such biases. Any cause of death that brings dead birds into close proximity to people will be over-recorded relative to those that kill birds quietly at night in the middle of fields. The causes of death of ringed birds reported by Spaepen (1991) illustrate this bias well, with the most frequently recorded causes of death being hunting and trapping, predation by domestic animals, and collision with vehicles and buildings. In the UK, where hunting Skylarks is prohibited by law, the most common recorded causes of death of ringed Skylarks are predation by cats and collision with cars (Dougall 1996). Around half of all ringing recoveries are from human-related causes (Wernham *et al.* 2002). Unusual deaths have included a bird hit by a golf ball and a bird caught in a mousetrap. Skylarks are apparently the birds most frequently killed by collision with aircraft in Britain, presumably during their aerial song flights.

Spaepen's ringing recoveries listed hunting as the most common cause of death of ringed birds, and in certain parts of Europe, particularly southwest France, hunting claims the lives of huge numbers of birds; this is discussed in more detail below. However there is little doubt that cold weather, starvation and predation are likely to be the most important causes of death of Skylarks. Although monitoring schemes started in the UK just too late to measure the impact of the famously cold winter of 1962/63, there is evidence that this had severe consequences for birds. The early years of the Common Birds Census recorded a significant rise in Skylark numbers as the population recovered from something like a 25% drop in the population. One observer walking along the cliffs of Cornwall immediately after the thaw found literally hundreds of complete Skylark wings littering the ground, an indication that predators and scavengers had done well from the mass death of Skylarks (Penhallurick 1978).

As with all small birds, Skylarks are vulnerable to a range of avian and mammalian predators. Of the avian predators, smaller falcons appear to be the most capable of catching Skylarks, possibly because they have a rate of climb close to that of a Skylark. Small birds can generally out-climb larger ones, but certain long-winged raptors, such as Eleonora's Falcon, Hobby and Merlin, have extremely high rates of climb for their size (Hedenström & Rosen 2001). In the UK, the main predator of Skylarks appears to be the Merlin, and it is this bird that has traditionally been used by falconers to catch larks. In his book *Birds of Northamptonshire and Neighbourhood* (1895), Lord Lilford wrote that

> The Sky-Lark affords very good sport for the falconer, the Merlin being the bird selected for this pursuit; but the best trained of these little Falcons rarely manage to take an adult Lark in full feather, though they will easily master young or moulting birds in August and the early part of September.

Despite Lilford's assertions, Merlins have a far higher rate of success when attacking Skylarks than do other birds of prey, and in some areas Skylarks account for a large part of the Merlin's diet. Indeed, larks appear to be an important item in the diet of the Merlin throughout its range, since another lark species, the Horned Lark, is one of the most frequent items in the diet of Merlins in North America (Sodhi & Oliphant 1993). Research carried out in Scotland by Will Cresswell (1994, 1996) suggests that Merlins have a far higher rate of success (12%) when attacking Skylarks than either Sparrowhawks (3%) or Peregrines (with no successes observed in this study), possibly because they chase Skylarks for longer. Cresswell's detailed observations of Merlin attacks on Skylarks show that there is a complex interaction between hunter and prey. As we saw in Chapter 4, Skylarks that start to sing when attacked are less likely to be caught than birds that do not sing, and even females will start to sing when attacked.

However, the ability to sing during attack is not the only factor determining the chances of surviving. One of the reasons that animals gather in large groups is that flocking reduces the chances of any individual being targeted by a predator, the dilution effect, and also that large numbers of birds may put the predators off, the confusion effect. Perhaps unexpectedly, therefore, flocking by Skylarks at Cresswell's estuary study site seemed to confer little protection against attack by Merlins, since the falcons selectively attacked very large flocks to such an extent that the benefits of the dilution and confusion effects were negated. An individual Skylark in a very large flock was around ten times more likely to be attacked by a Merlin than an individual in a smaller flock. The optimal size flock for an individual to be in to minimise the risk of being predated by a Merlin was in the range of 10 to 30 birds, yet only around a fifth of all birds at the Scottish study site were in flocks of that size. Merlins attack Skylarks both on the ground and in the air. Success rates for the falcon are greatest if the Skylark is on the ground and remains there, lower if the Skylark takes off on attack and lowest if the Skylark is already in the air when attacked and remains there. Sometimes Skylarks take extreme measures when trying to evade a Merlin attack, even using cars or passing people as shields to evade or deter the falcon. M.E. Taylor (1986) described how a Skylark being chased by a Merlin landed at the feet of two human observers and flattened itself against the ground between them, remaining there for half a minute. An even more unusual example of sanctuary from a Merlin attack was observed by Booth (1988, cited in Simms 1992), who saw the Skylark land at her feet as she examined a seal on the beach in Lincolnshire. The Skylark took off again and the Merlin resumed its chase, forcing the lark to seek shelter under an "overhang of blubber of an unconcerned bull seal. There it stayed for five or ten minutes before beginning a long, slow creep over the beach and out of sight". The usual raptor avoidance behaviour of Skylarks on the ground is to crouch, often not breaking cover until the last minute. When ground predators are detected, Skylarks may hover over them uttering an alarm call. I have seen groups of up to ten birds hovering around 2 m over the same spot, presumably marking the location of a predator, frequently looking down and calling quietly to each other.

Although the Merlin is probably the most important single predator of Skylarks, at least in the UK, a large number of other raptors have been observed to take larks. The Skylark is one of the twelve most frequent prey items in the diet of Peregrines in northern Britain, and one of the smallest birds regularly taken by this species (Ratcliffe 1980). Sparrowhawks can also be major predators, and studies in Germany and the Netherlands have shown that Skylarks comprise as much as 8% of all prey items taken by some birds, although other studies indicate a far lower proportion (Cramp 1980). The Hobby can be another important predator, and specialises in attacking birds during their song flights. An old method of catching Hobbies was to use tethered Skylarks coated with lime. Studies in central Europe and the Netherlands suggest that Skylarks comprise up to 25% of all birds taken by Hobbies, although birds form only a small part of this species' diet (Cramp 1980). Skylarks can form an important part of the diet of Montagu's and other harriers, and also Booted Eagles. Skylarks appear to be the songbird most frequently taken by Hen Harriers wintering in southern England (Clarke *et al.* 2003). Other birds of prey that have been observed to take Skylarks include larger species such as the Buzzard, Lesser Spotted Eagle and Golden Eagle. In Poland, Skylarks form one of the most important prey items of the Great Grey Shrike, and breeding densities of Skylarks are low around shrike nests (Hromada *et al.* 2002). The most important mammalian predators of Skylarks are likely to be mustelids (Weasels, Stoats etc.), Red Foxes, Badgers, Brown Rats, cats and dogs. It is unlikely that mammals account for more than a small proportion of adult Skylark predations, although female birds sitting on eggs might be particularly vulnerable.

## PREDATORS AND POPULATION DECLINES

As we saw in Chapter 3, populations of Skylarks and other farmland songbirds are in severe and sustained decline across much of western Europe, prompting much research into the causes. One hypothesis that is repeatedly put forward, particularly by those with interests in increasing game-bird stocks, is that these populations have declined because of increases in numbers of certain predators. In particular, numbers of some birds of prey, such as the Sparrowhawk, have increased greatly since 1980 following the banning of certain toxic pesticides, particularly the organochlorines. So have Skylark populations declined because more are being taken by Sparrowhawks? A number of detailed analyses of long runs of data have shown that there is, in fact, no relationship at all between declines in songbird populations and increases in numbers of birds of prey (Newton *et al.* 1997, Thomson *et al.* 1998a). Predation by Sparrowhawks is likely to account for only a relatively small proportion of deaths of adult Skylarks, and, at least in the UK, the Skylark is not a common prey species of this raptor. Indeed, the few data we have on Skylark survival rates actually suggest an increase in longevity during the period that bird-of-prey populations were recovering (Wolfenden & Peach 2001), quite the opposite of what we would expect to see if raptors were driving down Skylark populations.

A further consideration is that, while numbers of Sparrowhawks and certain other potential predators of Skylarks have certainly increased, this reflects in most cases simply a return to previous, pre-organochlorine levels. There is no evidence that numbers of Sparrowhawks are any higher now than they were in, say, the 1940s or 1950s. Yet we know that populations of Skylarks were very much higher in those decades than they are now. If Sparrowhawk numbers really do drive Skylark population trends, we would expect to have seen a huge increase in Skylark populations during the period that Sparrowhawks were virtually extinct in southern Britain, but this did not happen.

## HUNTING TODAY

Despite massive improvements in legal protection for Skylarks throughout Europe during the twentieth century, an estimated 4–6 million birds are still killed, legally or illegally, by hunters in Europe each year. This equates to two or three times the entire present British breeding population, and between 7% and 25% of the total European breeding population of 25–55 million pairs (Chapter 3). France and Italy together account for over three-quarters of these, and Greece most of the rest. Until 1997, a small number (less than 500 a year) were legally taken with Merlins by falconers in the UK, but this has now ceased. France, Italy and Greece are permitted to hunt Skylarks under Article 7(3) and Annex II/2 of the EU Birds Directive, one of the central pillars of bird conservation within the European Union. Article 7(4) states that the relevant Member States must ensure that levels of hunting comply with "the principles of wise use and ecologically balanced control of the species of birds concerned". Hunting is not permitted during the breeding season or, in the case of migrants, on their return to the breeding grounds.

French hunters using the traditional methods of double clap-nets and small drop-nets (*pantes* and *matoles*) have an authorised limit of 600,000–900,000 Skylarks per year, though many believe this is regularly exceeded. In 1979, it was estimated that around 12,000 *pantes* and over 200,000 *matoles* were set in France each autumn, the main target being Skylarks. The estimated catch of Skylarks for the 1998/99 season was 1.2 million birds. The season for this form of hunting is October and November, when millions of exhausted migrants arrive from the north and east. Many more birds are shot, with or without the use of dogs, during a season that lasts from mid September to 20 February. Until 1975, around 3–5 million Skylarks were killed in France each year (D'Elbée & Bried 1991), and in the mid 1980s Glutz von Blotzheim (1985) estimated the number killed at between 5 and 10 million birds. The number shot in the 1998/99 season was estimated at around 640,000, but this has subsequently risen as populations of other quarry species have fallen (Barbier 2001). The official figures of ONCFS, the French hunting and research body, suggest that between 1.2 and 1.6 million birds are now 'harvested' legally each year (Barbier 2001). In the single department of the Vendée in western France, hunters took over 15,000 Skylarks each year in the mid 1990s, despite the fact that only a small proportion of all the hunters in the department (6%) killed any larks at all (Barbier 2001). These birds are killed almost entirely in the autumn and winter and so comprise largely migrants from breeding grounds in central and northern Europe, where populations are in decline. Birds killed in western France are likely to originate from Scandinavia, the Baltic and (particularly in northwestern France) the Low Countries, whereas those falling victim to hunters in eastern France probably breed in central Europe (Hemery *et al.* 1991). The concentration of masses of migrants into small wintering grounds means that hunting in these areas could adversely affect populations over huge areas of Europe, particularly if they are largely females, as seems to be the case (see Chapter 9). The birds are generally hunted for recreational purposes or home consumption, although some hunters derive a small income from selling birds to local restaurants.

In Italy, the hunting of Skylarks is permitted in the autumn, the exact dates varying regionally. In Lombardy, for example, hunting is permitted from 15

September to 30 December, although the season lasts until the end of January in other areas. Skylark hunting is particularly popular in central and southern Italy, especially in Tuscany, Lazio, Campania, Puglia and Sardinia. This coincides with the main migration period, and takes place mostly in the northeast of the country, though hunters often travel southwards with the main movement of birds, hunting them en route. A maximum of 25 Skylarks per hunter may be taken each day, depending on the region, and no hunting is permitted on two days each week. Around 1.5 million birds are killed each year during this short period, most of them again migrants from central and eastern Europe on their way to French or Spanish wintering grounds. Birds are mostly shot from huts (*capanni*) set in trenches, and birds are attracted using live decoys, often illegally caught and held, or other lures such as mirrors, whistles and, also illegally, live Little Owls or amplified recordings of calls. There is a flourishing trade in illegal live decoys, which can fetch up to €100.

EU legislation has been largely responsible for a fall in the numbers of hunters in Italy, from 5 million to less than one million. However, many of these hunters are now travelling outside the EU, particularly to eastern Europe, where hunting laws are less strict and less well enforced. Searches of the Internet reveal the existence in Romania of companies specialising in leading Skylark hunting tours for foreign hunters. One requests that its clients do not bring their own guns, as the company offers "good quality semi-automatic shotguns". There are no estimates of how many birds are killed like this, but the Skylark appears to be a species targeted by travelling hunters. Since 1996, police forces in Hungary, Bulgaria, Slovenia and Italy have confiscated 180,000 dead birds from Italian hunters, a third of which were Skylarks (*British Birds* 95: 363). These birds were being ferried in refrigerated trucks, destined for the table in meals in the run-up to Christmas. Although commerce in legally hunted birds is illegal, there is a flourishing trade in these imports, and a plate of six larks may fetch up to €200 in expensive restaurants.

In Greece, Skylarks can only be killed with guns, as trapping is illegal. There are no quotas imposed on the number of birds that can be killed, but numbers of Skylarks killed each year are likely to be far smaller than the huge numbers slaughtered each year in France and Italy.

Whether hunting has contributed directly to the decline in the European population is unclear. However, the loss of possibly as much as 20% of the total European breeding Skylark population to legal hunting each year must be regarded as a serious threat to the species' conservation, particularly when all the available data show that populations are barely producing enough new birds to replace those lost naturally. The additional effects of illegal hunting can only be guessed at. A management plan for the species, produced for the European Union by the French hunting research organisation ONCFS, uses debatably inappropriate and selective data on productivity (some deriving from Delius's studies on coastal dunes in the early 1960s, and so clearly not applicable to the majority of current populations) to conclude that present levels of hunting are sustainable, and that "at the present time the annual production of birds can withstand such a bag" (Barbier 2001). Population trends in the UK clearly demonstrate, however, that annual productivity is unable to sustain stable populations even in the complete absence of hunting. Claims that current levels of hunting are sustainable need to be backed by far more rigorous analyses.

*Nesting Skylark disturbed by cereal harvesting*

CHAPTER 12

# Skylarks and modern agriculture

The hamlet stood on a gentle rise in the flat, wheat-growing north-east corner of Oxfordshire. We will call it Lark Rise because of the great number of skylarks which made the surrounding fields their springboard and nested on the bare earth between the rows of green corn.

Flora Thompson, *Lark Rise to Candleford* (1939)

The Skylark is certainly not a species which is injuriously affected by the improvements in agriculture, draining, enclosures, and the like.

Lord Lilford, *Notes on the Birds of Northamptonshire and Neighbourhood* (1895)

Not long before the fall of the Berlin Wall in November 1989, German ornithologists on both sides of the border carried out fieldwork to produce an atlas of the breeding birds for the whole of Germany (Rheinwald 1993). Of all the maps produced, the most striking was that for the Skylark, because the border between the two countries could be traced with some accuracy in the pattern of abundance of the birds (Figure 12.1). This pattern was not apparent in the distribution of other species, so this is clearly not just an artefact of something like different counting methods. Such a clear demarcation in population densities along a purely political boundary is very revealing, and suggests that Skylark numbers are dependent to a very large extent on types of land management that are themselves mediated through politics. The proportions and types of open habitats, mostly farmland, were, and remain, approximately the same in both of these former countries. What differed greatly between the two countries at the time, however, was the way that farmland was managed. In the former West Germany, agriculture was, as it still is, very intensive, using high levels of chemical inputs and mechanisation. In the for-

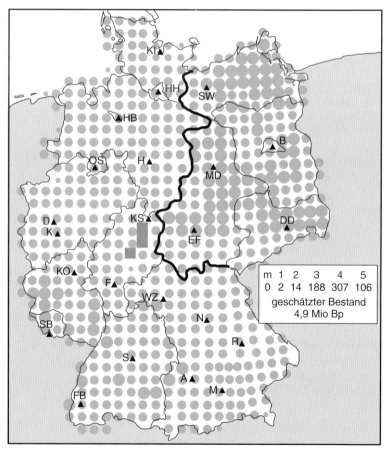

*Figure 12.1. Skylark distribution and abundance in Germany in 1985. The size of the dots represents levels of relative abundance. The thick line shows the border between the former West Germany and East Germany. From Rheinwald (1993).*

mer East Germany, on the other hand, agriculture at the time used few chemical inputs, and relied to a far greater degree on manual labour. As a result of these differences in farm management, crop yields were considerably higher in former West Germany than in its Communist counterpart: in the year this atlas was carried out, West German farmers were producing nearly twice as much wheat per hectare as their East Germany counterparts. This extraordinary 'eco-political' map is a striking introduction to the main theme of this chapter, the relationship between modern farming methods and Skylark populations.

Skylarks are intimately associated with farmland, an association that has been recognised for many years. We have already seen that throughout most of Europe, farmland is by far the most important habitat for Skylarks, largely because it provides the biggest area of suitably open habitat (Chapter 3). Although the territory density of Skylarks on farmland is often low compared with that on some other open habitats, the huge area of farmland available means that the majority of individual birds are found on land managed by people for food production. The Skylark would not be anything like as widespread and numerous as it is today were it not for the clearance for agriculture of most of the forests that covered much of Europe 10,000 years ago.

However, it has also become clear in the last 20 years that birds like the Skylark, which have benefited historically from the spread of agriculture, are now suffering severe population declines (Chapter 3). There has been considerable public concern about the disappearance of farmland birds from areas where they were once common. These declines have been recorded across Europe in a wide range of farmland species, and the Skylark has been one of the hardest hit (Tucker & Heath 1994). The number of birds lost is immense: the Skylark population of the UK declined by something like one and a half million pairs during the last quarter of the twentieth century. Because of its popularity, the Skylark has become a flagship species in the search for the causes of these declines and the fight to reverse them. Much effort has been invested in finding out why populations on farmland have collapsed and what can be done to reverse these declines. This research has provided a detailed insight into the many ways that modern agriculture can affect our environment.[1] Now that we have examined the ecology of the Skylark, it is time to return to the matter of these population declines, and to start to unravel their complex and often surprising causes. To do so requires us to look in detail at how Skylarks use their farmland environment.

The collapse of the populations of Skylarks and other farmland birds has coincided exactly with unprecedented changes in the way that farmland is managed. The similarity in timing of these two events is so close that it is difficult to ignore

---

[1] There is a vast amount of recent literature on the many and complex relationships between agricultural intensification and declines in farmland biodiversity. This is far too extensive to review in detail in this chapter, and the reader is referred to the Bibliography at the back of the book, which includes a number of sources not individually cited in this chapter.

the possibility that they are linked (Chamberlain *et al.* 2000a). Changes in agriculture have been driven by a need and a desire to produce more food per unit area. To achieve this increased output requires land to be managed in a more intensive manner, and the many different changes that have occurred to increase productivity are therefore often lumped under the umbrella term 'agricultural intensification'. As we shall see in this chapter, we can now be reasonably certain that Skylark population declines and agricultural intensification are connected in a causal manner; that is to say, the cause of the Skylark population decline has been agricultural change. Making this apparently obvious link has actually required a great deal of research, not least because a number of conflicting hypotheses have been, and continue to be, proposed and investigated.

Simply to assert, however, that agricultural intensification has caused Skylark populations to decline is insufficient if we are to fully understand the problem and suggest solutions. Agricultural intensification is the sum of a multitude of different and complex changes in land management, some of which might have implications for Skylarks, others of which might not. The search for the changes that have driven Skylark declines has identified some very surprising culprits.

The research required to tease apart all the complex interactions between Skylark population dynamics and agricultural change has generated much of what we know about the numbers, behaviour, distribution and ecology of Skylarks today, and therefore much of what has gone in the preceding chapters. My aim in this chapter is not to try to present everything that is known about Skylarks on farmland. Instead, I shall focus on a number of specific issues in modern agriculture that have, or may have, relevance to recent declines in Skylark populations. Before doing this, however, it is necessary to remember the 'eco-political' map of Skylarks in pre-unification Germany, and consider very briefly the political background to modern agriculture.


## THE POLITICS OF AGRICULTURAL INTENSIFICATION


As Robson (1997) has stated, agriculture is "an industry in which political intervention is a virtually permanent state of affairs". This intervention has its origins in two separate needs: to meet strategic food requirements in time of war, and to reduce poverty amongst food producers. Poverty amongst agricultural producers is a universal phenomenon that has its roots in three factors: a chronic tendency to overproduction, a proportional reduction in per capita income rise spent on food and the strong selection by industry of the lowest-priced products available on the world market. The modern agricultural revolution has its political roots in the Second World War. During this conflict, many European countries faced crippling food shortages that during peacetime were at least partly made up by imports from abroad. After the War, many saw self-sufficiency in agricultural produce as a strategic priority, and approached the problem through the creation of a 'common market' centred around the removal of protective tariffs to member nations, thereby allowing the free flow of labour, capital and services. The 1957 Treaty of Rome established the European Economic Community (EEC, later renamed the European Union), comprising Germany, France, Italy and the three Benelux countries, all of which were bound to a Common Agricultural Policy (CAP). The membership of the EU, and so the number of countries adhering to the CAP (for the CAP is one of the few truly common policies in the EU), rose from six in 1957 to nine (including the UK) in 1973, ten in 1981, twelve in 1986 and fifteen in 1995. This number is set to increase with the accession to the EU of up to ten central and eastern European countries in the near future.

The original aims of the CAP were to increase both agricultural productivity and the wealth of those engaged in food production within Member States. Implicit in Article 39 of the Treaty of Rome was the assumption that the latter would be brought about by the former and so "the politicians, by choosing the route of increasing productivity as the means of increasing earnings, had implicitly adopted the strategy of intensification. The alternative, of restructuring agriculture . . . and so allowing for more extensive farming, had thus been almost abandoned at the outset of the CAP" (Robson 1997). The CAP protected producers in the EEC (later EU) Member States by guaranteeing fixed prices (intervention prices), by imposing protective tariffs on cheaper imported produce and by paying export 'refunds' to allow competitive export onto the world market. This financial security proved the basis of subsequent intensification, since, for the first time, higher yields would be guaranteed to result in higher incomes. The CAP provided not only a guaranteed market for farmers but also provided capital grants to give farmers access to the machinery and technology they needed to increase output. The result has been the most rapid intensification of farming methods ever seen.

The CAP currently absorbs around half of all EU spending, costing around €40 billion each year. In addition, EU Member States all offer extra national subsidies. To this huge sum must be added the external costs of agriculture, such as water pollution, gas emissions and public health issues, costs that are met by the taxpayer and not by the farmer. In the UK, these external costs exceed £2 billion each year, approximately the same amount as total CAP spending (Pretty *et al.* 2000); in other words, it costs as much to clean up after modern agriculture as it costs to support it.

The CAP has many detractors, and is seen as being inefficient, inequitable, costly and, by many outside the EU, unfairly trade distorting. The future enlargement of the EU will necessitate a major overhaul of the CAP, providing the opportunity to funnel money from supporting the production of unwanted agricultural surpluses to enhancing the farmland environment and supporting rural development (Donald *et al.* 2002b). It remains to be seen whether this opportunity will be embraced.

# DECLINES IN BIODIVERSITY ON FARMLAND

After millennia of agricultural expansion, a high proportion of Europe's biodiversity now survives on farmland. Because of the very high proportion of land under agriculture in Europe and the very long history of environmental modification, the boundaries between food production areas, cultural resource areas and wildlife resource areas are often poorly defined, and in many areas they are one and the same. Some of the richest of Europe's wildlife habitats, and some of the most threatened, have been created by man to produce food. This is quite different to the situation in, for example, North America, where the wildlife resources are held in vast untouched wildernesses or national parks, and the food production areas are quite separate, in vast and relatively lifeless ranches or prairies.

European farmland therefore fulfils the dual, and often conflicting, roles of food production and wildlife habitat. Many agricultural areas in Europe are extremely important bird habitats and some, such as the Spanish *dehesas* and the Hungarian *pusztas*, support distinctive and rare assemblages of birds of international importance. Farmland in Europe supports 120 bird species of European conservation concern, more than any other habitat (Tucker 1997). Agricultural land also supports important and distinctive populations of other animals and of plants (Potts 1991). The massive changes in agriculture that have been brought about by the CAP are clearly of importance to these populations, since they profoundly affect the habitats they live in, and it is important to determine how they might affect biodiversity. In the case of farmland birds, the picture is all too clear. Farmland bird populations have declined in most European countries, and across the continent population declines have been greater in countries with the most intensive agriculture (Figure 12.2). Agricultural intensification appears therefore to be able to influence bird population levels on a truly continental scale.

This mass disappearance of birds and other wildlife has been described as the "Second Silent Spring" (Krebs *et al.* 1999), different to the first (Rachel Carson's 1963 vision of a land where all the birds have been killed by pesticides) in that it is actually happening. In the case of birds, the evidence overwhelmingly supports the Second Silent Spring hypothesis, as a very large number of studies demonstrate that agricultural intensification damages bird populations. In Britain, this pattern of decline is apparent only in specialist farmland species, and birds associated with other habitats have not shown the same trends (Siriwardena *et al.* 1998). For some species, it has even been shown that reversing agricultural intensification leads to a rapid recovery in bird populations (e.g. Peach *et al.* 2001), convincing evidence that changes in agriculture are responsible for the observed declines.

What is less clear is what has happened to other groups of wildlife during the same period. Birds are particularly well studied and monitored animals, and their trends are well known and documented in many countries. Other organisms are not so well monitored, and in many cases we have a very poor picture of what has happened. Nevertheless, it appears that the very conspicuous decline in bird popu-

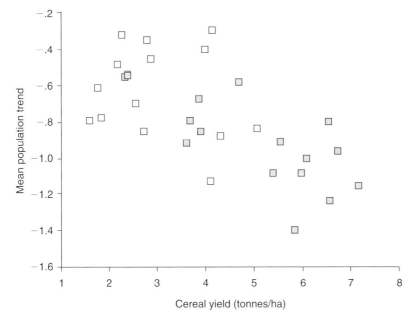

*Figure 12.2  The striking relationship between population declines of a range of declining farm-land bird species and cereal yield across Europe. Each point on the graph represents a different European country (Open squares = non-EU Member States, filled squares = EU Member States). Population declines between 1970 and 1990 were greater in countries with higher yields of cereals ($r_{30}$ = –0.66, P < 0.001), and greater in EU Member States than in other countries. From Donald* et al. *(2002b).*

lations represents just the tip of an iceberg of environmental collapse on farmland. The populations of many insects and plants have suffered huge declines in numbers and distribution, and many formerly common species are now rare (Donald 1998, Robinson & Sutherland 2002). This is important not only to those interested in nature conservation. The simplification of agricultural ecosystems represents a severe threat to those ecosystems themselves, since ecological simplification has long been known to favour massive pest outbreaks as the natural predators of pests are removed. It is ironic, though biologically predictable, that the only group of insects that has greatly increased in numbers during the last 20 years are the aphids, the crop pests against which most insecticide applications are directed.

In most cases, the mechanisms behind the declines in farmland biodiversity are unknown. Birds could be decreasing in numbers because the adults are dying younger, because more nests are failing, because more chicks are starving, because fewer nesting attempts are being made or many other reasons. It is likely that in most cases there is not one single cause but a combination of different factors acting to reduce populations. Proving beyond doubt that populations are declining for one of these reasons is extremely difficult, since data need to be collected on all stages of the life cycle. In the case of birds, for example, it is relatively easy to find and monitor nests, more difficult to assess exactly how many nesting attempts each pair make in a year and extremely difficult, or practically impossible, to determine how long birds live. Because of this, we cannot be absolutely certain why Skylark populations have declined, despite the enormous amount of research that has been carried out on the species. However, we do at least have enough information to start making well-informed suggestions as to which changes in agriculture have been the most important, and why. In the case of the Skylark, it seems that birds settling in different agricultural land-use types face different sorts of problems, so we shall deal with a number of different issues separately.

## SKYLARKS AND CEREALS

Cereal agriculture originated around 8000 BC in the Fertile Crescent, an arc of temperate uplands in what are now Turkey, Syria, Jordan and Iraq. The Mediterranean climate of this region favoured the evolution of large-grained, usually hermaphroditic self-pollinating annual grasses, which provided sufficient calories to be worth cultivating. Even wild, uncultivated cereals in this region could reward hunter-gatherers with up to a ton of seeds per hectare, representing an energetic profit of 50 kcal per 1 kcal expended (Diamond 1997). Their hermaphroditic nature aided early farmers by preserving selectively bred varieties, although infrequent cross-pollination allowed the development of new varieties such as bread wheat *Triticum*, now the single most important crop in the world. The use of these early cultivable cereals spread westwards across Europe, reaching Britain around 5000 BC (Edwards & Hirons 1984) and subsequently following explorers and colonists around the world. Today, cereals (including rice) account for well over half the calorific intake of the world's human population, and absorb over a third of all pesticide usage.

The arrival of cereals in Europe precipitated the clearance of large areas of the forests that had covered most of the land since the retreat of the last ice sheets around 8000 BC. The rate of woodland clearance accelerated with the advent of metal tools during the Bronze Age (2000 BC onwards in Britain) so that by the time of the Roman Conquest (AD 43) the area of woodland in parts of southern England was very similar to that found today (Rackham 1986). The clearance of forests for agriculture represents the single most profound anthropogenic change to Britain's landscape and wildlife habitats, and proved extremely beneficial to open-country species like the Skylark and the Corn Bunting.

As we saw in Chapter 3, cereals are an extremely important habitat for Skylarks. Although territory densities tend to be fairly low in cereals, their vast area means that cereals hold more pairs of Skylark than any other habitat in Britain and, probably, in the whole of Europe. In the UK, around 30% of all Skylarks are found in cereals. It has been calculated that the area of cereals planted each year in the UK is around 16 times greater than that of all the nature reserves in the country combined (Potts 1991). The total area of cereals planted each year in Europe is around 120 million hectares, a vast area roughly equivalent to that of France, Germany and Poland combined. Any changes in management that affect the suitability of cereals for Skylarks could clearly have a huge impact upon population levels across the continent. In fact, there have been a number of such changes in cereal management, and there is a growing body of evidence to suggest that these have indeed reduced the suitability of cereals for Skylarks and other farmland birds (Potts 1997). Changes in cereal management may, indeed, be the main cause of Skylark population declines.

The revolutionary nature of the changes in cereal agriculture that have taken place since the 1950s is perhaps best appreciated by looking at the extent to which such changes have achieved their goal of increasing yields. The increase in wheat yields has been almost exponential since the 1950s, having been relatively unchanged for the half century before this despite many attempts at improvement. Between 1961 and 2002, average UK wheat yields rose from 3.5 tonnes per hectare to over 8 tonnes.[2] Because of the importance of cereals to Skylarks, it is worth considering some of these changes in cereal management in some detail (pesticides will be discussed later in the chapter). It will become clear that all these changes have, or may have, contributed significantly to Skylark declines.

## 1. CHANGES IN THE TIME OF SOWING, HARVESTING AND PLOUGHING,

In traditional cereals systems, a high proportion of cereal crops are spring planted. This means that the new crop is planted some time between January and April. There is therefore very little green cover until April at the earliest, but spring-sown cereals (also known simply as spring cereals) tend to be harvested fairly late, between late July and late August. After harvest, the stubble of the crop is often left in the field over the winter, before the field is ploughed and re-sown the following spring. In the case of autumn-sown cereals (also known as winter cereals), sowing takes place in the autumn, often very shortly after the harvest of the previous crop. The crop grows throughout the winter and by the following spring is already a well-developed crop. Growth and maturation of the crop continue through the summer, and, as the crops have been developing for so much longer, harvesting occurs earlier in the summer than is the case with spring cereals, often as early as early July. After harvest, stubbles tend to be quickly ploughed in to prepare the field for resowing in early autumn. It is certainly not the case that autumn sowing is a new phenomenon: the Battle of Agincourt was fought on 25 October 1415 on a field recently ploughed and resown with wheat (a factor that contributed greatly to the

---

[2] Most of the agricultural statistics quoted in this chapter are drawn for the FAOSTAT database of the UN Food and Agriculture Organisation (http://apps.fao.org/).

French defeat that day). The first cereal varieties developed specifically for autumn sowing started to appear during the 1930s. However it was improvements in pest control and in soil drainage that led to the main transition from spring to the higher-yielding autumn plantings from the late 1960s onwards. In the early 1960s, around 80% of Britain's cereals were spring sown. By the 1990s, this had dropped to just 20%.

## 2. THE DEVELOPMENT OF TRAMLINE AGRICULTURE

Anyone looking at a modern cereal field will be struck by an extraordinarily geometric pattern of parallel lines running up and down through the crop. These so-called tramlines, each 30–50 cm wide, are left deliberately unplanted by the farmer, and are exactly wide enough to accommodate the wheels of a tractor (Plate 8). The advantage to the farmer of leaving a small proportion (less than 5%) of fields unproductive is that the tramlines guide the tractor through the crop in such way that during spraying or fertiliser applications, no parts of the crop are missed. This is because the distance between parallel tramlines is calculated to be exactly twice the width of the boom of the spraying machine. Because no parts of the crop are missed during spraying, modern cereal fields have a uniformly dense sward and populations of weeds and insects are effectively controlled. As we shall see, tramlines offer both opportunities and threats to Skylarks.

## 3. INCREASED USE OF INORGANIC FERTILISERS

The use of nitrogen- and phosphorous-based fertilisers has increased by more than 600% on British farmland since 1945, making a significant contribution to the rise in cereal yield. This increase in use was brought about by the development of artificial inorganic products which replaced imported guano from South America and the derived by-products of smelting which were used previously (Stoate 1996). Two significant effects of inorganic fertilisers have been to increase the structural density of cereal crops (particularly when used in conjunction with tramlines) and to allow continuous cropping on a scale never seen before. In some parts of southern England, winter cereals are now grown for eleven months of the year, and continuously from year to year (Potts 1997).

Much research has focused on the way Skylarks use cereal fields. A number of studies from the UK and elsewhere have yielded two consistent and important findings: spring cereals support higher territory densities of Skylarks than do winter cereals, and the territory density of Skylarks in both winter and spring cereals declines over the course of the breeding season (Figure 12.3). The higher numbers of Skylarks in spring cereals is clearly of significance in terms of recent population declines, since the area of this crop type has declined greatly in favour of winter cereals. The apparent decline in territory density over the course of the summer in

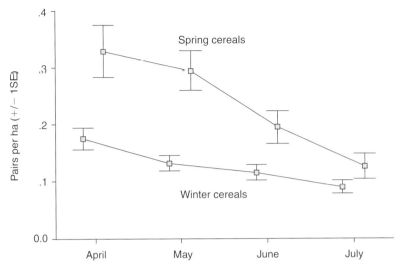

*Figure 12.3.    Seasonal changes in territory densities of Skylarks (pairs per hectare) in spring and winter cereals on lowland farmland in southern England. From Donald (1999).*

both cereal types is also of interest. Why are these birds apparently abandoning their territories so early in the summer? In fact, both the higher density of Skylarks in spring cereals and the seasonal declines in territory density in both cereal types can be explained by seasonal changes in crop structure. This is illustrated in Figure 12.4, which reveals a relationship of critical importance to understanding how Skylarks use cereals. In both types of cereal, numbers of territories decline as the crop becomes taller and denser. What is very important about the relationship illustrated in Figure 12.4 is that the same imaginary line of best fit (called a regression line by statisticians) fits equally well through both sets of points; in other words, the higher number of birds in spring cereals can be explained wholly by differences in crop structure (Donald *et al.* 2001c). Put simply, there is nothing special about spring cereals; Skylarks prefer them simply because, at any point in the breeding season, they are shorter and less dense than winter cereals. It is interesting to note that the highest densities of Skylarks recorded by RSPB researchers in winter cereals were found on a farm where the farmer had accidentally applied too high a dose of stem growth regulator. The resulting crop was very short, even at harvest (Figure 12.5), and Skylark numbers were abnormally high.

It is clearly important to understand why Skylarks establishing territories in both spring and winter cereals abandon their territories as the crop gets taller and thicker over the course of the summer. A clue to this mystery can be found in the opening lines of Flora Thompson's book *Lark Rise to Candleford*, quoted at the head of this chapter, in which the author makes the observation that Skylarks build their nests in the gaps between rows of cereals. Modern cereal fields, and particularly autumn-sown cereal fields, are too densely sown and fertilised for this to be possible once

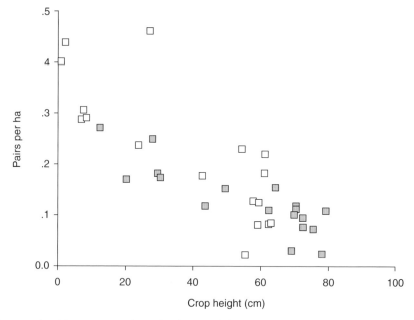

*Figure 12.4.    The important relationship between Skylark territory density and crop height in autumn-sown (closed symbols) and spring-sown (open symbols) cereals ($r_s = -0.82$, n = 35, P < 0.0001). Points represent two-weekly averages from two breeding seasons (1997 and 1998). Each point represents the average of a large number of fields. As cereal height increases, so densities of Skylarks fall in both cereal types. From Donald & Vickery (2000).*

the crop becomes well established. Indeed, it may be difficult for birds even to penetrate the growing crop, such is the density of its sward. As the crop develops, so Skylarks increasingly have to seek out patches of retarded growth or tramlines in which to nest and feed (Schön 1999, Stöckli 2002).

So could it be that Skylarks in modern cereal crops stop nesting early simply because they run out of nest sites? One way of testing this hypothesis is to look at how Skylarks use the one part of all modern cereal crops that does not become overgrown, the tramlines (Plate 8). Radio-tracking studies in Denmark have shown that as cereal crops develop, so the Skylarks in them are forced out of the crop and onto the tramlines, despite the fact that food availability is higher in the crop (Odderskær *et al.* 1997a). By the end of the breeding season, birds are spending around 70% of their time in tramlines, which occupy less than 5% of the total field area.

Further evidence for the effects of crop development on Skylark behaviour comes from examining the position of nests. If birds are being forced out of the crop by increasing sward density, it might be expected that the proportion of nests built on, or adjacent to, tramlines will increase as the crop develops. It might also be

*Figure 12.5. Harvesting winter wheat in Cambridgeshire, southern England. This crop was abnormally short due to application of a stem growth regulator, and the number of Skylarks using it was unusually high. Unfortunately, many of them were still nesting in it at harvesting, leading to high rates of chick loss (Plate 7). Photo: Paul F. Donald.*

expected that a lower proportion of nests in spring cereals are built on tramlines than is the case in winter cereals, simply because spring cereals are less tall and dense and so allow birds to nest away from tramlines. Both these expectations have been found to be true. The proportion of nests built on or immediately next to tramlines increases greatly in winter cereals, from zero in April, when birds were clearly avoiding tramlines, to around half of all nests in July (Figure 12.6). In spring cereals there is, as predicted, a far smaller increase in the incidence of nesting on tramlines. This provides further evidence that as the crop thickens and grows, particularly in winter cereals, so birds are increasingly forced out of the crop and onto the tramlines. By the middle of the breeding season, around 95% of the area of winter cereal fields is effectively useless to Skylarks. A very similar pattern of habitat exclusion has been observed in studies of the Brown Hare (Rühe 1999), a species that can be considered as the mammalian equivalent of the Skylark in terms of its use of different agricultural habitats.

Yet if Skylarks are capable of nesting on tramlines, as they clearly are, why should many pairs abandon breeding half way through the summer? The answer appears to lie at least partly with that most important determinant of productivity, nest predation. Nests on tramlines are extremely exposed, not only to the wheels of tractors but more importantly to the large numbers of mammalian predators that use them

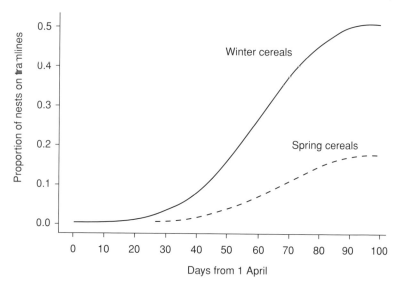

*Figure 12.6.* *Seasonal changes in the position of Skylark nests in spring and winter cereals in lowland England, derived from statistical models. The proportion of nests built immediately adjacent to tramlines increases in both crops as the season progresses, but is significantly greater in winter cereals. Data from the RSPB Skylark Research Project.*

as routes of access through the dense crop (Figure 12.7). In fact, nests built on or immediately adjacent to tramlines are twice as likely to fail as nests built further into the crop (Figure 12.8). Furthermore, because winter cereals are harvested earlier than spring cereals, a higher proportion of Skylark nests are lost to harvesting (Plate 7), although this is likely to account for relatively few nest losses as most nesting activity has already ceased by harvest time. So by mid to late summer, Skylarks in cereals, and particularly those in winter cereals, are increasingly forced to nest in places where their chances of success are reduced by an increased risk of predation. Whether this is the main reason for the seasonal fall in territory density in cereal crops, or whether the increase in sward density and consequent reduction in foraging area is more important, is not clear at present. Whatever the reason, it is clear that the rapid development of modern winter cereal crops is effectively curtailing the Skylark's breeding season at a time when it could continue breeding in spring cereals. Crude productivity estimates from a study carried out in France suggest that pairs in spring cereals are more productive in terms of chick output than are pairs in winter cereals (Eraud & Boutin 2002).

It is not only during the breeding season that the change from spring to autumn sowing of cereals has had an impact on Skylarks. As we saw in Chapter 10, the most important wintering habitat for Skylarks across much of Europe is cereal stubble. The autumn planting of cereals has meant that there has been a

*Figure 12.7. Skylark nest built on a tramline in winter cereals in late June, showing how exposed it is to predators. This nest was predated a couple of days after the photograph was taken. The tall and dense sward of winter cereals means that tramlines are the only places Skylarks can nest in these crops in the second half of the breeding season. Photograph: Paul F. Donald.*

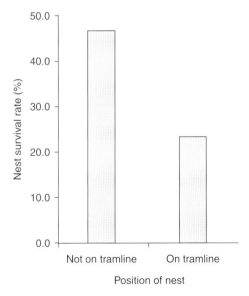

*Figure 12.8. Nest survival rates, expressed as the percentage of all nests that survive long enough for the chicks to leave the nest, of Skylark nests in cereals that are built immediately next to a tramline or further into the crop. The difference was statistically significant. From data in Donald* et al. *(2002a).*

decline in the area of this habitat available to wintering birds. Although it is not known whether this has led to an increase in the rate of winter mortality, it is likely that the loss of much of the species' most favoured winter habitat will have had some adverse effect, maybe in terms of reduced condition and fitness the following breeding season.

The loss of spring cereals to winter sowing has led to a reduction in the number of nesting attempts each pair is able to make in a year, and this is certainly an important, and perhaps the most important, cause of recent population declines. It appears that the loss of spring cereals has been sufficient wholly to account for the population declines recorded over the last 30 years (Siriwardena *et al.* 2001). The results of intensive studies are borne out by broad-scale historical data: the relationship between Skylark population levels in the UK and the area of spring cereals, although only correlative, is remarkably convincing (Figure 12.9).

The gradual discovery of the importance to Skylark populations of changes in cereal sowing times, which might once have appeared trivial in comparison to such factors as pesticide use, illustrates the subtle, complex and often unexpected nature of the interactions that can take place between a common bird and its apparently simple farmland environment.

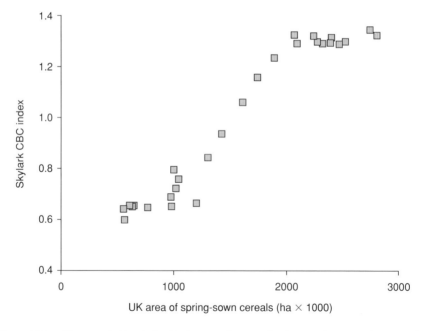

*Figure 12.9.   The remarkable relationship between the area of spring cereals sown each year in the UK between 1968 and 1996, and the population level of Skylarks as measured by the BTO's Common Birds Census index. From Donald & Vickery (2000).*

## SKYLARKS AND SET-ASIDE

The success of the CAP in raising productivity meant that by the 1970s agricultural production had begun to exceed demand. The production of these surpluses has become very expensive. Farmers have to be paid for producing them, and then there are considerable transport and storage costs. In dairy systems, these surpluses were reduced by the introduction of milk quotas. More recently, a similar system has been introduced to reduce surpluses of arable products, particularly cereals. In 1992, changes were made to the way in which farmers were paid subsidies through the CAP. These changes placed overwhelming financial pressure on most farmers to leave a proportion of their arable land uncultivated ('set-aside') each year. The scheme's introduction on a wide scale led to a reduction in the area of arable land in the European Union of around 9%, and the appearance in its place of fallow land. Set-aside became for a time the EU's second most extensive arable land use type after cereals.

The rules governing how set-aside must be managed are complex and have changed many times since its introduction, but general features are that there must be some green cover, either planted or naturally regenerating, that there are no, or very few, pesticide applications and that nothing may be removed from the land. A wide range of different habitats appeared as a result, and it became clear very soon after the introduction of the scheme that, although set-aside was introduced as a purely economic measure, here was a way of helping farmland birds (Wilson & Fuller 1992). Initial doubts about its potential to conserve farmland birds stemmed mainly from regulations requiring that set-aside be mown in the middle of the summer, causing the destruction of many nests of ground-nesting birds, including the Skylark. Changes to this regulation, resulting in later cuts, probably improved conditions for ground-nesting birds.

A number of research projects set out to examine whether or not set-aside was indeed the boon to farmland birds that conservationists hoped. A review of these studies by Juliet Vickery and David Buckingham (2001) clearly shows that set-aside fields can hold very high numbers of Skylarks relative to other farmland habitats, both during the breeding season and during the winter. However, the way in which set-aside is established and managed is crucial. Certain forms of set-aside are left in the same place each year, and if they become too tall or rank, Skylarks will not use them. Some set-aside is established as field margins, and if placed in a thin strip along a tall hedge or woodland edge, Skylarks will again avoid them. The most favourable type of set-aside for Skylarks is that created when the stubbles of the previous cereal crop are left unploughed and weeds are allowed to regenerate naturally. Because of this, Skylarks generally prefer set-aside that is moved around the farm each year (rotational set-aside), rather than set-aside that is left in the same place for several years (non-rotational set-aside). The optimal height of vegetation in set-aside appears to be around 20 cm, with patches of bare ground to allow foraging (Henderson *et al.* 2001).

In sympathetically managed set-aside fields, conditions appear ideal for Skylarks (Plate 8). As we have already seen, clutch sizes in set-aside are very high, indicating high food resources, territory densities can be very high, and birds appear capable of making more nesting attempts in a season than they do in cereal crops. Good set-aside is also a favoured habitat of Skylarks foraging for their chicks. The parents at one nest I observed in the middle of a cereal field regularly undertook flights of nearly half a kilometre to collect food for their chicks in set-aside. Chicks in nests in set-aside are fed soft-bodied, protein-rich foods like insect larvae, which promote rapid growth.

Why, then, with all these advantages, has the introduction of set-aside not led to a recovery in the Skylark population? It is possible that, as in cereals, nest predation may be the key. As we saw in Chapter 8, nests in set-aside have a particularly low survival rate (only around one in five nests survives long enough to produce chicks), since the food resources that attract Skylarks to set-aside also attract the predators of Skylark nests. So is it possible that set-aside, with its attractive habitat structure and high food resources, is actually luring Skylarks into some sort of ecological trap? This is an attractive theory when based solely upon an examination of individual nest survival rates, but becomes less convincing when another very important determinant of productivity, the number of nesting attempts, is considered. Because the habitat structure of most set-aside fields does not change greatly over the course of the breeding season, as it does in cereals, Skylarks are not forced to abandon nesting early in the breeding season, and so can more than compensate for lower success at the level of the individual nest by making a larger number of repeat nesting attempts. A study in France estimated that set-aside is in fact the most productive farmland habitat in terms of chicks produced per pair per year (Eraud & Boutin 2002).

A more likely explanation for the continued decline of Skylarks after the introduction of set-aside is that, despite the high densities found in some types of set-aside, the overall area of suitable set-aside is simply too small to make a difference. Based on the results of national surveys of Skylarks by the BTO, it can be estimated that only around a tenth of England's Skylarks nest in set-aside (Chapter 3); this may be too low a proportion to compensate for reductions caused by changes in other habitats. Perhaps as much as 80% of set-aside in the UK in the late 1990s was structurally sub-optimal for Skylarks (Henderson *et al.* 2001), no doubt contributing the absence of a recovery. The failure of set-aside to act as an environmental palliative to a general process of agricultural intensification suggests that it is better to strive for an overall reduction in agricultural intensity, rather than create small, unfarmed areas in a sea of otherwise intensive farmland (Potts 1991).

## SKYLARKS AND GRASSLAND

Grassland is the most extensive agricultural habitat in Europe, covering around 200 million hectares, and most of it is managed for meat and milk production. Just as the effects of intensification of arable land are reflected by changes in cereal yield, so intensification in pastoral systems is reflected in yield of milk. Milk is financially the single most important agricultural product in the UK, contributing 20% of total agricultural and horticultural output. The annual milk yield per cow in 1940 was around 2,200 litres per year, rising between 1950 and 1970 by around 60 litres annually. Yields reached a maximum of around 5,000 litres per cow per year in the early 1980s, although they could potentially increase further. This increase in yield has been brought about by better disease control, the increased use of artificial foodstuffs and the increased intensity of management of grassland used to grow grass for cutting. The demand for fodder crops has also increased because of the increasing tendency to winter dairy herds indoors. This demand has been met largely by the use of inorganic fertilisers and the introduction of silage to replace more traditional hay meadows.

Over 90% of British grassland has been 'improved' or 'semi-improved' during the twentieth century (Vickery *et al.* 2001). Around 86% of all agriculturally improved grassland receives annual applications of inorganic fertilisers, and 48% receives organic fertilisers. High usage of fertilisers greatly reduces the botanical diversity of grassland, and consequently its invertebrate diversity, and has led to the replacement of flower-rich, unimproved grassland with dense stands of monotypic grass (Stoate 1996, Vickery *et al.* 2001). Over 90% of unimproved grassland was lost between the 1930s and the 1980s. Silage began to replace hay meadows during the 1940s and currently supplies much of the winter feed of dairy herds. Cuts are made several times a season, usually starting in mid May, whereas in traditional hay systems only a single cut is taken at the end of the summer.

Changes in grassland management have impacted on farmland birds in a number of ways (Wakeham-Dawson & Smith 2000). Territory densities of Skylarks in grass have been shown by a number of studies to be generally low compared with densities in arable crops and non-agricultural habitats (see Chapter 3). This is due largely to the structure of modern grass fields, which, because of heavy grazing caused by high stock densities, are usually too short to provide adequate nesting cover (Plate 8). As shown in Chapter 3, the optimal vegetation height for nesting Skylarks is around 50 cm, but modern pastures offer vegetation that is generally lower than 10 cm. Detailed research on the response of Skylarks to changes in grassland structure has been undertaken in southern England by Andrew Wakeham-Dawson and his colleagues (Wakeham-Dawson & Aebischer 2001). In a series of carefully controlled experiments, they found that densities of breeding Skylarks were six times higher on long grazed grass than they were on short, heavily grazed pastures. Not only did the longer, less intensively grazed grass offer better nesting sites, it also provided more seed and invertebrate food. On the Dee Estuary in northwest England, Skylark breeding densities reach the very high levels of around 120 pairs per km$^2$ on ungrazed or moderately grazed coastal marshes, but fall to 52 pairs per km$^2$ on heavily grazed marshes (C.E. Wells, pers. comm.). Less intensively grazed grasslands allow not only the establishment of a suitable sward for nesting, but also adequate food supplies for wintering birds, particularly where grass species that bear seed throughout the winter are permitted to proliferate (Perkins *et al.* 2000).

In some habitats, however, increased grazing pressure appears to benefit Skylarks. On the grass moorland of northern Britain, increases in grazing pressure have resulted in the opening up of dense, heather-dominated habitats and so increased the amount of open grassy areas suitable for Skylarks to breed in (Pearce-Higgins & Grant 2002). The great reduction in overwinter outdoor grazing has indirectly led to a loss of winter food supplies for Skylarks, since the grain previously put out for winter stock to feed on is no longer available to the birds.

The frequent cutting of intensively managed grass fields can be absolutely devastating for Skylarks. Markus Jenny examined the productivity of nests in meadows on his study site in Switzerland and found that virtually all were destroyed when cuts were made on a monthly basis. In his study, 95 out 98 nests in meadows were destroyed, and the other three survived only because the farmers did not cut efficiently. The rate of production of chicks in these meadows was extremely low, averaging just 0.14 chicks per nesting attempt. In other words, it would take seven nesting attempts in these grasslands to produce a single chick. A further problem is that chicks surviving long enough to leave the nest are still vulnerable to cutting operations for at least another two weeks, by which time they are capable of flight. After cutting, it took around two weeks on Marcus's study site for the vegetation to grow sufficiently tall to allow further nesting attempts, but these were again destroyed since the grass was cut every four weeks. The period from the laying of the first egg to the chicks fledging and being able to fly from danger is around 32 days, so the minimum interval between successive cuts that would allow recovery of the sward and successful nesting is around 46 days. However the interval between successive cuts in most modern silage fields is less than this. Mowing not only destroys nests, it also makes the grass too short to provide cover for replacement nesting attempts. In one experiment in southern England, mowing of grass caused numbers of breeding skylarks to decline by around 80%.

Although there is considerable variation in the attractiveness to Skylarks of different types of grassland, it seems likely that even the better grassland habitats are not perfect. Even in the best grassland habitats, territory densities are generally low compared with those in arable crops. Chicks in nests in modern grass fields also tend to be in poor body condition, possibly the result of a poor diet. Because of the lack of nesting cover in heavily grazed grass fields, nest predation rates are often high, and of course many nests are crushed by the feet of livestock (Plate 7).


## SKYLARKS, HEDGEROWS AND CROP DIVERSITY


Hedgerow removal is a symptom of agricultural intensification that is as prominent in the public eye as is the use of pesticides. Around 50% of Britain's hedgerows were lost between 1947 and 1995 (Barr & Parr 1996), a loss that is likely to have contributed much to the decline in farmland wildlife. However hedgerow loss in itself is unlikely to have had any deleterious effects on Skylark populations. As we saw in Chapter 3, Skylarks actively avoid tall vertical structures such as trees and tall hedges, so hedgerow removal in the absence of any other changes would be likely to increase numbers of Skylarks. Removal of hedges at one farm in Norfolk led to a large increase in the number of Skylarks present (Bull *et al.* 1976). The reason that large-scale hedge removal has not led to an increase in Skylark numbers nationally is that hedgerow removal occurs for a purpose: to increase field size. As the CAP guarantees a market for all produce, farmers have tended to abandon traditional mixed farming, with its obsolete advantage of producing a variety of products to protect against a drop in the market for one of them, in favour of specialised production. Because of differences in climate, topography and soil types, farmers in eastern Britain have tended to specialise in arable production (Plate 8), whereas those in western and northern Britain do best by specialising in dairy and beef production. The result of this has been a polarisation in agriculture and a huge decline in habitat diversity at a regional level, something that has been clearly implicated in the declines of a number of farmland bird species (Evans 1997).

In the early 1980s, two important studies of Skylarks were undertaken in Switzerland, prompted by fears that bird populations were declining in that country because of changes in agriculture. Alex Schläpfer and Markus Jenny independently reached the same conclusion, that a reduction in habitat diversity on farmland reduces the number of nesting attempts each pair can make in a year, and increases the area of land a pair needs to support itself. Where there is high farmland habitat diversity, a typical Skylark territory might contain areas of grass, fallow, spring crops and winter crops, each at different stages of development. Schläpfer (1988, 2001) and Jenny (1990a) both demonstrated that Skylarks used different crops for nesting only at certain stages of their development. A territory containing a number of different crop types allows the birds to have, for example, a first nesting attempt in winter crops, then, as these become too tall and dense, to have a second nesting attempt in spring crops, then perhaps a third attempt in grass and a fourth in fallow. In areas of more intensive, less diverse farmland, such as are found across much of the EU, a typical territory is likely to contain just a single habitat type, such as winter cereal, giving the birds no opportunity to nest in other crops once the cereal has become too dense. Territories either have to become far larger, so reducing the number of pairs a given area can support, or the number of nesting attempts made by each pair is reduced.

The importance of habitat diversity is also evident in the results of a number of studies carried out in the UK, which demonstrate higher territory densities where the diversity of crop types is greater (Chamberlain *et al.* 1999a, 2000b, Chamberlain & Gregory 1999). The loss of arable pockets in predominantly grassland areas might be a particularly important form of habitat diversity loss for Skylarks, since even small areas of arable land might be sufficient to allow populations to survive in pasture-dominated areas (Robinson *et al.* 2001). The critical importance to Skylarks of crop structure, already demonstrated in discussions of the ecology of Skylarks in grassland and in cereals, is again apparent at the landscape scale.

As well as resulting in a reduction in habitat diversity, the loss of mixed farming has also led to the loss of one specific habitat, undersown cereals. Undersowing was a system whereby cereals acted as a precursor to grass leys, so that when the cereal was harvested, the stubbles were left to allow the undersown grass to emerge. A major cause of loss of stubbles during the last half-century has been the decline of undersowing, itself a direct result of the loss of mixed farming (Potts 2003). As we saw in Chapter 10, stubbles are a vital wintering habitat for Skylarks, and the loss of undersown stubbles may have greatly reduced this most important resource.

## PESTICIDES AND ORGANIC FARMING

Mankind has been using naturally occurring or artificial compounds to protect crops from pests since the time of the Sumerians, around 6,000 years ago. Nevertheless, it is the use of pesticides that people tend most to associate with recent agricultural intensification, and their use has indeed increased greatly. Around 3,400 chemical products are currently approved for use in the UK under the Food and Environment Protection Act. There have been significant increases in the number of chemical applications made to various crops, particularly cereals (Plate 8). Winter cereals can receive an average of ten different crop treatments during the course of the growing season (Figure 12.10). Furthermore, the efficacy of the chemicals used and the effectiveness of their delivery have also increased. Tramline systems ensure that no parts of the crop are missed, and advanced sprayers deliver exactly the right amounts of chemical to the crops.

On the other hand, the targeting of the chemicals towards specific pests has also improved. The indiscriminate use of certain chemicals that were directly toxic to non-target organisms, such as birds, was publicised and criticised in Rachel Carson's polemic book *Silent Spring* (1963), and the subsequent backlash against these chemicals led to their withdrawal in the USA and much of Europe. Chemicals such as DDT, which famously caused acute lethal and sub-lethal poisoning in birds, have been replaced largely with chemicals far more specific in their action and less persistent in the environment (though DDT and other toxic chemicals are still widely used in the developing world). Improved testing means that new chemicals are carefully vetted to ensure there are no direct toxic effects on non-target organisms. In the UK at least, there is no evidence that pesticides, when used correctly, are still poisoning large numbers of birds (Burn 2000).

However, the efficiency of modern chemicals and improvements in their application have almost certainly greatly reduced the insect, seed and weed food available to farmland birds, and it is these indirect effects of pesticides that now concern conservationists (Campbell *et al.* 1997b). In the case of one particularly well-

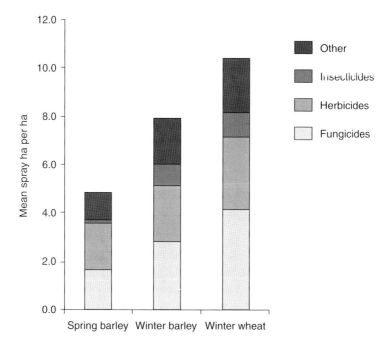

*Figure 12.10.  Pesticide applications (calculated as spray hectares per hectare of crop) in three different cereal types in 1996. The category 'Other' includes growth regulators, molluscicides and seed treatments. Data from Thomas* et al. *(1997).*

studied farmland bird, the Grey Partridge, the indirect effects of pesticides have been shown to be the main reason for the species' decline (Potts 1997). However the mechanism is far from simple, and it is, perhaps surprisingly, the use of herbicides, rather than insecticides, that has been responsible. Herbicides have reduced the number of weed plants on farmland, and this in turn has reduced the numbers of insects that feed upon such plants. The loss of these insects has been shown to reduce the survival rates of partridge chicks, and this in turn has driven the massive population decline of this species. This provides another good example of how the apparent simplicity of the agricultural ecosystem can sometimes mask a number of complex underlying processes.

So, has the increased use of pesticides had an effect upon Skylark populations, and, if it has, what has been the mechanism? This is a question that a number of recent research projects have set out to answer. Researchers have available to them a number of ways of addressing these questions, but all have their problems. As these problems are fundamental to interpreting the results of the research, I shall consider the evidence under headings that relate to how that research was carried out:

1. COMPARING ORGANIC AND CONVENTIONAL FARMS

A relatively small but increasing number of farms have dispensed with agrochemical use altogether, and turned to organic production. So a comparison of the numbers and ecology of Skylarks on organic farms with that of birds on farms where pesticides are still in use might yield clues about the effects of agrochemicals. However, there are considerable scientific difficulties with this approach. When farmers turn to organic production, they are generally obliged to make fundamental changes to the way they manage their land to control crop pests. For example, they might be forced to return to traditional grass–arable rotations to prevent the build-up of pests in the soil, or grow crops they would not necessarily grow under conventional, pesticide-based management. They might plant dense hedges to harbour the natural predators of crop pests. Therefore organic farms tend to be different to conventional farms in more ways than just pesticide use alone. This leaves the researcher with the problem of deciding whether any differences between organic and conventional farms in, for example, Skylark numbers or breeding success are due to pesticide usage or to one of these other changes. Nevertheless, such comparisons yield insights into what might happen if pesticide use is reduced or dispensed with altogether, irrespective of the direct cause.

A number of scientific studies have shown that there is sometimes, though certainly not always, a discernable difference in Skylark numbers between organic and pesticide-treated crops. For example, one study conducted on a sample of farms in southern England has shown that territory densities of Skylarks in organic cereal crops can be more than twice those in pesticide-treated crops, and organic grassland can hold up to five times the numbers found in treated grass (Wilson *et al.* 1997).

These differences are likely to be due to three factors: firstly the higher availability of invertebrate food in the organic crops, secondly the patchier, less dense sward structure of organic crops, providing suitable nesting sites throughout the breeding season, and thirdly the longer interval between silage cuts. Furthermore, organic systems generally contain a mixture of spring and winter crops at different stages of development, providing Skylarks with suitable breeding habitat throughout the nesting season. In contrast, a different study suggested that Skylark numbers do not differ greatly between organic and pesticide-treated farms in either the breeding season or winter (Chamberlain *et al.* 1999b). In this study, it was shown that the structure of fields on the organic farms was inherently less suitable for Skylarks than on the treated farms, as they were smaller and more enclosed. This might account for the lack of difference in the numbers of Skylarks that were recorded on each farm type.

2. COMPARING TREATED AND UNTREATED FIELDS

Another way of determining the effects of pesticides on Skylarks is to compare the ecology of birds on treated and untreated parts of the same farm. For example, we can compare differences in the diet and development of Skylark chicks in cereals, which receive pesticide applications, with those in set-aside, which does not, on the same sample of farms. However this approach shares with the organic/conventional comparison the problem that set-aside fields tend to be structurally very different from cereal fields, so isolating the effects of chemicals is extremely difficult, or even impossible. We have already seen that set-aside holds far higher densities of breeding Skylarks than do cereals, though how much of this difference is due to pesticide use and how much to differences in the structure of the habitat is unclear. Clutch sizes are higher in set-aside than in cereals, possibly reflecting higher food availability in set-aside, but the hatching success of eggs does not differ between sprayed cereals and unsprayed set-aside. The diet of chicks in sprayed and unsprayed crops shows clear differences in composition in a way that suggests that pesticides are affecting chick food availability. For example, Skylark chicks whose parents forage in unsprayed set-aside receive a large number of soft-bodied invertebrate larvae, nutritious food items that are particularly susceptible to pesticides. Chicks whose parents forage in sprayed cereals, on the other hand, bring them back a larger number of pesticide-tolerant ground beetles. Despite these differences in diet, there are apparently no differences in chick growth rates and body condition in sprayed and unsprayed crops (Donald *et al.* 2001e). Indeed, because of higher predation rates in set-aside, individual nesting attempts in sprayed cereals are actually the most productive of any nests on farmland.

Tony Morris (pers. comm.) has combined data on the growth rates and survival of Skylark nestlings with data on pesticide applications obtained from farmers. His ongoing analyses suggest that the body condition of Skylark chicks is slightly reduced in cereal fields that received a summer insecticide application compared with similar fields that received the usual pesticide applications but no summer insecticide. Although this did not adversely influence the survival of those chicks while they were in the nest, it is possible that chicks leaving the nest in poor body condition are less likely to survive to fledge.

## 3. EXPERIMENTAL MANIPULATION

Finally, researchers can experimentally manipulate pesticide applications to fields of a particular crop type and see what happens. This is by far the most rigorous approach, because the different fields differ only in pesticide application and the treatments can be swapped around between fields in different years to ensure that the results are consistent. However, it is also the most expensive approach, and requires farmers to accept losses in yield and other management problems.

The only example of this happening for the purposes of Skylark research has been the study by Peter Odderskær, Niels Elmegaard and their colleagues in Denmark (1997b), who examined the effects on Skylarks of insecticide applications in spring-sown cereals. Pesticide applications had no effect on the number or size of Skylark territories in spring cereals, and no effect on the distance parents flew to collect food for their chicks. However, pairs of Skylarks in the fields that were not sprayed consistently produced more chicks than those in sprayed fields. This increase in productivity was brought about by two factors, a higher rate of nest survival and a greater number of nesting attempts. However the difference in Skylark productivity between sprayed and unsprayed fields was smaller than the differences in productivity attributable to the weather. In poor weather, Skylarks in insecticide-treated fields did worse than those in unsprayed fields, but in good weather there was no discernable difference between sprayed and unsprayed fields.

The results of a large number of studies, using all the various comparative methods described above, are clearly equivocal. Some studies suggest a demonstrable effect of pesticides on Skylark numbers or ecology, some suggest an effect only under certain conditions, such as bad weather, and others do not suggest any differences at all. In general, those studies demonstrating an effect of pesticides suggest a relatively small effect. A summary of the indirect effects of pesticides on a range of farmland birds yielded equally equivocal conclusions (Campbell *et al.* 1997b). A reasonable summary of all this work might be that while pesticides may have adversely affected Skylarks in a number of ways, their use is unlikely to be the most important cause of recent population declines.

## GENETICALLY MODIFIED CROPS

Recent advances in biotechnology have permitted agricultural scientists to develop crops that are resistant to the effects of certain agrochemicals. Genetically modified herbicide-tolerant (GMHT) crops allow farmers to use broad-spectrum herbicides in the knowledge that the crop plants are safe and all the pest plants vulnerable, thus allowing more effective weed control. Such crops have been grown in the USA since the mid 1990s and are, at the time of writing, undergoing trials in the UK.

Among the many fears that have been raised by the introduction of such crops is that this will greatly increase the rate of loss of biodiversity on farmland (Firbank & Forcella 2000). The Skylark, being a bird that is largely confined to farmland through most of its European range, might be particularly badly affected by the loss of insect and plant food that may result from the large-scale use of GM crops. In order to investigate this possibility, Alan Watkinson and his colleagues at the University of East Anglia attempted to model the effects of GMHT sugar beet on Skylark food supplies. They concluded that the impact on Skylark populations of a wide take-up of GM crops will vary from negligible, if the farmers taking up the technology tend to be those with already low weed densities, to severe, if GM crops are adopted mainly by farmers whose fields currently have high weed-seed densities (Watkinson *et al.* 2000).

Clearly more research is necessary not only into how GM crops will affect bird food availability, but also where such crops are likely to be grown. At present, the

GM varieties being tested are of crops, such as sugar beet, that are of relatively minor importance for Skylarks. The potential impacts of GMHT cereals, which are not currently available but are in an advanced stage of development, are likely to be far greater. If GMHT cereals have lower food availability for Skylarks than current varieties, which may already not always hold enough, the effects on Skylark populations could be very severe.

## SKYLARKS AS CROP PESTS

While modern agriculture has certainly damaged Skylark populations, it is also clear that Skylarks have, in the past, damaged agriculture. As we shall see in the next chapter, the Skylark's reputation as a crop pest greatly slowed the progress of the early conservation movement in trying to afford the species full legal protection, and led to some of the earliest ever applied ornithological research. This research, conducted by Dr W.E. Collinge (1913) nearly a century ago, concluded that, although some of the food eaten by Skylarks is injurious to crops, a far greater proportion of its consumption was of benefit to the farmer, as it included large numbers of noxious insects and weeds. Nevertheless, at times the Skylark could, and occasionally still does, cause considerable damage to crops. Cecil Smith, in his *Birds of Somersetshire* (1869), suggested that although the good done to the farmer by Skylarks in eating harmful insects generally outweighed the bad, huge arrivals of birds in hard weather could wreak considerable damage. He quotes from his diary, in which he wrote:

Since the late frost set in very unusual numbers of Sky Larks made their appearance, both in flocks and singly: they have nearly destroyed a field of rape for me, there being nothing left but the thick stems; the whole field looks like a field of turnips that had been attacked by the 'black army', nothing but the skeletons of the leaves being left. I had one shot at this flock, and killed enough for a good dish of Larks, but they were very thin and not good eating; their crops and throats were full of green rape. Had I been so disposed I might have killed almost any number, for they were so thick on the ground that the one shot I had killed thirteen, and the whole flock almost immediately settled down again in the same field again. I also noticed some of the same sort of mischief done to some cabbages in an allotment field near.

In winter and spring, according to the Reverend C.A. Johns in *British Birds in their Haunts* (1920), the Skylark eats

the tender stalks of sprouting corn. Hence it is regarded with deadly hostility by farmers, and hence, too, the quiet of the country is much disturbed at these seasons, by boys employed to frighten it away by screaming and plying a peculiar sort of rattle.

There are several similar accounts in early ornithological literature of Skylarks causing damage to crops, but such damage seems to have occurred only infrequently, and generally only during mass hard-weather movements (see Chapter 9). In the breeding season, when the diet switches largely to invertebrates, Skylarks appear to cause little damage.

Sugar beet appears to be a crop that is particularly susceptible to damage by Skylarks, probably because it is a delicate crop that requires an intensive herbicide regime to minimise weed competition. Where it is the primary spring crop, therefore, Skylarks have little option, in the absence of other foods, but to attack the cotyledons of emerging beet plants. Research carried out in the early 1970s suggested that, although Skylarks, as well as Woodpigeons and mice, caused some damage to beet seedlings, this was not reflected in reduced yields at harvest (Edgar & Isaacson 1974). More detailed research into the problem by Rhys Green (1980) found that over 60% of the diet of Skylarks feeding in sugar beet fields was made up of beet leaves and cotyledons. However crop damage declined greatly (and Skylark food intake efficiency rose greatly) as the availability of weed seeds and invertebrates increased, suggesting that the latter are more profitable food items.

Sugar beet is not the only crop to suffer damage form Skylarks. Lettuce seedlings can sometimes suffer severe damage, although even very badly damaged plants recover to give the same yield as undamaged ones (Edgar & Isaacson 1974). Medic pastures in northwestern Iraq, where Skylarks (probably of the subspecies *dulcivox*) winter in large numbers, suffer a loss of up to 60% of their leaf area, resulting in a halving of seed yield (Halse & Trevenen 1985). Different species of medic appear to suffer different levels of damage, possibly related to variation in nutritive content. Also in Iraq, Halse & Trevenen (1986) recorded severe grazing damage to young cereal crops. Although not as serious as the damage to medic pastures, grazing by Skylarks led to measurable reductions in yield. These reductions were lowest for cultivars that were widely established in Iraq and highest for cultivars recently imported from elsewhere, probably because of their higher nutrient content. In Tasmania, the introduced Skylark population is apparently causing problems as a pest of opium poppy crops at the cotyledon stage (Dr M Statham, pers. comm.). The Skylark is not the only lark to cause problems for farmers. In North America, the Horned Lark is also a pest of lettuce leaves, and chemicals are applied to seedlings to reduce their palatability to the birds (York *et al.* 2000). In Iraq, cereal crops suffer damage from Calandra Larks, which dig up the seedlings (Halse & Trevenen 1986).

## THE CONSERVATION OF SKYLARKS ON FARMLAND

The overwhelming weight of scientific evidence suggests that the massive declines in Skylark populations described in Chapter 3, and similarly massive declines in other farmland species, have been caused largely or wholly by agricultural intensification. Research on a large number of other farmland bird species and other wildlife support the same hypothesis: increases in agricultural output have led to declines in farmland wildlife. The cases for other hypotheses to explain biodiversity loss on farmland have proved weak and inadequate to account for the scale of the problem.

Now that intensive research has established the link between agricultural change and biodiversity loss, and in many cases revealed the underlying mechanisms, conservationists are in the position of being able to advocate measures to reduce the impacts of modern farming practices on Skylark populations. However, any such measures must be pragmatic; advocating a return to the agricultural practices of the 1850s would be naive and doomed to failure. Instead, those wishing to introduce measures to help Skylark populations to recover need to consider the practicality of those measures. Farmers are businesspeople who, quite understandably, may not be prepared to forgo a substantial part of their income to protect Skylark populations. In many respects, farmers have been forced to intensify production by the economics of European agriculture; many low-intensity systems have simply not been profitable enough to survive the economics of the CAP. Solutions to the problem of declining farmland wildlife therefore need to be cheap, economically neutral or even, ideally, profitable for the farmers if they are to have any chance of succeeding. The economics of agriculture are determined within the EU, largely by the CAP, so it is with the CAP that the search for a solution to the Skylark problem needs to begin.

As we have already seen, much of the agricultural intensification that has taken place in western Europe during the last 30 years or so has been driven by the Common Agricultural Policy. Subsidies paid through the CAP to farmers have so far been based largely upon price support, meaning that prices, held above world market prices, are guaranteed. Price support has been the single largest stimulus to agricultural intensification, and so to the loss of farmland wildlife (Donald *et al.* 2002b). Not only has it led to increases in inputs and the loss of marginal land, it has also contributed to a decline in the area of mixed farming, since farmers no longer need to diversify in order to protect themselves from fluctuations in the market prices of different commodities.

It may appear tempting to advocate the complete removal of agricultural subsidies as a measure to protect Skylarks and farmland wildlife, but paradoxically this too could have severe negative impacts. If farmers in the EU had to compete on world markets, it is entirely possible that larger farms would intensify further to increase yields while smaller farms, often those supporting the best wildlife habitats, might not be able to compete and could disappear completely. In the three years following the removal of agricultural subsidies in New Zealand in 1989, for example, pesticide use actually increased by over 40% as farmers strived to raise productivity. Whatever the effects on wildlife of totally removing agricultural subsidies in the EU, complete liberalisation would certainly lead to unemployment and falling incomes, so is unlikely to occur in the near future. However, changes will need to be made to the way subsidies are distributed, since overproduction is likely to become an increasing problem. It has been predicted that the UK's demand for food in 2015 will be only 5% higher than it was in 1987, and that demand in 2015 could be met even if 40% of the UK's currently farmed land were to fall out of production (North 1990).

A more sensible option than complete abandonment of agricultural subsidies would be to change the way agricultural subsidies are paid, so as to support more sustainable farming systems; in other words, to stop paying farmers to produce unwanted agricultural surpluses and instead pay them to produce more wildlife. Under such a system, Skylarks, Cornflowers and nature trails could be seen as being just as much a farm product as wheat (Musters *et al.* 2001).

In 1992 and again in 1999, changes were made to the way subsidies are paid to farmers by reducing price support in favour of area payments. These mean that farmers receive a fixed amount of subsidy for each hectare of land they farm, irrespective of how much is produced from that land, providing less of an incentive to intensify. These changes also led to the introduction of set-aside, which, as we have seen, can be a valuable wildlife habitat if managed correctly. Even more importantly, reforms of the CAP since 1985 have included the provision of agri-environment measures, which have been shown to be successful in enhancing bird populations (Aebischer *et al.* 2000). Such schemes have been delivered both through the CAP and through nationally funded schemes. Although these measures currently make up a small proportion (less than 5%) of the total CAP budget, it is likely that falling demand, public and political pressure and changes to the CAP to accommodate the enlargement of the EU will bring about changes that increase this amount. Indeed, the UK government now recognises the decline in farmland bird populations as being of public, rather than just scientific, concern, and now has a commitment to reverse the declines in farmland bird populations by 2025.

It therefore appears likely that future changes in the way that agricultural subsidies are paid and government policy is formulated will create a situation in which measures to protect Skylarks will become economically feasible. But what changes should be made to agricultural methods to help Skylark populations to recover? If agri-environment schemes are to work, they need to be carefully designed to achieve the best results, and changes that benefit one species will not necessarily benefit another. The power of 'smart' agri-environment schemes to deliver birds is well illustrated by the case of the Cirl Bunting in southern England, where the prescriptions were based upon detailed ecological research and so achieved a high rate of success (Peach *et al.* 2001). The large body of recent research on Skylarks suggests a number of possible solutions to the problems Skylarks face in the modern agricultural environment:

- *Increasing the area of spring cereals.* We have already seen that spring cereals have a number of considerable advantages for Skylarks compared with winter cereals. Some agri-environment schemes, such as the UK's Arable Stewardship Scheme, already provide economic incentives for farmers to plant spring, rather than winter, crops. As the gross margin (a measure of the amount of profit achieved) of spring cereals is often very close to that of winter cereals, large areas of winter cereals could be converted to spring cereals at relatively little cost. Any scheme that encourages farmers to plant spring cereals is likely to be very effective at restoring Skylark numbers.

- *Managing winter cereals to mimic the benefits of spring cereals.* Where it is unfeasible or undesirable to revert to spring cereal systems, it might be possible to manage winter cereals in such a way as to mimic some of the advantages of spring crops. Leaving small, unplanted patches of ground ('Skylark scrapes') within winter cereal crops might provide birds with safe nesting and feeding sites and so encourage more late broods. Early results from some experimental work in southern England (Plate 8) suggest that this is a highly efficient, and very cheap, way of boosting Skylark productivity and numbers in otherwise inhospitable winter cereals.
- *Encouraging winter stubbles.* Any schemes that provide financial encouragement to farmers to return to spring planting methods could provide additional payments to ensure that the option of a period of winter stubbles that such systems offer is taken up. Where stubbles are left for Skylarks, they should be provided away from field margins or woodland edges. Barley stubbles are preferable to wheat stubbles.
- *Encouraging mixed farming.* Encouraging mixed farming, with the resultant benefits of habitat heterogeneity and consequent opportunities for multiple nesting attempts, is likely to restore Skylark populations in landscapes dominated by arable or pastoral agriculture. Particularly effective in boosting Skylark numbers would be the integration of arable systems, particularly cereals, into predominantly grassland areas.
- *Reducing pesticide applications.* As markets for organic foods have started to outstrip supply, many farmers are considering changing to specialist organic production. Conversion to organic production requires a transition period of several years before produce can be labelled as fully organic, a period during which farmers are forced to tolerate lower yields without the benefits of the premium organic crops attract. Schemes to support farmers during this transition period would encourage conversion to organic agriculture, with resultant benefits to Skylark populations.

The extent to which farmers adopt the conservation options outlined above depends to a large extent on agri-environment schemes making these options economically viable for farmers. However, there are also a number of simple measures that farmers can adopt to make their farms more suitable for Skylarks through simple management changes without losing large amounts of income. Such measures include leaving cereal stubble for as long as possible over the winter, delaying the cutting of set-aside for as long as possible at the end of the summer, and increasing as much as possible the interval between successive cuts of silage. The conservation of the Skylark will depend upon favourable changes being made in international and national policies and in local land management practices.

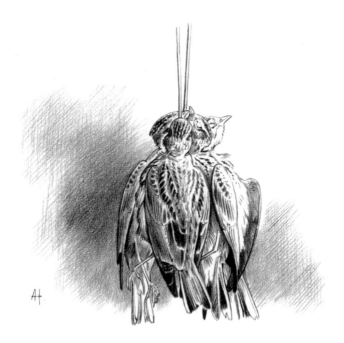

*Skylarks on sale in a Victorian butcher's shop*

## CHAPTER 13

# Poetry, persecution and the rise of popular protest

Judging by the ordinary laws of probability the English Skylark ought long ago to have gained the distinction that belongs to the Dodo and the Great Auk, for the Lark abides in the midst of foes.

Society for the Protection of Birds, Educational Series No. 22— *Skylark* (1897)

In the land of plenty, the larks fall ready roasted

John Ray, *A Compleat Collection of English Proverbs* (1670)

Robert Boyle (1627–91) is regarded as one of the founding fathers of modern science. Among his many achievements, he used experiments on animals in a vacuum pump (his own invention) to prove that respiration is necessary to sustain life, a discovery that led to an understanding of the workings of the respiratory system and so made a major contribution to modern anatomy. His description of the first experiment with the pump (Boyle 1662) is interesting, and introduces a theme that will recur throughout this chapter:

> To satisfie ourselves in some measure, about the account upon which Respiration is so necessary to the Animals, that Nature hath furnished with Lungs, we took (being then unable to procure any other lively Bird, small enough to be put into the Receiver) a Lark, one of whose Wings had been broken by a shot, of a Man that we had sent to provide us with some Birds for our Experiment; but notwithstanding this hurt, the Lark was very lively, and did, being put into the Receiver, divers times spring up in it to a good height.

However, as the air was pumped out and a vacuum created in the receiver,

> she began manifestly to droop and appear sick, and very soon after was taken with as violent and irregular Convulsions, as are wont to be observ'd in Poultry, when their heads are wrung off: For the Bird threw herself over and over two or three times, and dyed with her Breast upward, her Head downwards, and her Neck awry.

Seeing the convulsions, the experimenters quickly readmitted air through the stopcock,

> yet it came too late . . . we found that the whole Tragedy has been concluded within ten Minutes of an hour.

This account is interesting as a record of an important moment in the history of science, but it is also interesting as an early example of the strange relationship that has existed for centuries between our own species and the Skylark. Sparrows, mice, cats and dogs were routinely sacrificed by Boyle and his contemporaries without a qualm, yet Boyle is at pains to point out that he used a Skylark because he had no option, and describes the bird's death as a tragedy. Perhaps better than any other bird, the Skylark illustrates our own species' ambivalent and contradictory attitudes towards wildlife. On the one hand, poets and musicians have adopted it as the epitome of freedom and the emblem of a rich and varied countryside, on the other it has for centuries been mercilessly hunted in vast numbers for food and the cagebird industry. This contradiction has been recognised in a number of artistic allusions to the poignancy of the song of caged birds. Indeed, the metaphor of the caged lark appears to have entered common parlance in Victorian England. In his speech at the opening of the Manchester School Board Higher Grade School in 1884, the

Senior Inspector of Schools, a Mr H.E. Oakeley, spoke of how "the other day he was inspecting a school in Ancoats, and the boys in the first class were repeating some poetry they had learnt about a Skylark. He enquired whether anyone had seen a Skylark; there was a silence, but a boy presently held out his hand to signify he wished to speak, and on his saying, 'Well, where did you see a lark' he answered 'In the public-house at the corner of the street, in a cage'. He (Mr Oakeley) thought 'Poor caged lark, and poor caged little lad'."

Capture for the cagebird industry was not the only exploitation of Skylarks. For centuries, astonishing numbers of Skylarks were killed for food, and despite the famous British love of wildlife, this practice was probably more prevalent in England (although not, apparently, in other parts of Britain) than anywhere else. Today, despite strict legal protection elsewhere, huge numbers of Skylarks are hunted legally and illegally in certain European countries (Chapter 11). As a poetic emblem of freedom and beauty, as a highly desirable cagebird, and as a tasty pie filling, the Skylark has entered popular culture to a degree disproportionate to the appeal of its physical appearance.

## THE SKYLARK IN ART AND POPULAR CULTURE

The Romans were the first to glorify the larks, when Julius Caesar raised the *Legio V Alaudae* in Gallia Transalpina in around 52 BC (Bishop 1990). This legion, last heard of in fighting on the Danube in around AD 70, was so named because of the distinctive crests on the soldiers' helmets, although exactly which species they were supposed to resemble is unclear.

The extent to which a bird features in popular culture can be assessed by the number of different local names it acquires. The Skylark, perhaps unsurprisingly, has many. These fall into a number of groups. First are the descriptive names, such as Rising Lark (Northamptonshire), Field Lark (Surrey), Short-heeled Lark (Scotland), Clod Lark and Clodhopper (both Sussex), and Ground Lark and Sky-flapper (Somerset). Another group of names are variants on Laverock, from *láwerce*, the Anglo-Saxon word for a lark. This may derive from the word for one guilty of treason, an allusion to the difficulty of finding a lark's nest (see Chapter 7). Another possibility is that it derives from the early German word *Lievling*, from *Liebling der Gottheit*, stemming from the belief that the lark was under the protection of the Virgin Mary (the Skylark was known as Lady Hen, or Our Lady's Hen, in Shetland). Variants include Laverak and Lavrock (Scotland), Lerruck and Lavro (Orkney), Learock (Lancashire) and Sky Laverock (Northamptonshire). Laverock and Lavro are still in use in some of the Scottish islands, and the word survives in the contemporary words for a lark in Dutch (*leeuwerik*) and Afrikaans (*lewerik*). A third group of names are variants of various medieval Celtic words, such as Ehidit (Cornwall), Ehedydd or Uchedydd (Wales), Fuiseog (Ireland) and Melhuez and Pelhuez, meaning 'high flight'. A few other names are clearly local inventions with no known origins, such as Lintwhite (Suffolk). The word 'lark' is also intriguingly close to the Middle English word *laik*, meaning to play or fool around, and there is a possibility that the two words are connected. The expression 'larking about' may derive from the behaviour of fighting Skylarks (see Chapter 5), but it may be separately derived from *laik* — which also gives us the lek of the Black Grouse and the Ruff and even, via modern Danish, the construction toy Lego®. There are two collective nouns for Skylarks, an exaltation and a bevy.

Skylarks have also given their name to a number of places, such as Caerlaverock and Larkhill, and, by fictional extension, to the setting of one of the best-loved books in the English language, *Lark Rise to Candleford*, Flora Thompson's evocative account of her childhood in rural Oxfordshire at the end of the nineteenth century.

It is the Skylark's place in poetry that has won it such wide recognition. An extraordinary number of poems have been written with the Skylark as a central theme. One of the earliest poems written in readable English (by John Lyly, 1553–1606) contains the lines:

> . . . Who is't now we hear?
> None but the lark so shrill and clear
> Now at heaven's gate she claps her wings
> The morn not waking till she sings

This perhaps set the trend for many of the early poets who wrongly ascribed the song they sought to describe to the female.

A recent anthology contains over 150 items of poetry and prose written in praise of the Skylark (Beer 1995), and this compilation is far from comprehensive. The anthology contains writings by a remarkably wide range of authors. How many other thematic anthologies could bring together the writings of Theocritus, Shakespeare, Siegfried Sassoon and Enid Blyton? An earlier collection of bird-related poetry, Robinson's *The Poets' Birds* of 1883, devotes nearly 30 pages to the Skylark, more than to any other species. Robinson classified the classical poetry on the species into four groups, those extolling 'the morning lark', those celebrating 'the merry lark', those describing 'the soaring lark' and those concentrating on 'the low-roosted lark' (a lark in descending song flight). He also pointed out the high proportion of poems that describe the song of the Skylark as a religious outpouring. To these can perhaps now be added the lark as emblem of freedom, as emblem of the countryside, and even the lark as emblem of hope in war (my favourite in Stewart Beer's anthology is the poignant 'Shelley in the Trenches' by John William Streets, who died in 1916). One of the better known of the Skylark poems, Meredith's 'The Lark Ascending', provided the inspiration for Vaughan Williams' orchestral piece of the same name, one of the surprisingly few musical tributes to the species.

It is well beyond the scope of this book (and the ability of its author) to offer anything more than a passing mention of this huge body of artistic endeavour. However it is worth mentioning one poet who stands out from the rest in two ways.

During his troubled life (many of his poems were written in Northampton Asylum, where he was confined for much of his life), John Clare (Figure 13.1) not only wrote an unusually large number of poems with the Skylark as a major theme, but he also knew the bird far better than any other poet. His poems clearly show that he was intimately familiar with the Skylark as a part of the living landscape rather than just as a poetic metaphor, though like most other poets of the time he thought

*Figure 13.1.    A portrait of John Clare (1793–1864), by William Hilton (1786–1893). During his troubled life, Clare wrote a number of poems about Skylarks. His intimate knowledge of the Skylark sets Clare apart from the multitude of other poets who have eulogised the species. Reproduced with permission of the National Portrait Gallery, London.*

it was the female who sang. Poems such as that at the head of Chapter 6 display a profound knowledge of the species that borders on the scientific. Other poems by Clare describe examples of behaviour that would only become apparent with many hours of keen and critical observation, no doubt made during his childhood in rural Northamptonshire.

Clare's poems certainly contain more detailed information on the species' behaviour than some of the early 'scientific' ornithological treatises. For example, Eleazar Albin, in his *Natural History of Birds* (1731–38), does not even mention the song flight, concentrating instead on giving advice on how to keep birds in captivity. Despite his humble origins and lack of formal education, John Clare was perhaps the first person really to study and record the intimate details of the Skylark's natural history.

## INTRODUCED POPULATIONS

It was the beauty of the Skylark's song and its insectivorous habits, rather than the taste of its flesh, that stimulated the introduction of the species to parts of the world well outside its native range. These introductions have resulted in the successful establishment of populations in Australia, New Zealand, Canada and even the Hawaiian Islands. Skylarks were first introduced to southern Australia in 1850, and to New Zealand in 1864. The New Zealand introductions have been chronicled in Lamb's (1964) book about the North Canterbury Acclimatisation Society. Releases in New Zealand of Skylarks and other European bird species were organised largely by the Acclimatisation Societies, in an effort to make British settlers moving abroad feel more at home, to recreate a piece of England in another hemisphere. In New Zealand, however, a greater need was for the biological control of crop pest populations, which, following the destruction and removal of many of their natural predators, reached plague proportions. Indeed, several of the Acclimatisation Societies in New Zealand were formed as sections of Agricultural Societies.

The Societies recognised three characteristics of desirable species to introduce: they should be omnivorous, to enable them to overwinter when one or the other food source was unavailable; they should be non-migratory, to avoid their all disappearing and possibly not returning; and they should be prolific breeders. The Skylark clearly fitted all these criteria. At first, success rates were very low, as most birds died on passage, particularly when passing through the tropics. All the 66 Skylarks sent out on the steamer *British Empire* in 1864 perished on board during the three-month journey. Three years later, the *Matoaka* arrived in Canterbury with 13 surviving Skylarks, which were put on sale on condition they be liberated immediately, and in the same year the Auckland and Nelson Acclimatisation Societies also started to import Skylarks. In 1872, the *Charlotte Gladstone* arrived in Christchurch with a consignment of 1,000 birds bound for the Acclimatisation Society's aviaries. Although none of these were Skylarks, it was discovered that one of the stewards on board had brought five larks with him, for which he received the handsome payment of £1 each. The Society employed the services of one Richard Bills, a bird-catcher who, over a period of years, exported many thousands of birds to New Zealand. How and where Skylarks were first permanently established as breeding birds in New Zealand is unclear, although it is likely to have been somewhere on the Canterbury Plains, where the species still flourishes in very large numbers.

The Skylark was introduced to the Hawaiian Archipelago from England in 1865 and from the introduced New Zealand population in 1870. It became established on all islands, but has subsequently disappeared from Kauai and possibly from Oahu (Campbell *et al.* 1997a). The current population probably exceeds 10,000 birds.

The last of the successful introductions was to western Canada, where several hundred English birds of the nominate subspecies *A. a. arvensis* were released in a series of importations between 1903 and 1919. In 1903, the British Colombia Natural History Society, with financial support from the provincial government and local residents, imported and released 100 pairs of Skylark. In 1913, an additional 49 birds were released. Six more birds were released in 1919. The first census of the new Vancouver Island population, carried out in 1935, found 219 Skylarks at nine different locations on the Saanich Peninsula at the southeastern tip of the island. A series of mild winters and the clearance of forests allowed the species to proliferate, and by the 1950s birds appeared to have occupied all suitable habitats on the island. A second census of Vancouver Island in 1962 recorded 694 Skylarks, and in 1965 around 1,000 Skylarks were present. Birds colonised nearby San Juan Island (Washington State, USA), some 18 km east of Vancouver Island, in 1960, and by the 1980s the Skylark was considered a locally common breeding resident there, though it has now declined to very low numbers and is likely to disappear in the near future. Since the 1980s, the Vancouver Island population has also greatly declined, largely because of loss of habitat through urban encroachment, and there are fears that it may soon become extinct (Campbell *et al.* 1997a). Current efforts are being made by the Victoria International Airport Authority (on whose land much of the remaining population survives) and the Victoria Natural History Society to manage remaining habitats for Skylarks. Introductions have been attempted in many other parts of North America, including Delaware, Ohio, New York, California, Oregon, Quebec, Massachusetts, New Jersey, Michigan and Montana, but these all proved unsuccessful. The single success of the Vancouver introductions might be due to the fact that temperature and rainfall on Vancouver Island are more similar to that of the native range of the subspecies that was imported.

The introduced populations of Skylarks in Australia, New Zealand and Canada clearly became very important to many of the residents of these countries, evoking strong passions in those who had (or often had not) chosen to leave Britain. A family reference book of 1861 (compiled by S.O. Beeton, husband of the famous cookery writer) describes the arrival of an English Skylark in a tough gold-mining community in Australia:

It was on a Tuesday when they arrived, and the next morning the lark was hung outside the tent, and at once commenced piping up. The effect was electric. Sturdy diggers—big men with hairy faces and great brown hands—paused in the midst of their work, and listened reverently. Drunken, brutal diggers left unfinished the blasphemous sentence, and looked bewildered and ashamed. Far and near the news spread like lightning—"Have you heard the lark?" "Is it true, mate, that there is a real English skylark up at Jack Wilsted's?"

So it went on for three days, and then came Sunday morning. Such a sight had not been seen since the first spadefull of the golden earth had been turned! From every quarter, from far off hills and from creeks twenty miles away, came a steady concourse of great rough Englishmen, all brushed and washed as decent as possible. The movement was by no means preconcerted, as was evident from the half-ashamed expression on every man's face. There they were, however, and their errand was—to hear the lark!

Nor were they disappointed. There, perched in his wood and iron pulpit, was the little minister, and, as though aware of the importance of the task before him, he plumed his crest, and, lifting up his voice, sung them a sermon infinitely more effective than the bishop himself could have preached. It was a wonderful sight to see that three or four hundred men, some reclining on the ground, some sitting with their arms on their knees and their heads in their hands, some leaning against the trees with their eyes closed, so that they might the better fancy themselves at home and in the midst of English corn fields once more; but sitting, standing or lying, all were equally quiet and attentive, and when, after an hour's steady preaching, the lark left off, his audience soberly started off, a little low-spirited perhaps, but on the whole much happier than when they came.

"I say, Joe", one digger was heard to say to another, "do you think that Wilsted would sell him,—the bird, you know; I'll give as much gold-dust for him as he weighs, and think him cheap."

"Sell him, be blowed!" was the indignant response; "how would you like a feller to come to our village at home and make a bid for our parson?"

While such accounts are likely to be greatly embellished, it is clear that nostalgia for the sights and sounds of the British countryside ran deep in expatriate communities, at least initially. The establishment of a breeding population of Skylarks in New Zealand was, at first, greeted with huge enthusiasm: "a ride through the country area awakened many recollections, and travellers stopped frequently to watch larks as they soared on high, pouring forth volumes of song, ample appreciation of this their new home" (McDowall 1994). Initial enthusiasm waned, however, when farmers began to complain that Skylarks had become so numerous as to become a serious crop pest. These complaints led some Acclimatisation Societies to falsify their records to make it appear that they had not, in fact, introduced Skylarks after all! Bounties were introduced on a number of introduced species, and in only two months in 1918 Ashburton County

Council paid out £495 17s 6d in bounties on over 150,000 birds, mostly Skylarks and House Sparrows. Nevertheless, strong passions were aroused when moves were made in New Zealand to eradicate introduced species such as the Skylark to help restore native wildlife. One critic of the eradication plans wrote in the 1950s:

> We, the descendants of these early settlers, were born and reared here. The song of the skylark, blackbird and thrush, the splash of the rising trout in the river, and the roar of the red stag in the forest, all of these things we take for granted. Why? Because they were here when we were born; they are as much a part of New Zealand's environment as we are ourselves. With God's help they will remain here despite the mouthing stupidity of politicians, money greedy individuals, senseless critics and empire-building bureaucrats who, to suit their own selfish purposes, would label many animals 'noxious' to our way of life, a term that if applied in its true sense . . . should include these self-same individuals (McDowall 1994).

In the very severe winter of 1969, local inhabitants supplied the introduced population of Skylarks on Vancouver Island with copious amounts of grain to see them through the worst of the weather, and small, privately funded introductions took place in 1953 and 1977 in areas the species had not already occupied. On Vancouver Island, conservation efforts are currently under way to prevent the dwindling Skylark population there from dying out.


## HUNTING THROUGH HISTORY


Despite its popularity as a songbird with poets and colonialists, the Skylark has been regarded as a delicacy and slaughtered for food in its millions for many centuries, as economic records indicate. Prices of Skylarks started to be recorded systematically from the reign of Edward I, due largely to the formation and strengthening of poulterers' guilds during this turbulent period. The Worshipful Company of Poulters of the City of London, whose history has been described by P.E. Jones (1965), may have been established to control prices of birds sent to London markets. This guild regularly published official prices to prevent 'forestalling', the purchase by middlemen of dead birds on their way to market and the inflation of their prices (Table 13.1).

Comparison of these prices with those charged for other birds indicates that a dozen Skylarks would cost around the same as one Mallard, and one could obtain around a hundred larks for the price of one Crane or Great Bustard. These low prices suggest that during the thirteenth to sixteenth centuries Skylarks were regarded more as a staple food than as an occasional luxury. Prices of Skylarks were also controlled in the other main European centre of lark consumption, Leipzig, "whose Larks are famous all over Germany, as having the most delicate flavour", and

*Table 13.1. Rated prices of Skylarks, 1274–1633, from Jones (1965) and other sources. These were maximum prices, and birds were often available more cheaply. All Saints, Allhallows and Hollantide all denote 1 November; Bartholemewtide is 24 August.*

| Year | Price per dozen | Notes |
| --- | --- | --- |
| 1274 | 1d | |
| 1363 | 3d | |
| 1370 | 3d | |
| 1388 | 3d | |
| 1393 | 2d | |
| 1425 | 4d | |
| 1507 | 4d | |
| 1512 | 4d | |
| 1517 | 4d | |
| 1521 | 4d–5d | 4d Easter to All Saints, 5d All Saints to Shrovetide |
| 1535 | 4d | |
| 1537 | 5d–8d | |
| 1538 | 3d–5d | 3d 'mean', 5d 'best' |
| 1541 | 6d | |
| 1559 | 6d–8d | 6d Michaelmas to Allhallows, 8d Allhallows to Shrovetide |
| 1571 | 7d–9d | 7d in the markets, 9d in the poulters' shops |
| 1572 | 6d–8d | 6d in the markets, 8d in the poulters' shops |
| 1575 | 4d–6d | 4d Bartholomewtide to Hollantide, 6d Hollantide to Shrovetide |
| 1633 | 10d | |

where the excise on sales of Skylarks alone raised 6,000 dollars (around £50,000 in today's terms) each year during the late eighteenth century.

Over the centuries, mankind has developed a huge number of techniques for catching larks. The most frequently used method of catching Skylarks for food was to flush birds into a 'night-lark-net', or trammel, a net around 20 m wide and braced by poles along each edge that was dropped onto the sleeping birds. This method was apparently ineffective on bright, moonlit nights and required absolute darkness, when up to 400 birds could be caught each night. A variant of this method was called 'low-belling', in which the net was preceded by men wearing or tolling bells similar to those worn by cattle, which apparently caused the birds to remain on the ground until the net was over them. The method probably relied on the birds mistaking the sound of approaching footsteps for cows wearing bells, a sound familiar to them and not threatening. This method of catching Skylarks was so highly valued in the sixteenth century that it was restricted to the owners of the land it was practised on, and the 'right to go with low-bell' was often specifically included in legal documents relating to land tenure.

Not all methods of catching Skylarks were so economical. One method, depicted around 1640 by the painter of hunting scenes Wolfgang Birkner (Figure 13.2), was so heavy in costs of manpower and materials that it was reserved for princes. A series of eight parallel nets, each 200 m long, was set in a field where large numbers

*Figure 13.2.   A Skylark hunting scene completed around 1640 by Wolfgang Birkner. A large num-
ber of people dragged ropes across a field towards a series of parallel nets.*

of Skylarks were known to roost. The nets were placed increasingly far apart, such
that the first two nets were 6 m apart, the last two 9 m apart. Long lines of people,
dragging ropes between them, drove the larks into the nets. The timing of the
drives was apparently very important, and the first big drives were not started until
the first stars had started to show, particularly a medium-sized star low on the
southern horizon known as the 'Lark Star'. One or two thousand larks were
considered a normal nightly catch using this method (Bub 1991).

The vast numbers of Skylarks captured in southern England to supply the
London meat markets were caught largely by dragging nets over fields at night
and by using double clap-nets during the day. Two men were required for drag-
netting at night, one at each end of the net to keep it taut. The net was held
at approximately 45 degrees, the rear end of the net dragging along the ground.
As soon as a lark was flushed, the net would be dropped and the bird removed.
The method was successful because flushed larks invariably try to rise vertically,
causing them to hit the net.

Double clap-nets, still used in France for catching Skylarks for food, and in
Belgium for ringing, resemble a pair of double doors opened and placed flat on
the ground. In the space between bait might be scattered, or a live decoy bird
tethered. As larks pass overhead, the hunter pulls on the string holding the
decoy bird, causing it to flap around. Any birds attracted to the decoy are
caught when the pull of a string causes the doors to flip up and over them.
Other bird-catchers preferred setting snares, usually made of horsehair, to entan-
gle the legs of birds attracted to bait. A less common method was to use birds
of prey, particularly the Hobby, to prevent Skylarks from taking flight and so
make easier their capture by nets. The Hobbies themselves were initially caught
by coating bound Skylarks with twigs smeared with birdlime and encouraging

the Hobby to strike at them, so becoming entangled. All these methods were in use at least as early as the 1770s, since all are described in *The Sportsman's Dictionary; or, The Gentleman's Companion* of 1778.

Large numbers of migrating Skylarks were also shot in Victorian England, more for sport than for food, since arriving migrants, the main quarry of the shooters, were lean and in poor condition after their long journey. Birds were attracted to the field during the day either by use of live decoys or by using a 'lark mirror' or 'lark glass'. Lark mirrors have a fascinating history that stretches back to at least 1583. Herman Arentsen and Natalino Fenech have described this history in great detail in their unpublished manuscript *Lark Mirrors: folk art from the past*. Lark mirrors were widely used throughout Europe and Asia, and particularly in France and Italy, where they were manufactured industrially during the nineteenth and twentieth centuries. In France, they were sufficiently familiar to have entered common idiom, a *miroir aux alouettes* meaning an illusion, and *alouettes au miroir* meaning a strong but dangerous attraction, something rather like 'moths to a flame'.

Lark mirrors came in many shapes and designs, but the most popular was a rectangular block of wood about 30 to 50 cm long and inset with small mirrors or pieces of glass (Figure 13.3). When migrating Skylarks were passing over (mirrors were only used at migration times), the hunter would pull on a string, or rely on a clockwork motor, to spin the mirror rapidly. The patterns of reflected light this produced seem to have proved fatally attractive to migrating birds (though not, apparently, to resident birds). In a detailed description of Skylark hunting in the

A LARK-GLASS.

*Figure 13.3. A Skylark mirror, or lark glass. From Rowley (1877).*

nineteenth century, A.E. Knox, in his book *Ornithological Rambles in Sussex* (1850), described how "the reflection of the sun's rays from these little revolving mirrors seems to possess a mysterious attraction for the larks, for they descend in great numbers from a considerable height in the air, hover over the spot, and suffer themselves to be shot at repeatedly without attempting to leave the field or to continue their course". This was a popular sport, though much frowned upon by purists such as Knox, and a single field could hold up to five lark mirrors, each with as many guns covering it. However, "notwithstanding the crowd, and the noise of voices mingled with the continual roar of guns, the infatuated birds advance stupidly to their doom, hover in numbers over the decoy, and present the easiest possible mark to the veriest tyro that ever pulled a trigger". The scathing tone of Knox's description of hunting with lark mirrors suggests that this method was the preserve of the wealthy arriviste:

> Presently a voice exclaims "Here they are, look out!" and a cluster of dark specks becomes visible at a great distance. In a few moments he perceives that this is a flock of larks: but surely it is not possible that they will notice that miserable toy which is now spinning rapidly, urged by the frantic exertions of a gentleman in bright yellow gaiters and brand-new shooting coat, crossed with a virgin shot belt, who pulls the string violently with one hand, while with the other he wields his full-cocked gun as carelessly as if it were a shillelagh! He is mistaken: they suddenly descend with rapidly closed pinions, to within a few yards of the very spot where he stands, or perhaps to a rival lure in the same or in an adjoining field, and, hovering over it in apparent delight and admiration, patiently suffer themselves to be shot at and massacred in considerable numbers.

The French hunter Reymond, writing in 1882, was a keen user of lark mirrors:

> When the passage of larks is abundant and the larks are animated with this goodwill to pitch upon the mirror, one should have a wheelbarrow full of cartridges — one can shoot all morning having trouble to load the gun, the barrels scorching the fingers. One finished by being deaf; the eyes are dazed, and, although seated quietly on a mound of turf or on a folding seat, the perspiration courses down the face as if taking violent exercise. The slain scattered on the ground, the feathers flying on all sides — this is a scene full of pleasure and animation which would cheer up an Englishman attacked by the spleen.

There are records of over 1,000 Skylarks being shot at a single mirror on a single day, and the popularity of shooting larks at mirrors in Italy is well illustrated by the publication of a book on the subject in 1941, during the austerity of the Second World War. A number of contemporary scenes of shooting at mirrors are shown in Figure 13.4. Victorian accounts unconvincingly suggest that the birds are attracted because they think the flashing mirror is a fire, an owl, another Skylark or a pool of water. Nobody really knows why Skylarks find these little spinning trinkets so fatally attractive.

*Figure 13.4.    Three late nineteenth- and early twentieth-century images of hunting with lark mirrors in France. In the upper two, the hunter has employed someone to pull a string to activate the mirror; in the lower picture it is operated by clockwork. Images provided by Natalino Fenech and Herman Arentsen.*

# VICTORIAN MARKETS AND THE RISE OF PROTEST

Small numbers of larks were eaten in rural areas in the belief that their flesh was a cure for diseases affecting the throat and voice, and parents in Belgium believed that if the first meat their children ate was a Skylark, they would grow up to be God-fearing. In Italy, it was thought that eating larks cured ailments of the liver. However, the vast majority of Skylarks killed during the nineteenth century were destined for consumption by wealthy gourmands.

Protest at the killing of vast numbers of Skylarks for food dates back well before the establishment of the Victorian conservation societies. In 1826, Thomas Bewick, in his popular *A History of British Birds*, added as a footnote to his account of the Skylark:

> We must here dismiss the disgusting task of noting the edible qualities of these tiny creatures, the ornament of our fields, our gardens, and groves; nor can we help regarding their destruction for the purposes of gormandism, as not a little reproachful to humanity, in countries abounding with every species of food fit for the use of man.

At this time, however, the fashion amongst the rich for eating Skylarks was only in its infancy. The Wild Birds Protection Act of 1881 prohibited the capture or killing of Skylarks during the close season, which in most counties ran from March to August, the penalty for breaking this law being up to £1 per bird. In 1884, protection was extended to the eggs of the Skylark in a small number of counties, the penalty again being up to £1 per egg. In 1886, the penalty for taking Skylarks during the close season was increased to include the forfeit of any traps or snares used. Skylarks were protected throughout the year in a small number of counties that applied for such protection (including parts of Essex, London, Middlesex and the boroughs of Kingston-upon-Hull, Middlesborough, South Shields and Cardiff). But there was nothing to prevent the wholesale capture of the vast numbers of Skylarks arriving in Britain from the Continent in autumn, or of the massive immigrations of birds from the Low Countries during hard weather. These were the targets of the bird-catchers, and it was these birds that met the growing demand from the London markets, for cagebirds, meat and the feather industry (which used to dye the wing feathers to imitate those of exotic species).

Skylark hunting was carried out mostly in southeast England, particularly along the Sussex coast around Brighton, in the Home Counties and in Cambridgeshire and Lincolnshire. Skylarks were taken in southern England to supply not only the London market, but also the *Halles* market in Paris, where in the 1830s nearly a million Skylarks were sold each year. This trade was centred on the port of Brighton, and many of the birds supplied to Paris markets were trapped on the nearby Sussex Downs. Skylarks have long been considered a delicacy in France, and the popular children's song '*Alouette, gentille alouette*' is little more than a list of the parts of the Skylark's body the singer is going to pluck before eating it. In the winter of 1867–68, an estimated 1,255,500 Skylarks were brought to markets in Dieppe alone (Pycraft 1911).

A high proportion of the Skylarks sent to the London markets were captured in a small area of the Dunstable Downs in Bedfordshire, largely because the area had free access, allowing the lark catchers to work unhindered. Larks caught in this area were considered to be of the very finest quality, and Dunstable Larks appeared on the menus of many of the most fashionable London restaurants. At one site near Dunstable, nearly 50,000 birds were captured during the course of a single winter to supply the London markets. The fate of the birds depended upon the current price for birds. When prices were high, both males and females were sent live to London, but when prices were low the males alone were sent alive for the more lucrative cagebird market (in the 1850s a good male Skylark could fetch up to 15 shillings), while the females were killed for the poulterer.

Henry Mayhew's book *London Labour and the London Poor*, first published in 1851, provides a unique eyewitness account of the London bird markets. Mayhew distinguishes in his account between Skylarks taken for the cagebird industry and those sent, already dead, to Leadenhall Market:

> The yearly 'take' of larks is 60,000. This includes sky-larks, wood-larks, tit-larks and mud-larks. The sky-lark is in far better demand than any of the others for his 'stoutness of song', but some prefer the tit-lark, for the very absence of such stoutness. 'Fresh-catched' larks are vended in the streets at 6*d*. and 8*d*., but a seasoned bird is worth 2*s*. 6*d*. One tenth is the street-sale. The larks for the supply of fashionable tables are never provided by the London bird-catchers, who catch only 'singing larks,' for the shop and street-traffic. The edible larks used to be highly esteemed in pies, but they are now generally roasted for consumption. They are principally the produce of Cambridgeshire, with some from Bedfordshire, and are sent direct (killed) to Leadenhall-market, where about 215,000 are sold yearly, being nearly two-thirds of the gross London consumption.

Birds awaiting sale as songbirds were often kept in appalling conditions. One eyewitness wrote in the 1860s:

> Almost daily I pass a shop in Old-street, St Luke's, and there, exhibited in the open window, may always be seen a sight loathsome and sickening. Store-cage packed on store-cage, and each one literally crammed with birds of various kinds, larks, linnets, thrushes &c. To say the least, each cage is half-full of birds, so that they perch on each other's backs, while, at the same time, the cages themselves are as filthy and disgusting as can be imagined. I wonder what prevents the officers of the Society for the Prevention of Cruelty to Animals from giving the bird dealer in question a call.

The situation had clearly not improved by 1920, when the RSPB's publication *Bird Notes & News* drew attention to the plight of Skylarks "destined for the bird markets of big towns, such as the disgraceful one in Sclater Street, E., where they may, if they live, be sold from street stalls into a life whose chief advantage is that it will probably not last long".

The fashion for eating Skylarks had not yet reached its height when Mayhew was writing around 1850, and the numbers sent to the London markets increased greatly in the 50 years following the publication of his book. In 1854, the number of Skylarks reaching the London Meat Markets had already almost doubled to 400,000 (Pycraft 1911). Early efforts to protect the Skylark provide an interesting insight into the way the fledgling British bird conservation movement mobilised its resources and its influence. The initiative was taken by the Society for the Protection of Birds (SPB), founded in Didsbury, Manchester, in 1891. In 1904 the SPB received Royal Charter and became the RSPB, now Europe's largest conservation organisation. The plight of the Skylark formed one of the main thrusts of this organisation's early work, and the species appeared frequently in the pages of the Society's quarterly publication *Bird Notes & News*, from which many of the following quotations are taken. As early as 1897, the SPB produced a leaflet on the Skylark and its plight, Number 22 in its *Educational Series* (Figure 13.5).

The SPB developed a number of strategies both to secure legal protection for Skylarks and to encourage public protest at the continued slaughter. Calls for an end to the killing played simultaneously upon people's sense of moral repugnance and upon the importance of Skylarks in controlling the numbers of agriculturally harmful insects. One of the leading lights in the early SPB, Edith Carrington (whose writings appeared in the *Reprints of the Humanitarian League*), wrote that "a London shop-front recently exhibited the painful sight of festoons of larks, with the notice attached, 'Special order, ten thousand larks, one and sixpence a dozen'." *The Star* newspaper investigated the trade in 1894, and sent a reporter to Leadenhall Market. On asking the chief salesman how many birds arrived each week, he was told "I have seen truck after truck on the Great Eastern loaded with nothing but larks". This mass slaughter of Skylarks for food in Victorian England evoked passions amongst members of the early conservation movement the likes of which had rarely been aroused before. William Henry Hudson (1841–1922), a leading figure in the early SPB (and one of the few men to take an active role in this largely female organisation), spoke for many when he wrote:

> Lark-eating, which revolts us even more than wheatear eating, is, alas! too common and wide-spread in the country to be suppressed. . . It will not soon be ended—there are too many Britons with the Italian's debased passion for a song-bird's flesh. But the feelings of intense disgust and even abhorrence the practice arouses in all lovers of nature grows, and will continue to grow; and we can look forward to the time when the feeders on Skylarks of today will be dead and themselves eaten by worms, and will have no successors in all these islands.

**Society for the Protection of Birds.**

EDUCATIONAL SERIES. Edited by H. E. DRESSER, F.L.S., F.Z.S.

## No. 22.—SKYLARK.

By FLORENCE ANNA FULCHER.

SKYLARK.

### I. Name.—SKYLARK.

Family—*Alaudidæ.*
Genus—*Alauda arvensis.*

### II. General Description.

Upper parts varied with three shades of brown, the darkest of which lies along the shaft of each feather; a faint whitish streak over the eye; throat white; under parts yellowish white tinged with brown; the throat and sides of neck with dark brown lanceolate spots, which form a gorget just above the breast. Length 7¼ inches (W. H. Hudson).

Illustration, by kind permission of Messrs. Gurney & Jackson, from "Manual of British Birds," by Mr. Howard Saunders.

*Figure 13.5.    Front cover of the SPB's educational leaflet of 1897.*

The SPB's Leaflet No. 16, published in 1900, consisted solely of a single poem, written in the style of the time by Rennell Rodd. As an interesting historical document, though not necessarily as a good example of the body of fine artistic endeavour the species has inspired, this is worth quoting in full:

## The Skylarks
### In an East End bird market

Oh, the sky, the sky, the open sky
For the home of a song-bird's heart!
And why, why and forever why
Do they stifle here in the mart?
Cages of agony, rows on rows,
Torture that only a wild thing knows:
Is it nothing to you to see
That head thrust out through the hopeless wire,
And the tiny life, and the mad desire
To be free, to be free, to be free?
Oh, the sky, the sky, the blue wide sky,
For the beat of a song-bird's wings!
And why, why, and forever why? –
Is the only song it sings.

Great sad eyes with a frightened stare,
Look through the 'wildering darkness there,
The surge, the crowd, and the cry;
Fluttering wild wings beat and bleed,
And it will not peck at the golden seed,
And the water is almost dry:
Straight and close are the cramping bars,
From the dawn of mist to the chill of stars,
And yet it must sing or die!
Will its marred hoarse life in the city street
Make any heart of you glad?
It will only beat with its wings and beat
It will only sing you mad.

Better to lie like this one, dead,
Ruffled plumage of breast and head,
Poor little feathers forever furled,
Only a song gone out of the world!
Where the grasses wave like an emerald sea,
And poppies nod in the corn,
Where the fields are wide and the winds blow free,
This joy of the spring was born,
Whose passionate music, long and loud
In the hush of the rose of morn,
Was a voice that fell from a sailing cloud
Midway to the blue above –
A thing whose meaning was joy and love,

Whose life was one exquisite outpouring
Of a sweet, surpassing note,
And all you have done is to break its wing,
And to blast God's breath in its throat!

If it does not go to your heart to see
The helpless pity of those bruised wings,
The tireless effort with which it clings
To the strain and the will to be free,
I know not how I shall set in words
The meaning of God in this,
For the loveliest things in this world of His
Are the ways and the songs of birds!
But the sky, the sky, the wide free sky,
For the home of the song-bird's heart!
And why, why, forever why
Do they stifle here in the mart?

Although too cloyingly sentimental and anthropomorphic for today's tastes, emotive outpourings like this did much to raise the plight of Skylarks in the Victorian public conscience, but the habits of the relatively few able and willing to buy Skylarks for food or as cagebirds were slow to change. In her book *Animal Rights: Political and Social Change in Britain since 1800*, Hilda Kean (1998) describes the sentiments of the early conservation movement:

The selling of larks at Leadenhall had been recorded by Henry Mayhew in the 1850s but the recent fashion for such delicacies set in train an even greater slaughter of these songbirds. By the 1890s between 20,000 and 40,000 larks were sold in the London markets alone every day. Arriving in sackfuls, these dead birds were sold wholesale to poultry and game dealers by the bushel. Their purchasers were not working people but those with money to spend on fashionable dinners with lark pudding, *mauviettes en surprise aux truffes*. Gourmands, not the hungry poor, were responsible for this slaughter. According to correspondence in *The Times*, while it was wealthy women who wore the feathered hats it was men who were fond of lark puddings, crimped cod and oysters. At this time the only meat the poor in Suffolk could find to eat was sparrow pie. Fuelled by apparent necessity, this was not the focus of the SPB's concerns; its contempt was reserved for ostentatious consumption.

To put this level of slaughter into perspective, at the lower estimate of 20,000 birds per day, a number equivalent to the entire present British population would have been consumed by Londoners in a little less than three months.

The RSPB's contempt for this rising level of destruction is well illustrated in an article published in its *Bird Notes & News* of 1912, which described how:

The birds . . . are tempted in hard weather by a spread of food, and are caught in horsehair snares, which remain set all day. There they struggle piteously through the long hours, starving in sight of the food round about, until in the evening the snarer comes round and wrings their necks. And then smart society can have *mauviettes* on the *menu*.

As the *Leeds Mercury* reported at this time, "The stomach triumphs over sentiment, and the choir of birds, whose music is the best and cheapest that the world has to offer, is thinned with the recklessness that usually obtains when there is £ s d as the reward". The RSPB's 1912 article, sparked by news that a ton and a half of Skylarks had been transported from Royston to the London food markets in a single week, concludes with an allusion to the hypocrisy of those condemning the slaughter of birds elsewhere: "Whether they [the Skylarks] are British-born or merely immigrants, England, it must be admitted, is somewhat unpleasantly weighted with a ton and a half of Skylarks on her shoulders, when she expressed natural indignation at the export of her songbirds and at the terrific destruction of migrants in Italy".

The 1912 article created such a public outcry that bird-catchers were forced into making excuses for their work, protesting that the birds they were killing were not, in fact, Skylarks, but some other type of lark arriving from the Continent, or claiming they were killing larks to help prevent damage to crops. In an interview with the *Daily News* in 1913 one Skylark catcher is reported as saying, "I mind snaring larks this forty year, and I never see any wrong in it. Snaring larks has put many a shilling into the pockets of a poor man when he wanted the money badly. I've earned a pound a day lark snaring easy. They're wicked, mischievous birds". A letter to the *Shooting Times* in 1903 stated, "A correspondent writes in reference to the strings of larks hanging in the poulterer's shops and laments the cruelty of killing such lovely song birds. The writer is evidently under a misapprehension, as these birds are not the English sky-lark but birds that have come over here from abroad". This excuse was used repeatedly by those opposed to a ban on the killing of Skylarks. The RSPB's response was that "the profiteer dubs himself philanthropist, and places a lively faith in public ignorance". The RSPB fought back by asking its members to write to shops and markets still selling Skylarks to protest at the practice, and to threaten to withdraw their custom pending the removal of Skylarks from their stock. By this time, and probably largely due to the RSPB's efforts, the habit of eating Skylarks was starting to go out of fashion, and many firms were only too happy to withdraw birds from sale. In 1914 the RSPB was able to announce that 'through the efforts of a member of this Society, the Committee of the Albemarle Club decided some little time since to discontinue providing Larks as an article of food at the Club'. In 1923, the Chairman of the RSPB wrote an open letter to the Incorporated Association of Retail Distributors:

The Council of the Royal Society for the Protection of Birds desire to bring to your notice the growing dislike among the public to Skylarks and other Songbirds being used for food and to the appeals which have been made to many large firms to discontinue the sale of these birds in their Poultry Departments. By some dealers difficulty with regard to acceding to this suggestion is felt, unless all firms of a similar nature are generally agreed on the subject, and we have therefore been advised to ask you if the matter could be favourably considered by your Directors, with a view to firms being affiliated to the Incorporated Association of Retail Distributors being recommended to abandon the practice of putting these birds on the market. To bird lovers, the eating of Larks is such an offence against good taste and the best kind of sentiment, that they feel compelled to refrain from making purchases at shops or stores where these birds are exposed for sale. Among others, Mr Selfridge and Sir Woodman Burbidge have expressed their desire to suppress this trade.

Later that year, the famous company of Messrs Selfridge & Co. wrote to the RSPB, "We will not allow the department to expose Larks for sale, and only supply orders which we have specially contracted to supply". The Haymarket Stores followed suit, writing to a member of the RSPB who had written a letter of complaint that "I am pleased to be able to inform you that instructions have been given for the discontinuance of the sale of Larks in the Poultry Department". In the same year the RSPB produced a postcard (available to members at 9d a dozen), bearing a picture of a Skylark by the famous artist Archibald Thorburn and a plea for a cessation of the trade, for its members to send to shops still selling Skylarks.

The Society also elicited letters of support for a ban on the Skylark trade from such luminaries as the Duchess of Portland, Earl Buxton and Sir Montagu Sharpe, who wrote "I fail to comprehend how any man who has stopped and listened to the thrilling notes of the ascending Lark can afterwards sit down and knowingly eat the bird. He might just as well feed on his canaries, and probably would not detect any difference". The following year, Harrods joined the ranks of the converted, writing to the RSPB's Chairman of the Publicity Committee "As an outcome of the requests we have received from your Society and also from some of our customers, we have now decided to entirely cease from selling these birds in any of our departments".

Interestingly, requests to Scottish firms to cease selling Skylarks received the response that the habit of eating Skylarks, or indeed any other songbird, was practically unknown in Scotland; indeed very little is recorded of the trade outside London. In Scotland the absence of a trade in dead Skylarks may have been the result of a superstition relating to the three small black spots on the tongues of chicks. Local beliefs held that eating a lark would cause three black spots matching those on the tongue of a Skylark chick to appear on the tongue of the diner, or that killing a lark would bring the perpetrator three curses. It appears that virtually the whole market for Skylarks was amongst the affluent gourmands and the 'smart set' in London.

Some of the Society's tactics may just have bordered upon the extreme. In 1914 (note the year), an anonymous 'German Friend of Birds' published a letter in the RSPB's *Bird Notes & News* expressing his or her surprise that the killing of Skylarks was still practised in England, and stating that in Germany "hardly anybody would think of killing that lovely little bird, which is a delight to see rising towards the sky

and warbling its little tune". Whether the publication of this letter on the eve of the
First World War was a deliberate attempt to shame English lark-eaters by asserting
the moral superiority of the enemy in such matters will never be known, but the
timing and anonymity of the letter is intriguing. Trade in Skylarks in Germany had
been centred on the city of Leipzig, where in the middle of the nineteenth century
as many as one and a half million birds were collected in the three months from
September to November from the surrounding areas for export throughout the
world. Leipzig Skylarks had a reputation for quality that matched that of the
Dunstable Larks. However, growing public disapproval, led by the early conservation activist Friedericke Kempner, together with a freak hailstorm on 27 August
1860 that apparently wiped out most of the birds around the city, led to an almost
complete collapse of the Skylark industry there by around 1870. The memory of
the Leipzig Skylarks lives on in the form of Leipziger Lerchen, sweet biscuits
embossed with a cross, which, according to some, commemorates the millions of
birds that were killed there.

At the same time that it was trying to secure protection for the Skylark by play-
ing on the national conscience, the RSPB was also busy promoting the Skylark as
an indispensable ally of the farmer. The SPB's 1897 Educational Leaflet on the
Skylark was pragmatic in stressing not only the cultural value of the species, but
also its economic value:

> Let us consider, ere it be too late, if it be worth while to avert this threatened
> loss. It is not from a sentimental point of view only that the question of pro-
> tection for the birds must be approached, even by those who value them as
> one of nature's best modes of expressing poetic thought and beauty, and some-
> thing more that we can neither name nor fathom. Let us pass, therefore, and
> let us consider how the little creature that sings at heaven's gate is hard at work
> at earth's portal. The economic value of insectivorous birds is untold, and it is
> for its work in this direction during the winter that the Lark is so precious.

As early as 1908, scientific research into the diet of Skylarks was being undertaken with the support of the Society (Collinge 1913), possibly the earliest example of applied research being used to support a conservation campaign. This
research was summarised in the RSPB's *Bird Notes & News,* showing that Skylarks
are largely beneficial to agriculture. Economic ornithology was a subject of considerable interest at the time, and there was a regular feature under this heading in
*Bird Notes & News.* A letter by 'A Farmer' in *The Times* in 1922 asserted that
Skylarks had to be killed because of the damage they caused to crops. This was
answered by a letter to *The Times* by Dr W.E. Collinge, author of much of the
research on the diet of the species, who claimed that "50.5 per cent. of the total
food is of a neutral nature, 36.5 per cent. beneficial and only 13 per cent. injurious. The injuries are far outweighed by the benefits conferred". This same Dr
Collinge calculated that 10,000 Skylarks would, over the course of a year, consume
as many as 80 million insects, or around 27 tons of them.

Despite the wave of public condemnation stirred up by the RSPB, Skylarks continued to be killed and consumed in great numbers well into the 1920s. A letter to *The Times* of 25 February 1922 asserted "No one can pass a poulterer's shop at present without seeing piles of larks for sale. They are sometimes in boxes, sometimes strung on a string with their throats twisted. In all the stores one meets the same heaps of pathetic little corpses". The writer went on to say that in his opinion, slaughter for food was causing Skylark numbers to decline greatly in parts of southeast England. Efforts were made to increase the protection afforded to Skylarks by the existing legislation. Questions were asked in the House of Commons in 1926 and 1927 to request a ban on imports of Skylarks and to ban the exposure for sale of Skylarks during the close season. Issues relating to the legal protection of Skylarks rumbled on well into the 1930s, although by this time the consumption of larks was no longer in fashion and keeping them in cages was illegal. Section 6 of the Wild Birds Protection Act of 1931 provided all birds with year-round protection, but certain species, including the Skylark, were exempt in certain regions if they were thought to pose a threat to agriculture. Attempts to secure year-round protection for Skylarks in Norfolk in 1934 failed because of the reluctance of farmers to relinquish the power of killing birds when they reached what were thought to be pest levels. This incident sparked considerable national debate, with headlines in the Press sympathetic to farmers blaring 'The crop destroyer', 'No protection for Skylarks' and even, in reference to the migratory nature of the species and ominous political events abroad, 'Skylarks that sing to Nazis will get no mercy here'. These sentiments stimulated some witty responses in the pro-Skylark press. Someone writing under the pseudonym 'Touchstone' wrote in rhyme to the *Morning Post* of the beneficial effect of Skylarks on agriculture:

> Post-mortems, skilfully conducted
> Have clearly shown that this is so;
> But farmers will not be instructed,
> And when they vow the lark must go
> Insects in endless ranks
> Unanimously pass a vote of thanks

In *The Guardian*, another wit, Frank Buckland, also defended 'The Undesirable Alien' in verse, concluding:

> They say that you arrive on alien wings
> To spoil the grain, and maybe it is true;
> But I can only think that there are things
> That go against the grain far more than you

Eventually, the RSPB's efforts at changing public opinion and improving protective legislation proved successful, as the exemptions were removed from subsequent versions of the 1931 act, providing Skylarks with complete legal protection.

Thus one of the first, and longest, conservation campaigns in Europe reached its successful conclusion. A fascinating aspect of this early campaign to provide protection for Skylarks is that it contained all the elements of a modern conservation campaign, comprising a mixture of popular protest, fundraising, direct action, scientifically credible research and high-level political lobbying. The Skylark can therefore be regarded as one of the battlefields upon which the early conservation movement first learned its tactics.


# EPILOGUE


A century later, and the RSPB and other conservation organisations are once again fighting to save the Skylark, this time from a far more serious threat, agricultural intensification. Hunting in Victorian England was an emotive issue, but may have had relatively little impact on Skylark populations. Agricultural intensification, on the other hand, is causing populations to crash across the whole of western Europe. Skylarks have already disappeared from much of their former range, a terrible indictment of our ability to manage our natural resources, and Rachel Carson's *Silent Spring* is no longer a science fiction but a likelihood. It is still too early to assess whether the second battle to save the Skylark will achieve the success of the first, or whether our legacy to future generations will be silent skies above lifeless fields.

# APPENDIX 1

# The world's larks

This list is drawn from Sibley & Monroe (1990), with updates from the literature (Alström 1998, Ryan *et al*. 1998, Ryan & Bloomer 1999) and recommendations for further changes by Peter Ryan and Keith Barnes, University of Cape Town (pers. comm.). Common alternative English names are given in parentheses.

| Scientific name | English name | Distribution |
|---|---|---|
| *Mirafra passerina* | Monotonous Lark | Southern Africa |
| *Mirafra cantillans* | Singing Bushlark | Northern Africa, Middle East, Asia |
| *Mirafra javanica* | Australasian Bushlark | Southern Asia, Australia |
| *Mirafra cheniana* | Melodious (Latakoo) Lark | Southern Africa |
| *Mirafra albicauda* | White-tailed Lark | Central and Eastern Africa |
| *Mirafra hova* | Madagascar (Hova) Lark | Madagascar |
| *Mirafra cordofanica* | Kordofan Lark | Central Africa |
| *Mirafra williamsi* | Williams's Lark | Kenya |
| *Mirafra pulpa* | Friedmann's Lark | Kenya and Ethiopia |
| *Mirafra hypermetra* | Red-winged Bushlark | North-east Africa |
| *Mirafra somalica* | Somali Long-billed Lark | Somalia |
| *Mirafra ashi* | Ash's Lark | Somalia |
| *Mirafra africana* | Rufous-naped Lark | Sub-Saharan Africa |
| *Mirafra sharpii* | Somali Lark | Somalia |
| *Mirafra angolensis* | Angola Lark | Southern Central Africa |
| *Mirafra rufocinnamomea* | Flappet Lark | Sub-Saharan Africa |
| *Mirafra apiata* | Cape Clapper Lark | South Africa and Namibia |
| *Mirafra (apiata) marjorae* | Agulhas Clapper Lark | South Africa |
| *Mirafra (apiata) fasciolata* | Eastern Clapper Lark | Southern Africa |
| *Mirafra collaris* | Collared Lark | Ethiopia, Somalia and Kenya |
| *Mirafra africanoides** | Fawn-coloured Lark | Eastern and Southern Africa |
| *Mirafra (africanoides) alopex** | Abyssinian (Foxy) Lark | Ethiopia and Somalia |
| *Mirafra erythroptera* | Indian Bushlark | India and Pakistan |
| *Mirafra assamica* | Rufous-winged Lark (Bengal Bushlark) | Southern Asia |
| *Mirafra rufa* | Rusty Lark | Central Africa |
| *Mirafra gilletti* | Gillett's Lark | Ethiopia, Somalia and Kenya |
| *Mirafra poecilosterna** | Pink-breasted Lark | East Africa |
| *Mirafra degodiensis* | Degodi Lark | Ethiopia |
| *Mirafra marionae* | Indochinese Bushlark | South East Asia |

| Scientific name | English name | Distribution |
|---|---|---|
| *Mirafra mic     ptera* | Burmese Bushlark | Burma (Myanmar) |
| *Mirafra affinis* | Jerdon's Bushlark | India and Sri Lanka |
| *Mirafra (sabota) bradfieldi** | Bradfield's Lark | Southern Africa |
| *Mirafra sabota** | Sabota Lark | Southern Africa |
| *Pinarocorys erythropygia* | Rufous-rumped Lark | Western and Central Africa |
| *Pinarocorys nigricans* | Dusky Lark | Central and Southern Africa |
| *Heteromirafra archeri* | Archer's Lark | Somalia |
| *Heteromirafra ruddi* | Rudd's Lark | South Africa |
| *Heteromirafra sidamoensis* | Sidamo Lark | Ethiopia |
| *Certhilauda curvirostris* | Cape Long-billed Lark | South Africa |
| *Certhilauda brevirostris* | Aghulas Long-billed Lark | South Africa |
| *Certhilauda semitorquata* | Eastern Long-billed Lark | South Africa |
| *Certhilauda subcoronata* | Karoo Long-billed Lark | South Africa and Namibia |
| *Certhilauda benguelensis* | Benguela Long-billed Lark | Namibia and Angola |
| *Certhilauda chuana* | Short-clawed Lark | Southern Africa |
| *Certhilauda burra** | Red Lark | South Africa |
| *Certhilauda erythrochlamys** | Dune Lark | Namibia |
| *Certhilauda albescens** | Karoo Lark | South Africa |
| *Certhilauda barlowi** | Barlow's Lark | South Africa and Namibia |
| *Chersomanes albofasciata* | Spike-heeled Lark | Southern Africa |
| *Chersomanes (albofasciata) beesleyi* | Beesley's Lark | Tanzania |
| *Eremopterix leucotis* | Chestnut-backed Sparrow-Lark | Sub-Saharan Africa |
| *Eremopterix australis* | Black-eared Sparrow-Lark | Southern Africa |
| *Eremopterix verticalis* | Grey-backed Sparrow-Lark | Southern Africa |
| *Eremopterix leucoparia* | Fischer's Sparrow-Lark | East Africa |
| *Eremopterix signata* | Chestnut-headed Sparrow-Lark | East Africa |
| *Eremopterix nigriceps* | Black-crowned Sparrow-Lark | Northern Africa, Southern Asia |
| *Eremopterix grisea* | Ashy-crowned Sparrow-Lark | Southern Asia |
| *Ammomanes cincturus* | Bar-tailed Desert Lark | Northern Africa, Southern Asia |
| *Ammomanes deserti* | Desert Lark | Northern Africa, Southern Asia |
| *Ammomanes phoenicurus* | Rufous-tailed Lark | India |
| *Ammomanes (Ammomanopsis) greyi* | Gray's Lark | Angola and Namibia |
| *Alaemon alaudipes* | (Greater) Hoopoe-Lark | Northern Africa, Middle East |
| *Alaemon hamertoni* | Lesser Hoopoe-Lark | Somalia |

| Scientific name | English name | Distribution |
|---|---|---|
| *Rhamphocoris clot-bey* (*clotbey*) | Thick-billed Lark | North Africa, Middle East |
| *Melanocorypha calandra* | Calandra Lark | Europe, North Africa, Middle East |
| *Melanocorypha bimaculata* | Bimaculated Lark | Western and Central Asia |
| *Melanocorypha maxima* | Tibetan Lark | Central and Southern Asia |
| *Melanocorypha mongolica* | Mongolian Lark | Eastern Eurasia |
| *Melanocorypha leucoptera* | White-winged Lark | Central Eurasia |
| *Melanocorypha yeltoniensis* | Black Lark | Central Eurasia |
| *Calandrella brachydactyla* | (Greater) Short-toed Lark | Eurasia, North Africa, Middle East |
| *Calandrella blanfordi* | Blanford's Lark | Ethiopia, Somalia, Arabian Peninsula |
| *Calandrella erlangeri* | Erlanger's Lark | Ethiopia |
| *Calandrella cineria* | Red-capped Lark | Eastern and Southern Africa |
| *Calandrella acutirostris* | Hume's Lark | Southern Eurasia, Central Asia |
| *Calandrella rufescens* | Lesser Short-toed Lark | North Africa, Southern Eurasia |
| *Calandrella cheleensis* | Asian Short-toed Lark | Southern Central Asia |
| *Calandrella raytal* | Indian Short-toed Lark (Sand Lark) | Southern Eurasia |
| *Calandrella somalica* | Rufous (Somali) Short-toed Lark | Somalia and Ethiopia |
| *Calandrella* (*somalica*) *athensis* | Athi Short-toed Lark | Kenya and Tanzania |
| *Spizocorys conirostris* | Pink-billed Lark | Southern Africa |
| *Spizocorys sclateri* | Sclater's Lark | South Africa and Namibia |
| *Spizocorys obbiensis* | Obbia Lark | Somalia |
| *Spizocorys personata* | Masked Lark | Ethiopia and Kenya |
| *Spizocorys fringillaris* | Botha's Lark | South Africa |
| *Eremalauda* (*Spizocorys*) *starki* | Stark's Lark | South Africa and Namibia |
| *Eremalauda dunni* | Dunn's Lark | Northern Africa, Arabian Peninsula |
| *Chersophilus duponti* | Dupont's Lark | Iberia, North Africa |
| *Galerida cristata* | Crested Lark | Eurasia, Northern and East Africa |
| *Galerida theklae* | Thekla Lark | Southern Europe, North and East Africa |
| *Galerida malabarica* | Malabar Lark | India |
| *Galerida deva* | Tawny (Sykes's) Lark | India |
| *Galerida modesta* | Sun Lark | Sub-Saharan Africa |
| *Galerida magnirostris* | Large-billed Lark | South Africa |

| Scientific name | English name | Distribution |
|---|---|---|
| *Pseudalaemon freemantlii* | Short-tailed Lark | East Africa |
| *Lullula arborea* | Woodlark | Western Eurasia |
| *Alauda arvensis* | Skylark | Europe, Central Asia, North Africa |
| *Alauda gulgula* | Oriental (Small) Skylark | Southern and South East Asia |
| *Alauda (arvensis) japonica* | Japanese Skylark | Eastern Asia, Japan |
| *Alauda razae* | Raso Lark | Cape Verde |
| *Eremophila alpestris* | Horned (Shore) Lark | North America, Colombia, Europe, Asia, North Africa |
| *Eremophila bilopha* | Temminck's Horned Lark | North Africa, Middle East |

* it has been suggested by Peter Ryan and others that the species marked with an asterisk should be placed in a new genus, tentatively called *Calendulauda*.

# APPENDIX 2

# Scientific names of plants and animals mentioned in the text

PLANTS

| | |
|---|---|
| Black-bindweed | *Fallopia convolvulus* |
| Cornflower | *Centauria cyanus* |
| Fat-hen | *Chenopodium album* |
| Knotgrass | *Polygonum aviculare* |

INVERTEBRATES

| | |
|---|---|
| Devil's Coach Horse | *Staphylinus olens* |

MAMMALS AND REPTILES

| | |
|---|---|
| Aardvark | *Orycteropus afer* |
| Badger | *Meles meles* |
| Brown Hare | *Lepus europaeus* |
| Brown Rat | *Rattus norvegicus* |
| Cape Verde Giant Gecko | *Tarentola gigas* |
| Grass Snake | *Natrix natrix* |
| Grey Squirrel | *Sciurus carolinensis* |
| Hedgehog | *Erinaceus europaeus* |
| Racoon Dog | *Nyctereutes procyonoides* |
| Red Fox | *Vulpes vulpes* |
| Stoat | *Mustela erminea* |
| Weasel | *Mustela nivalis* |
| Wild Boar | *Sus scrofa* |

BIRDS

| | |
|---|---|
| Arctic Warbler | *Phylloscopus borealis* |
| Australasian Harrier | *Circus approximans* |
| Australasian Magpie | *Gymnorhina tibicen* |
| Black Grouse | *Tetreo tetrix* |
| Blackcap | *Sylvia atricapilla* |
| Bobolink | *Dolichonyx oryzivorus* |

BIRDS *CONT.*

| | |
|---|---|
| Booted Eagle | *Hieraaetus pennatus* |
| Broad-billed Sandpiper | *Limicola falcinellus* |
| Brown-headed Cowbird | *Molothrus afer* |
| Buzzard | *Buteo buteo* |
| Carrion Crow | *Corvus corone* |
| Cirl Bunting | *Emberiza cirlus* |
| Cloud-scraping Cisticola | *Cisticola dambo* |
| Common Tern | *Sterna hirundo* |
| Corn Bunting | *Miliaria calandra* |
| Crane | *Grus grus* |
| Cuckoo | *Cuculus canorus* |
| Curlew | *Numenius arquata* |
| Eleonora's Falcon | *Falco eleonorae* |
| Goldcrest | *Regulus regulus* |
| Golden Eagle | *Aquila chrysaetos* |
| Great Grey Shrike | *Lanius excubitor* |
| Greenshank | *Tringa nebularia* |
| [Grey] Heron | *Ardea cinerea* |
| Grey Partridge | *Perdix perdix* |
| Hen Harrier | *Circus cyaneus* |
| Hobby | *Falco subbuteo* |
| House Sparrow | *Passer domesticus* |
| Kestrel | *Falco tinnunculus* |
| Lammergeier | *Gypaetus barbatus* |
| Lapland Bunting | *Calcarius lapponicus* |
| Lapwing | *Vanellus vanellus* |
| Lesser Spotted Eagle | *Aquila pomarina* |
| Linnet | *Carduelis cannabina* |
| Little Owl | *Athene noctua* |
| Little Ringed Plover | *Charadrius dubius* |
| Magpie | *Pica pica* |
| Mallard | *Anas platyrhynchos* |
| Marsh Harrier | *Circus aeruginosus* |
| Marsh Warbler | *Acrocephalus palustris* |
| Meadow Pipit | *Anthus pratensis* |
| Merlin | *Falco columbarius* |
| Montagu's Harrier | *Circus pygargus* |
| Nightingale | *Luscinia megarhynchos* |
| Oystercatcher | *Haematopus ostralegus* |
| Pacific Golden Plover | *Pluvialis fulva* |
| Passenger Pigeon | *Ectopistes migratorius* |
| Peregrine | *Falco peregrinus* |
| Quail | *Coturnix coturnix* |
| Raven | *Corvus corax* |
| Red-billed Quelea | *Quelea quelea* |
| Redshank | *Tringa totanus* |
| Redstart | *Phoenicurus phoenicurus* |

| Reed Bunting | *Emberiza schoeniclus* |
|---|---|
| Richard's Pipit | *Anthus richardi* |
| Ruff | *Philomachus pugnax* |
| Shelduck | *Tadorna tadorna* |
| Snipe | *Gallinago gallinago* |
| Song Thrush | *Turdus philomelos* |
| Sparrowhawk | *Accipiter nisus* |
| Spotted Redshank | *Tringa erythropus* |
| Swallow | *Hirundo rustica* |
| Tree Pipit | *Anthus trivialis* |
| Tree Sparrow | *Passer montanus* |
| Whimbrel | *Numenius phaeopus* |
| Wood Warbler | *Phylloscopus sibilatrix* |
| Woodcock | *Scolopax rusticola* |
| Woodpigeon | *Columba palumbus* |
| Yellowhammer | *Emberiza citrinella* |

# Bibliography

AEBISCHER, N.J., GREEN, R.E. & EVANS, A.D. (2000) From science to recovery: four case studies of how research has been translated into conservation action in the UK. In: Aebischer, N.J., Evans, A.D., Grice, P.V. & Vickery, J.A. (eds) *Ecology and Conservation of Lowland Farmland Birds*, 43–54. BOU, Tring.

AFIK, D., WARD, D. & SHKEDY, Y. (1991) A test of the self-incubation hypothesis for desert birds that build a rampart of stones in front of their nests. *Journal of Thermal Biology*, 16: 255–260.

AHAS, R. (1999) Long-term phyto-, ornitho- and ichthyophenological time-series analyses in Estonia. *International Journal of Biometeorology*, 42: 119–123.

ALBIN, E. (1731–38) *A Natural History of Birds*. 3 vols. W. Innys, London.

ALDER, L.P. (1982) Feeding behaviour of Skylarks in hard winters. *British Birds*, 75: 33.

ALSTRÖM, P. (1998) Taxonomy of the *Mirafra assamica* complex. *Forktail*, 13: 97–107.

ANDREW, D.G. (1952) Flock of Skylarks singing on ground. *British Birds*, 45: 408–409.

ANON. (1778) *The Sportsman's Dictionary; or, The Gentleman's Companion*. Fielding & Walker, London.

AUBIN, T. (1982) Habituation to territorial song in the skylark (*Alauda arvensis* L.): diversity and monotony. *Biology of Behaviour*, 7: 353–362.

AUBIN, T. & BREMOND, J.-C. (1983) The process of species-specific song recognition in the skylark: an experimental study by means of synthesis. *Zeitschrift für Tierpsychologie*, 61: 141–152.

AUNINŠ, A., PETERSEN, B.S., PRIEDNIEKS, J. & PRINS, E. (2001) Relationships between birds and habitats in Latvian farmland. *Acta Ornithologica*, 36: 55–64.

BAICICH, P.J., HEINL, S.C. & TOOCHIN, M. (1996) First documented breeding of the Eurasian skylark in Alaska. *Western Birds*, 27: 86–88.

BARBIER, L. (2001) Elements for a Skylark *Alauda arvensis* management plan. *Game and Wildlife Science*, 18: 45–83.

BARKER, F.K., BARROWCLOUGH, G.F. & GROTH, J.G. (2002) A phylogenetic hypothesis for passerine birds: taxonomic and biogeographic implications of an analysis of nuclear DNA sequence data. *Proceedings of the Royal Society of London (B)*, 269: 295–308.

BARNES, K. (ED) (2000) *The Eskom Red Data Book of Birds of South Africa, Lesotho and Swaziland*. BirdLife South Africa, Johannesburg.

BARR, C.J. & PARR, T.W. (1996) Hedgerows: linking ecological research and countryside policy. In: Watt, T.A. & Buckley, G.P. (eds) *Hedgerow Management and Nature Conservation*, 119–136. Wye College Press, Wye.

BARRETT, J.H. (1966) Symmetrical albinism in a Skylark. *Bulletin of the BOC*, 86: 124.

BAUER, H.-G. & RANFTL, H. (1996) Die Natzung Überwinternder Stoppelbrachen durch Vögel. *Ornithologischer Anzeiger*, 35: 127–144.

BAXTER, E.V. & RINTOUL, L.J. (1953) *The Birds of Scotland: their History, Distribution and Migration*. Oliver & Boyd, Edinburgh.

BEER, S. (1995) *An Exaltation of Skylarks*. SMH Books, Pulborough.

BEETON, S.O. (ED) (1861) *Beeton's Book of Home Pets*. S.O. Beeton, London.

BEWICK, T. (1826) *A History of British Birds*. Newcastle.

BIRDLIFE INTERNATIONAL (2000) *Threatened Birds of the World*. Lynx Edicious, Barcelona and BirdLife International, Cambridge.

BIRDLIFE INTERNATIONAL/EUROPEAN BIRD CENSUS COUNCIL (2000) *European Bird Populations: Estimates and Trends*. BirdLife Conservation Series 10. BirdLife International, Cambridge.

BIRKHEAD, T. (2000) *Promiscuity; an evolutionary history of sperm competition and sexual conflict*. Faber and Faber, London.

BISHOP, M.C. (1990) *Legio V Alaudae* and the crested lark. *Journal of Roman Military Equipment Studies*, 1: 161–164.

BOYER, H.J. (1988) Breeding biology of the Dune Lark. *Ostrich*, 59: 30–37.

BOYLE, R. (1662) *New Experiments, Physico-Mechanical*. Thomas Robinson, London.

BRACKENBURY, J.H. (1978) A possible relationship between respiratory movements, syringeal movements and the production of song by skylarks *Alauda arvensis*. *Ibis*, 120: 526–529.

BROWN, A.F. & ATKINSON, P.W. (1996) Habitat associations of coastal wintering passerines. *Bird Study*, 43: 188–200.

BROWN, A.F. & STILLMAN, R.A. (1993) Bird–habitat associations in the eastern Highlands of Scotland. *Journal of Applied Ecology*, 30: 31–42.

BROWN, A.J. (1986) Hour long song flight by skylark. *British Birds*, 79: 136.

BROWN, J.S., KOTLER, B.P. & MITCHELL, W.A. (1997) Competition between birds and mammals: a comparison of giving-up densities between crested larks and gerbils. *Evolutionary Ecology*, 11: 757–771.

BROWNE, S.J., VICKERY, J.A. & CHAMBERLAIN, D.E. (2000) Densities and population estimates of breeding Skylarks *Alauda arvensis* in Britain in 1997. *Bird Study*, 47: 52–65.

BUB, H. (1991) *Bird trapping and bird banding: a handbook for trapping methods all over the world*. Cornell University Press, Ithaca.

BUCKINGHAM, D.L. (2001) Within-field habitat selection by wintering skylarks *Alauda arvensis* in southwest England. In: Donald, P.F. & Vickery, J.A. (eds) *The Ecology and Conservation of Skylarks* Alauda arvensis, 149–158. RSPB, Sandy.

BUCKINGHAM, D.L., EVANS, A.D., MORRIS, A.J., ORSMAN, C.J. & YAXLEY, R. (1999) Use of set-aside land in winter by declining farmland bird species in the UK. *Bird Study*, 46: 157–169.

BULL, A.L., MEAD, C.J. & WILLIAMSON, K. (1976) Bird-life on a Norfolk farm in relation to agricultural changes. *Bird Study*, 23: 163–182.

BURN, A.J. (2000) Pesticides and their effects on lowland farmland birds. In: Aebischer, N.J., Evans, A.D., Grice, P.V. & Vickery, J.A. (eds) *Ecology and Conservation of Lowland Farmland Birds*, 89–104. BOU, Tring.

BUSCHE, G. (1989) Drastische Bestandseinbussen der Feldlerche *Alauda arvensis* auf Grünlandflächen in Schleswig-Holstein. *Die Vogelwelt*, 110: 51–59.

BUSCHE, G. (1994) Zum Niedergang von 'Wiesenvögeln' in Schleswig-Holstein 1950 bis 1992. *Journal für Ornithologie*, 135: 167–177.

BUTLER, A.G. (1896–98) *British Birds with their Nests and Eggs*. Brumby & Clarke, London.

CAMPBELL, R.W., VAN DAMME, L.M. & JOHNSON, S.R. (1997a) Sky Lark (*Alauda arvensis*). In: Poole, A. & Gill, F. (eds) *The Birds of North America*, No. 286. The Academy of National Sciences, Philadelphia, PA, and The American Ornithologists' Union, Washington D.C.

CAMPBELL, L.H., AVERY, M.I., DONALD, P.F., EVANS, A.D., GREEN, R.E. & WILSON, J.D. (1997b) *A review of the indirect effects of pesticides on birds*. Joint Nature Conservation Committee Report 227. JNCC, Peterborough.

CARSON, R. (1963) *Silent Spring*. Hamish Hamilton, London.

CHAMBERLAIN, D.E. (2001) Habitat associations and trends in reproductive performance of skylarks *Alauda arvensis* breeding in the uplands of the UK. In: Donald, P.F. & Vickery, J.A. (eds) *The ecology and conservation of skylarks* Alauda arvensis, 25–39. RSPB, Sandy.

CHAMBERLAIN, D.E. & CRICK, H.Q.P. (1999) Population declines and reproductive performance of skylarks *Alauda arvensis* in different regions and habitats of the United Kingdom. *Ibis*, 141: 38–51.

CHAMBERLAIN, D.E. & GREGORY, R.D. (1999) Coarse and fine scale habitat associations of breeding skylarks *Alauda arvensis* in the UK. *Bird Study*, 46: 34–47

CHAMBERLAIN, D.E., WILSON, A.M., BROWNE, S.J. & VICKERY, J.A. (1999a). Effects of habitat type and management on the abundance of skylarks in the breeding season. *Journal of Applied Ecology*, 36: 856–870.

CHAMBERLAIN, D.E., WILSON, J.D. & FULLER, R.J. (1999b) A comparison of bird populations on organic and conventional farm systems in southern Britain. *Biological Conservation*, 88: 307–320.

CHAMBERLAIN, D.E., FULLER, R.J., BUNCE, R.G.H., DUCKWORTH, J.C. & SHRUBB, M. (2000a) Changes in the abundance of farmland birds in relation to the timing of agricultural intensification in England and Wales. *Journal of Applied Ecology*, 37: 771–788.

CHAMBERLAIN, D.E., VICKERY, J.A. & GOUGH, S. (2000b) Spatial and temporal distribution of breeding Skylarks *Alauda arvensis* in relation to crop type in periods of population increase and decline. *Ardea*, 88: 61–73.

CHERNYSOV, V.M. (1998) [Cases of aberrant flight feather counts in *Alauda arvensis*, *Saxicola torquata* and *Parus major*]. *Russian Journal of Ornithology*, 52: 21–22.

CLARK, R.B. (1947) Seasonal fluctuations in the song of the sky-lark. *British Birds*, 40: 34–43.

CLARK, R.B. (1948) A display flight of the sky-lark. *British Birds*, 41: 244–246.

CLARKE, R., COMBRIDGE, P. & MIDDLETON, N. (2003) Monitoring the diets of farmland winter seed-eaters through raptor pellet analysis. *British Birds*, 96: 360–375.

COLLINGE, W.E. (1913) *The food of some British wild birds*. Dulau, London.

CÔTÉ, I.M. & SUTHERLAND, W.J. (1997) The effectiveness of removing predators to protect bird populations. *Conservation Biology*, 11: 395–405.

COWAN, P.J. & BROWN, G.M. (2001) Prostrate gourd plants as apparent cooling sites for larks in the heat of the day. *Sandgrouse*, 23: 59–60.

COX, G.W. (1983) Foraging behaviour of the Dune Lark. *Ostrich*, 54: 113–120.

CRAMP, S. (ED) (1980) *Handbook of the Birds of Europe, the Middle East and North Africa: The Birds of the Western Palearctic*. Volume 2. Oxford University Press, Oxford.

CRAMP, S. (ED) (1988) *Handbook of the Birds of Europe, the Middle East and North Africa: The Birds of the Western Palearctic*. Volume 5. Oxford University Press, Oxford.

CRESSWELL, W. (1994) Song as a pursuit-deterrent signal, and its occurrence relative to other anti-predation behaviours of skylark (*Alauda arvensis*) on attack by merlins (*Falco columbarius*). *Behavioural Ecology and Sociobiology*, 34: 217–223.

CRESWELL, W. (1996) Surprise as a winter hunting strategy in Sparrowhawks *Accipiter nisus*, Peregrines *Falco peregrinus* and Merlins *F. columbarius*. *Ibis*, 138: 684–692.

CRICK, H.Q.P., GIBBONS, D.W. & MAGRATH, R.D. (1993) Seasonal changes in clutch size in British birds. *Journal of Animal Ecology*, 62: 263–273.

CSICSÁKY, M. (1978) [The song of the skylark (*Alauda arvensis*) and its relation to respiration]. *Journal für Ornithologie*, 119: 249–264.

DAUNICHT, W.D. (1998) *Zum Einfluss der Feinstruktur in der Vegetation auf die Habitatwahl, Habitatnutzung, Siedlungsdichte und Populationsdynamic von Feldlerchen* (Alauda arvensis) *in grosparzelligem Ackerland*. Unpublished PhD thesis, University of Bern.

DAVIES, N.B. (2000) *Cuckoos, Cowbirds and Other Cheats*. T. & A.D. Poyser, London.

DEAN, W.R.J. (1989) A review of the genera *Calandrella*, *Spizocorys* and *Eremalauda* (Alaudidae). *Bulletin of the BOC*, 109: 95–110.

DEAN, W.R.J. & HOCKEY, P.A.R. (1989) An ecological perspective of lark (Alaudidae) distribution and diversity in the southwest-arid zone of Africa. *Ostrich*, 60: 27–34.

DE CARLI E., FORNASARI L., BANI L. & BOTTONI L. (1998) Trend in distribution, abundance and habitat features of skylark (*Alauda arvensis*) in Northern Italy. *Gibier Faune Sauvage*, 15: 387–396.

D'ELBÉE, E. & BRIED, J. (1991) Alouette des champs *Alauda arvensis*. In: Yeatman-Berthelot, D. (ed) *Atlas des Oiseaux de France en Hiver*, 356–357. Société Ornithologique de France, Paris.

DELGADO, A. & MOREIRA, F. (2000) Bird assemblages of an Iberian cereal steppe. *Agriculture, Ecosystems and Environment*, 78: 65–76

DELGADO, A. & MOREIRA, F. (2002) Do wheat, barley and oats provide similar habitat and food resources for birds in cereal steppes? *Agriculture, Ecosystems & Environment*, 93: 441–446.

DELIUS, J.D. (1963) Das Verhalten der Feldlerche. *Zeitschrift Tierenpsychologie*, 20: 297–348.

DELIUS, J.D. (1965) A population study of skylarks *Alauda arvensis*. *Ibis*, 107: 466–492.

DIAMOND, J. (1997) *Guns, germs and steel*. Jonathan Cape, London.

DÍAZ, M. & TELLERÍA, J.L. (1994). Predicting the effects of agricultural changes in central Spanish croplands on seed-eating overwintering birds. *Agriculture, Ecosystems & Environment*, 49: 289–298.

DIERSCHKE, V. & VOWINKEL, K. (1990) [Breeding bird census and habitat selection of the Skylark *Alauda arvensis* on arable land in southern Lower Saxony]. *Verhandlungen der Gesellschaft für Okologie*, 19: 216–221.

DIXON, C. (1897) *Our Favourite Song Birds*. Lawrence & Bullen, London.

DOBINSON, H.M. & RICHARDS, A.J. (1964) The effects of the severe winter of 1962/63 on birds in Britain. *British Birds*, 57: 373–434.

DONALD, P.F. (1998) Changes in the abundance of invertebrates and plants on British farmland. *British Wildlife*, 9: 279–289.

DONALD, P.F. (1999) *The Ecology and Conservation of Skylarks* Alauda arvensis *on Lowland Farmland*. Unpublished DPhil thesis, University of Oxford.

DONALD, P.F. & VICKERY, J.A. (2000) The importance of cereal fields to breeding and wintering skylarks *Alauda arvensis* in the UK. In: Aebischer, N.J., Evans, A.D., Grice, P.V. & Vickery, J.A. (eds) *Ecology and Conservation of Lowland Farmland Birds*, 140–150. BOU, Tring.

DONALD, P.F. & VICKERY, J.A. (EDS) (2001) *The Ecology and Conservation of Skylarks* Alauda arvensis. RSPB, Sandy.

DONALD, P.F., WILSON, J.D. & SHEPHERD, M. (1994) The decline of the corn bunting. *British Birds*, 87: 106–132.

DONALD, P.F., BUCKINGHAM, D.L., MOORCROFT, D., MUIRHEAD, L.B., EVANS, A.D. & KIRBY, W.B. (2001a) Habitat use and diet of skylarks *Alauda arvensis* wintering on lowland farmland in southern Britain. *Journal of Applied Ecology*, 38: 536–547.

DONALD, P.F., BUCKINGHAM, D.L., MUIRHEAD, L.B., EVANS, A.D., KIRBY, W.B. & SCHMITT, S.I.A. (2001b) Factors affecting clutch size, hatching rates and partial brood losses in skylark *Alauda arvensis* nests on lowland farmland. In: Donald, P.F. & Vickery, J.A. (eds) *The Ecology and Conservation of Skylarks* Alauda arvensis, 63–77. RSPB, Sandy.

DONALD, P.F., EVANS, A.D., BUCKINGHAM, D.L., MUIRHEAD, L.B. & WILSON, J.D. (2001c) Factors affecting the territory distribution of Skylarks *Alauda arvensis* breeding on lowland farmland. *Bird Study*, 48: 271–278.

DONALD, P.F., GREEN, R.E. & HEATH, M.F. (2001d) Agricultural intensification and the collapse of Europe's farmland bird populations. *Proceedings of the Royal Society of London (B)*, 268: 25–29.

DONALD, P.F., MUIRHEAD, L.B., BUCKINGHAM, D.L., EVANS, A.D., KIRBY, W.B. & GRUAR, D.J. (2001e) Body condition, growth rates and diet of Skylark *Alauda arvensis* nestlings on lowland farmland. *Ibis*, 143: 658–669.

DONALD, P.F., EVANS, A.D., MUIRHEAD, L.B., BUCKINGHAM, D.L., KIRBY, W.B. & SCHMITT, S.I.A. (2002a) Survival rates, causes of failure and productivity of Skylark *Alauda arvensis* nests on lowland farmland. *Ibis*, 144: 652–664.

DONALD, P.F., PISANO, G., RAYMENT, M. & PAIN, D.J. (2002b) The Common Agricultural Policy, EU enlargement and the conservation of Europe's farmland birds. *Agriculture, Ecosystems & Environment*, 89: 167–182.

DONALD, P.F., DE PONTE, M., PITTA GROZ, M.J. & TAYLOR, R. (2003) Status, ecology, behaviour and conservation of Raso Lark *Alauda razae*, *Bird Conservation International*, 13: 13–28.

DOUGALL, T. (1996) Movement and mortality of British-ringed Skylarks *Alauda arvensis*. *Ringing & Migration*, 17: 81–92.

DOUGALL, T. (1997) Biometrics and sex ratios of Skylarks *Alauda arvensis* in winter in south-east Scotland. *Ringing & Migration*, 18: 37–49.

DOUGALL, T. (1998) Wing length and undertail covert markings in the Skylark: a museum perspective. *Ringing & Migration*, 19: 86–90.

DOUGALL, T. (1999) Mass and visible fat scores of Skylarks *Alauda arvensis* in winter in south-east Scotland. *Ringing & Migration*, 19: 283–297.

DOWSETT-LEMAIRE, F. & DOWSETT, R.J. (1978) Vocal mimicry in the lark *Mirafra hypermetra* as a possible species isolating mechanism. *Bulletin of the BOC*, 98: 140–144.

D'URBAN, W.S.M. & MATHEW, M.A. (1892) *The Birds of Devon*. R.H. Porter, London.

EDGAR, W.H. & ISAACSON, A.J. (1974) Observations on skylark damage to sugar beet and lettuce seedlings in East Anglia. *Annals of Applied Biology*, 76: 335–337.

EDWARDS, K.J. & HIRONS, K.R. (1984) Cereal pollen grains in pre-elm decline deposits: implications for the earliest agriculture in Britain and Ireland. *Journal of Archaeological Science*, 11: 71–80.

ELMEGAARD, N., ANDERSEN, P.N., ODDERSKÆR, P. & PRANG, A. (1999) Food supply and breeding activity of skylarks in fields with different pesticide treatment. In: Adams, N.J. & Slotow, R.H. (eds) *Proceedings of the 22nd International Ornithological Congress, Durban*, 1058–1069. BirdLife South Africa, Johannesburg.

ERAUD, C. & BOUTIN, J.-M. (2000) Application of the ACT programme to identify Skylark habitat in France. *Alauda*, 69: 63–74.

ERAUD, C. & BOUTIN, J.-M. (2002) Density and productivity of breeding Skylarks *Alauda arvensis* in relation to crop type on agricultural lands in western France. *Bird Study*, 49: 287–296.

ERAUD, C., BOUTIN, J.-M. & ROUX, D. (2000) Breeding habitat of the Skylark (*Alauda arvensis*) in a Mediterranean agroecosystem. *Gibier Faune Sauvage*, 17: 147–163.

EVANS, A.D. (1997) The importance of mixed farming for seed-eating birds in the UK. In: Pain, D.J. & Pienkowski, M.W. (eds) *Farming and Birds in Europe: the Common Agricultural Policy and its Implications for Bird Conservation*, 331–357. Academic Press, London.

FAHSE, L., DEAN, W.R.J. & WISSEL, C. (1998) Modelling the size and distribution of protected areas for nomadic birds: Alaudidae in the Nama-Karoo, South Africa. *Biological Conservation*, 85: 105–112.

FEFELOV, I.V. (1997) [Fragments of bird sounds in songs of the Skylark *Alauda arvensis* and Starling *Sturnus vulgaris* in the Cis-Baikal Region]. *Russian Journal of Ornithology*, 22: 19–22.

FEFELOV, I.V., TUPITSYN, I.I., PODKOVYROV, V.A. & ZHURALEV, V.E. (2001) [*Birds of the Selenga River Delta*]. Eastern Siberian Publishing Company, Irkutsk.

FINLAYSON, C. (1992) *Birds of the Strait of Gibraltar*. T. & A.D. Poyser, London.

FIRBANK, L.G. & FORCELLA, F. (2000) Genetically modified crops and farmland biodiversity. *Science*, 289: 1481–1482.

FORCHHAMMER, M.C., POST, E. & STENSETH, N.C. (1998) Breeding phenology and climate. *Nature*, 391: 29–30.

FULLER, E. (2000) *Extinct Birds*. Oxford University Press, Oxford.

FULLER, R.J., WARD, E., HIRD, D. & BROWN, A.F. (2002) Declines of ground-nesting birds in two areas of upland farmland in the south Pennines of England. *Bird Study*, 49: 146–152.

GARB, J., KOTLER, B.P. & BROWN, J.S. (2000) Foraging and community consequences of seed size for coexisting Negev Desert granivores. *Oikos*, 88: 291–300.

GERSS, W. (1989a) [Estimating the average strophe length of the song of the skylark (*Alauda arvensis*)]. *Zoologischer Anzeiger*, 222: 27–36.

GERSS, W. (1989b) [Measuring influences on the strophe length of the song of the skylark (*Alauda arvensis*)]. *Zoologischer Anzeiger*, 223: 33–42.

GIBBONS, D.W., REID, J.B. & CHAPMAN, R.A. (1993) *The New Atlas of Breeding Birds in Britain and Ireland: 1988–91*. T. & A.D. Poyser, London.

GIBSON, L. (1977) Breeding the Skylark in Canada. *Avicultural Magazine*, 84: 74–77.

GILLINGS, S. (2001) Factors affecting the distribution of skylarks *Alauda arvensis* wintering in Britain and Ireland during the early 1980s. In: Donald, P.F. & Vickery, J.A. (eds) *The Ecology and Conservation of Skylarks* Alauda arvensis, 115–128. RSPB, Sandy.

GILLINGS, S. & FULLER, R.J. (2001) Habitat selection by Skylarks *Alauda arvensis* wintering in Britain in 1997/98. *Bird Study*, 48: 293–307.

GLADWIN, T.W. (1985) Skylarks and Yellowhammers roosting under snow. *British Birds*, 78: 109–110.

GLUTZ VON BLOTZHEIM, U.N. & BAUER, K.M. (1985) *Handbuch der Vögel Mitteleuropas*. Band 10/1. AULA-Verlag, Wiesbaden.

GOODBODY, I.M. (1950) Sky-lark migration in S.E. Ireland. *British Birds*, 43: 265–271.

GÖTMARK, F., BLOMQVIST, D., JOHANSSON, O.C. & BERGKVIST, J. (1995) Nest site selection: a trade-off between concealment and view of the surroundings? *Journal of Avian Biology*, 26: 305–312.

GRAHAME, J. (1806) *The Birds of Scotland*. Longman, London.

GREEN, R.E. (1978) Factors affecting the diet of farmland skylarks *Alauda arvensis*. *Journal of Animal Ecology*, 47: 913–928.

GREEN, R.E. (1980) Food selection by skylarks and grazing damage to sugar beet seedlings. *Journal of Applied Ecology*, 17: 613–630.

GRØNSTØL, G.B. (1996) Aerobatic components in the song-flight display of male lapwings *Vanellus vanellus* as cues in female choice. *Ardea*, 84: 45–55.

GUYOMARCH, J.C. & GUILLET, S. (1996) *La Migration Postnuptiale Chez l'Alouette des Champs* Alauda arvensis *en Captivité*. University of Rennes I/ FDC Landes.

HAGEMEIJER, W.J.M. & BLAIR, M. (EDS) (1997) *The EBCC Atlas of European Breeding Birds: their Distribution and Abundance*. T. & A.D. Poyser, London.

HALSE, S.A. & TREVENEN, H.J. (1985) Damage to medic pastures by skylarks in north-western Iraq. *Journal of Applied Ecology*, 22: 337–346.

HALSE, S.A. & TREVENEN, H.J. (1986) Damage to cereal crops by larks in north-western Iraq. *Annals of Applied Biology*, 108: 423–430.

HALUPKA, K. (1998a) Partial predation in an altricial bird selects for the accelerated development of young. *Journal of Avian Biology*, 29: 129–133.

HALUPKA, K. (1998b) Nest-site selection and nest predation in meadow pipits. *Folia Zoologica*, 47: 29–37.

HANCOCK, M. & AVERY, M. (1998) Changes in breeding bird populations in peatlands and young forestry in north east Sutherland and Caithness between 1988 and 1995. *Scottish Birds*, 19: 195–205.

HARDY, E. (1933) Skylark nesting in October in Lancashire. *British Birds*, 33: 198.

HARRISON, C. (1988) *The History of the Birds of Britain*. Collins, London.

HARRISON, J.M. (1966) A case of symmetrical albinism in a Skylark. *Bulletin of the BOC*, 86: 11–15.

HART, J.D., MURRAY, A.W.A., MILSOM, T.P., PARROTT, D., ALLCOCK, J., WATOLA, G.V., BISHOP, J.D., ROBERTSON, P.A., HOLLAND, J.M., BOWYER, A., BIRKETT, T. & BEGBIE, M. (2002) The abundance of farmland birds within arable fields in relation to seed density. *Aspects of Applied Biology*, 67: 221–228.

HEDENSTRÖM, A. (1995) Song flight performance in the skylark *Alauda arvensis*. *Journal of Avian Biology*, 26: 337–342.

HEDENSTRÖM, A. & ALERSTAM, T. (1996) Skylark optimal flight speeds for flying nowhere and somewhere. *Behavioural Ecology*, 7: 121–126.

HEDENSTRÖM, A. & MØLLER, A.P. (1992) Morphological adaptations to song flight in passerine birds: a comparative study. *Proceedings of the Royal Society of London (B)*, 247: 183–187.

HEDENSTRÖM, A. & ROSEN, M. (2001) Predator versus prey: on aerial hunting and escape strategies in birds. *Behavioral Ecology*, 12: 150–156.

HEMERY, G., GORIN, R. & RANAULT, O. (1991) Origines géographiques et périodes de migration des Alouettes des champs (*Alauda arvensis*) en France d'aprés les resultants du baguage. *Gibier Faune Sauvage*, 9: 229–241.

HENDERSON, I.G., CRITCHLEY, N.R., COOPER, J. & FOWBERT, J.A. (2001) Breeding season responses of Skylarks *Alauda arvensis* to vegetation structure in set-aside (fallow arable land). *Ibis*, 143: 317–321.

HERRANZ, J., YANES, M. & SUÁREZ, F. (1994) The nestling diet of two sympatric larks: Thekla Lark (*Galerida theklae*) and Lesser Short-toed Lark (*Calandrella rufescens*). *Actas de las XII Jornadas Ornitológicas Españolas*, 123–133.

HERREMANS, M. (1984) [Biased sex ratios in catches of Skylarks (*Alauda arvensis*)]. *Le Gerfaut*, 74: 401–405.

HOCKEY, P.A.R., ALLAN, D.G., REBELO, A.G. & DEAN, W.R.J. (1988) The distribution, habitat requirements and conservation status of Rudd's Lark *Heteromirafra ruddi* in South Africa. *Biological Conservation*, 45: 255–266.

HOESCH, W. (1958) Uber die Auswirkung der Gefieder-Einstäubung auf die Federfarbe bei Lerchen. *Journal für Ornithologie*, 99: 367–371.

HROMADA, M., TRYJANOWSKI, P. & ANTCZAC, M. (2002) Presence of the great grey shrike *Lanius excubitor* affects breeding passerine assemblage. *Annales Zoologici Fennici*, 39: 125–130.

JAMES, D., JARRY, G. & ERARD, C. (2000) Influence of the moon on the nocturnal postnuptial migration of the skylark *Alauda arvensis* L. in France. *Comptes Rendus de l'Academie des Sciences, Serie III—Life Sciences*, 323: 215–224.

JENNY, M. (1990a) Territorialität und Brutbiologie der Feldlerche *Alauda arvensis* in einer intensiv genutzten Agrarlandschaft. *Journal für Ornithologie*, 131: 241–265.

JENNY, M. (1990b) Nahrungsökologie der Feldlerche *Alauda arvensis* in einer intensiv genutzten Agrarlandschaft des schweizerischen Mittellandes. *Ornithologische Beobachter*, 87: 31–53.

JENNY, M. (1990c) Populationsdynamic der Feldlerche *Alauda arvensis* in einer intensiv genutzen Agrarlandschaft des schweizerischen Mittelandes. *Ornithologische Beobachter*, 87: 153–163.

JEROMIN, K. (2002) Zur Ernährungsökologie der Feldlerche (*Alauda arvensis* L. 1758) in der Reproduktionsphase. Unpublished dissertation, Christian-Albrechts-Universität, Kiel.

JOHNS, C.A. (1920) *British Birds in their Haunts*. London. First published 1862.

JONES, P.E. (1965) *The Worshipful Company of Poulters of the City of London: a Short History*. Oxford University Press, London.

KALEJTA-SUMMERS, B. (1997) Diet and habitat preferences of wintering passerines on the Taff/Ely saltmarshes. *Bird Study*, 44: 367–373.

KEAN, H. (1998) *Animal Rights: Political and Social Change in Britain since 1800*. Reaktion Books, London.

KHOKHLOV, A.N. (1990) [Peculiarities of distribution, number and ecology of Alaudidae in anthropogenic landscapes of the central Front-Caucasian area]. [*Little-studied birds of North Caucasia*, 196–222]. Russia.

KIRKWOOD, J.K., DUIGNAN, P.J., KEMBER, N.F., BENNETT, P.M. & PRICE, D.J. (1989) The growth rate of the tarsometatarsus bone in birds. *Journal of Zoology, London*, 217: 403–416.

KNOX, A.E. (1850) *Ornithological Rambles in Sussex*. Van Voorst, London.

KOTLER, B.P. & BROWN, J.S. (1999) Mechanisms of coexistence of optimal foragers as determinants of local abundances and distributions of desert granivores. *Journal of Mammalogy*, 80: 361–374.

KOVSHAR, A.F. & BEREZOVIKOV, N.N. (1995) [The biology of the Small Skylark (*Alauda gulgula* Franklin, 1831) in south-east Kazakhstan]. *Selevinia*, 3: 63–68.

KREBS, J.R., WILSON, J.D., BRADBURY, R.B. & SIRIWARDENA, G.M. (1999) The second Silent Spring? *Nature*, 400: 611–612.

LACK, P.C. (1986) *The Atlas of Wintering Birds in Britain and Ireland*. T. & A.D. Poyser, Calton.

LAMB, R.C. (1964) *Birds, beasts and fishes: the first hundred years of the North Canterbury Acclimatisation Society*. The North Canterbury Acclimatisation Society, Christchurch.

LANGE, H. (1951) On the song-length of the sky-lark (*Alauda arvensis* L.). *Dansk Ornitologisk Forenings Tidsskrift*, 45: 34–43.

LAURSEN, K. (1981) Birds on roadside verges and the effect of mowing on frequency and distribution. *Biological Conservation*, 20: 59–68.

LILFORD, LORD (1895) *Notes on the Birds of Northamptonshire and Neighbourhood*. R.H. Porter, London.

LÜPS, P., BIBER, O. & NUSSBAUMER, M.A. (1993) [Did sexual dimorphism in Sky Larks *Alauda arvensis* evolve as a consequence of male song flight?]. *Bulletin of the Natural History Museum of Bern*, 11: 117–124.

MACLEAN, G.L. (1970) The biology of the larks (Alaudidae) of the Kalahari sandveld. *Zoologica Africana*, 5: 7–39

MAEDA, T. (2001) Patterns of bird abundance and habitat use in rice fields of the Kanto Plain, central Japan. *Ecological Research*, 16: 569–585.

MAL'CHEVSKIY, A.S. & PUKINSKIY, Y.B. (1983) [*Birds of the Leningrad Region and adjacent territories*]. Leningrad University Press, Leningrad.

MASON, C.F. & MACDONALD, S.M. (1999) Winter bird numbers and land-use preferences in an arable landscape in eastern England. *Bird Conservation International*, 9: 119–127.

MATHER, M.H. & ROBERTSON, R.J. (1992) Honest advertisement in flight displays of bobolinks (*Dolichonyx oryzivorus*). *Auk*, 109: 869–873.

MAYFIELD, H. (1975) Suggestions for calculating nest success. *Wilson Bulletin*, 87: 456–466.

MAYHEW, H. (1851) *London Labour and the London Poor*. G. Newbold, London.

MCDOWALL, R.M. (1994) *Gamekeepers for the Nation: the story of New Zealand's acclimatisation societies 1861–1990*. Canterbury University Press, Christchurch.

MCGREGOR, P.K., HOLLAND, J. & SHEPHERD, M. (1997) The ecology of corn bunting *Miliaria calandra* song dialects and their potential use in conservation. In: Donald, P.F. & Aebischer, N.J. (eds) *The ecology and conservation of corn buntings* Miliaria calandra, 76–87. Joint Nature Conservation Committee, Peterborough.

MEINERTZHAGEN, R. (1951) Review of the Alaudidae. *Proceedings of the Zoological Society of London*, 121: 81–132.

MILSOM, T.P., LANGTON, S.D., PARKIN, W.K., ALLEN, D.S., BISHOP, J.D. & HART, J.D. (2001) Coastal grazing marshes as a breeding habitat for skylarks *Alauda arvensis*. In: Donald, P.F. & Vickery, J.A. (eds) *The Ecology and Conservation of Skylarks* Alauda arvensis, 41–51. RSPB, Sandy.

MØLLER, A.P. (1991) Influence of wing and tail morphology on the duration of song flight in skylarks. *Behavioral Ecology and Sociobiology*, 28: 309–314.

MØLLER, A.P. (2002) North Atlantic Oscillation (NAO) effects of climate on the relative importance of first and second clutches in a migratory passerine bird. *Journal of Animal Ecology*, 71: 201–210.

MOORCROFT, D., WHITTINGHAM, M.J., BRADBURY, R.B. & WILSON, J.D. (2002) The selection of stubble fields by wintering granivorous birds reflects vegetation cover and food abundance. *Journal of Applied Ecology*, 39: 535–547.

MOUNTFORT, G.R. (1939) Skylark carrying young birds. *British Birds*, 32: 79.

MURRAY, K.A., WILCOX, A. & STOATE, C. (2002) A simultaneous assessment of farmland habitat use by breeding skylarks and yellowhammers. *Aspects of Applied Biology*, 67: 121–128.

MUSTERS, C.J.M., KRUK, M., DE GRAAF, H.J. & TER KEURS, W.J. (2001) Breeding birds as a farm product. *Conservation Biology*, 15: 363–369.

NATION, R. (1996) Skylarks displaying in Qatar. *Phoenix*, 13: 2.

NEWTON, I., DALE, L. & ROTHERY, P. (1997) Apparent lack of impact of Sparrowhawks on the breeding densities of some woodland songbirds. *Bird Study*, 44: 129–135.

NORBERG, R.Å. (1991) The flappet lark *Mirafra rufocinnamomea* doubles its wingbeat rate to 24Hz in wing-clap display flight: a sexually selected feat. *Journal of Experimental Biology*, 159: 515–523.

NORTH, J. (1990) Future agricultural land use patterns. In: Britton, D. (ed) *Agriculture in Britain: changing pressures and policies*, 69–93. CABI, Wallingford.

NORTHCOTE, J. (1833) *Fables, Original and Selected*. John Murray, London.

NUSSBAUMER, M.A. (1992) Die Messbarkeit kleiner Vogelskelette am Beispiel der Feldlerche *Alauda arvensis* nebst Angaben zum Geschlechtdimorphismus am Skelett. *Ornithologischer Beobachter*, 89: 245–251.

ODDERSKÆR, P., PRANG, A., POULSEN, J.G., ANDERSEN, P.N. & ELMEGAARD, N. (1997a). Skylark (*Alauda arvensis*) utilisation of micro-habitats in spring barley fields. *Agriculture, Ecosystems and Environment*, 62: 21–29.

ODDERSKÆR, P., PRANG, A., ELMEGAARD, N. & ANDERSON, P.N. (1997b) *Skylark reproduction in pesticide treated and untreated fields*. Pesticides Research 32. Danish Environmental Protection Agency, Copenhagen.

OELKE, H. (1968) Wo beginnt bzw. wo endet der Biotop der Feldlerche? *Journal für Ornithologie*, 109: 25–29.

ORR, Y. (1970) Temperature measurements at the nest of the desert lark (*Ammomanes deserti deserti*). *Condor*, 72: 476–478.

PAIN, D.J. & PIENKOWSKI, M.W. (EDS) (1997) *Farming and Birds in Europe: the Common Agricultural Policy and its Implications for Bird Conservation*. Academic Press, London.

PAYNE, R.B. (1978) Local dialects in the wingflaps of Flappet Lark *Mirafra rufocinnamomea*. *Ibis*, 120: 204–207.

PEACH, W.J., LOVETT, L.J., WOTTON, S.R. & JEFFS, C. (2001) Countryside stewardship delivers cirl buntings (*Emberiza cirlus*) in Devon, UK. *Biological Conservation*, 101: 361–373.

PEARCE-HIGGINS, J.W. & GRANT, M.C. (2002) The effects of grazing-related variation in habitat on the distribution of moorland skylarks *Alauda arvensis* and meadow pipits *Anthus pratensis*. *Aspects of Applied Biology*, 67: 155–163.

PENHALLURICK, R.D. (1978) *The Birds of Cornwall and the Isles of Scilly*. Headland, Penzance.

PERKINS, A.J., WHITTINGHAM, M.J., BRADBURY, R.B., WILSON, J.D., MORRIS, A.J. & BARNETT, P.R. (2000) Habitat characteristics affecting use of lowland agricultural grassland by birds in winter. *Biological Conservation*, 95: 279–294.

POLOZOV, S.A. (1989) [Feeding behaviour of larks wintering in West Kopetdag]. In: [*Ecological aspects of study, practical use and conservation of birds in the mountain ecosystems*], 82–83. Aspects of All-Union Symposium. Frunze, Russia.

POTTS, G.R. (1991) The environmental and ecological importance of cereal fields. In: Firbank, L.G., Carter, N., Darbyshire, J.F. & Potts, G.R. (eds) *The Ecology of Temperate Cereal Fields*, 3–21. Blackwell Scientific, Oxford.

POTTS, G.R. (1997) Cereal farming, pesticides and grey partridge. In: Pain, D.J. & Pienkowski, M.W. (eds) *Farming and birds in Europe: the Common Agricultural Policy and its Implications for Bird Conservation*, 150–177. Academic Press, London.

POTTS, G.R. (2003) The myth of the overwintered stubble. *Bird Study*, 50: 91–93.

POULSEN, J.G. (1996) Behaviour and parental care of skylark *Alauda arvensis* chicks. *Ibis*, 138: 525–531.

POULSEN, J.G., SOTHERTON, N.W. & AEBISCHER, N.J. (1998) Comparative nesting and feeding ecology of skylarks *Alauda arvensis* on arable farmland in southern England with special reference to set-aside. *Journal of Applied Ecology*, 35: 131–147.

PRETTY, J.N., BRETT, C., GEE, D., HINE, R.E., MASON, C.F., MORISON, J.I.L., RAVEN, H., RAYMENT, M.D. & VAN DER BIJL, G. (2000) An assessment of the total external costs of UK agriculture. *Agricultural Systems*, 65: 113–136.

PYCRAFT, W.P. (1911) The Larks. In: Kirkman, F.B. (ed) *The British Bird Book*. T.C. & E.C. Jack, London.

RABØL, J. & NOER, H. (1973) Spring migration of the Skylark (*Alauda arvensis*) in Denmark: influence of environmental factors on the flocksize and correlation between flocksize and migratory direction. *Die Vogelwarte*, 27: 50–65.

RACKHAM, O. (1986) *The History of the Countryside*. Dent, London.

RADFORD, A.P. (1988) Skylark singing close to hovering kestrel. *British Birds*, 81: 72.

RATCLIFFE, D. (1980) *The Peregrine Falcon*. T. & A.D. Poyser, Calton.

RAY, J. (1670) *A Compleat Collection of English Proverbs*. W. Morden, Cambridge.

REIJNEN, R., FOPPEN, R. & MEEUWSEN, H. (1996). The effects of traffic on the density of breeding birds in Dutch agricultural grasslands. *Biological Conservation*, 75: 255–260.

RHEINWALD, G. (1993) *Atlas der Verbreitung und Häufigkeit der Brutvögel Deutschlands*. *Dachverband Deutscher Avifaunisten*, Germany.

RJABOW, W.F. (1968) Die Nahrung der Feldlerche in der Kustanai-Steppe. *Falke*, 15: 112–118.

ROBERTSON, J. & BERG, A. (1992) Status and population changes of farmland birds in southern Sweden. *Ornis Svecica*, 2: 119–130.

ROBINSON, P. (1883) *The Poets' Birds*. Chatto & Windus, London.

ROBINSON, R.A. (1997) *Ecology and Conservation of Seed-eating Birds on Farmland*. Unpublished PhD thesis, University of East Anglia.

ROBINSON, R.A. (2001) Feeding ecology of skylarks *Alauda arvensis* in winter: a possible mechanism for population decline? In: Donald, P.F. & Vickery, J.A. (eds) *The Ecology and Conservation of Skylarks* Alauda arvensis, 129–138. RSPB, Sandy.

ROBINSON, R.A. & SUTHERLAND, W.J. (1999) The winter distribution of seed-eating birds: habitat structure, seed density and seasonal depletion. *Ecography*, 22: 447–454.

ROBINSON, R.A. & SUTHERLAND, W.J. (2002) Post-war changes in arable farming and biodiversity in Great Britain. *Journal of Applied Ecology*, 39: 157–176.

ROBINSON, R.A., WILSON, J.D. & CRICK, H.Q.P. (2001) The importance of arable habitat for farmland birds in grassland landscapes. *Journal of Applied Ecology*, 38: 1059–1069.

ROBSON, N. (1997) The evolution of the Common Agricultural Policy and the incorporation of environmental considerations. In: Pain, D.J. & Pienkowski, M.W. (eds) *Farming and Birds in Europe: the Common Agricultural Policy and its Implications for Bird Conservation*, 43–78. Academic Press, London.

ROLLIN, N. (1943) Sky-lark song. *British Birds*, 36: 146–150.

ROLLIN, N. (1956) Song output of unstimulated Skylark. *British Birds*, 49: 218–221.

ROWLEY, G.D. (1877) *Ornithological Miscellany*. Trübner, London.

ROYLE, N.J., HARTLEY, I.R., OWENS, I.P.F. & PARKER, G.A. (1999) Sibling competition and the evolution of growth rates in birds. *Proceedings of the Royal Society of London (B)*, 266: 923–932.

RÜHE, F. (1999) Effects of stand structures in arable crops on Brown Hare (*Lepus europaeus*) distribution. *Gibier Faune Sauvage*, 16: 317–337.

RYAN, P.G. & BLOOMER, P. (1999) The Long-Billed Lark complex: a species mosaic in southwestern Africa. *Auk*, 116: 194–208.

RYAN, P.G., HOOD, I., BLOOMER, P., KOMEN, J. & CROWE, T.M. (1998) Barlow's Lark: a new species in the Karoo Lark *Certhilauda albescens* complex of southwest Africa. *Ibis*, 140: 605–619.

SAFRIEL, U.N. (1990) Winter foraging behaviour of the Dune Lark in the Namib Desert, and the effect of prolonged drought on behaviour and population size. *Ostrich*, 61: 77–80.

SCEBBA, S. (2001) Biometrics and sex ratios of Skylarks *Alauda arvensis* during migration in southern Italy. *Ringing and Migration*, 20: 364–370.

SCHAEFER, T. (2001) Die Feldlerche *Alauda arvensis* als Brutvogel halboffener Landschaften. *Vogelwelt*, 122: 257–263.

SCHEKKERMAN, H. (1999) Sex bias and seasonal patterns in tape-lured samples of migrating skylarks *Alauda arvensis*. *Ringing and Migration*, 19: 299–305.

SCHLÄPFER, A. (1988) Populationsökologie der Feldlerche *Alauda arvensis* in der intensiv genutzten Agrarlandschaft. *Ornithologische Beobachter*, 85: 305–371.

SCHLÄPFER, A. (2001) A conceptual model of skylark *Alauda arvensis* territory distribution in different landscape types. In: Donald, P.F. & Vickery, J.A. (eds) *The Ecology and Conservation of Skylarks* Alauda arvensis, 3–9. RSPB, Sandy.

SCHÖN, M. (1999) On the significance of micro-structures in arable land: does the Skylark (*Alauda arvensis*) show a preference for places with stunted growth? *Journal für Ornithologie*, 140: 87–91.

SEEBOHM, H. (1882–85) *A History of British Birds*. Porter, London.

SHARALDAEVA, V.D. (1999) [The role of larks in the structure of bird populations on the steppes of the Torei Lakes Hollow, south-eastern Trans-Baikalia]. *Bulletin of Buryat University (2)*, 2: 127–134.

SHARROCK, J.T.R. (1976) The Atlas of Breeding Birds in Britain and Ireland. T. & A.D. Poyser, Berkhamsted.

SHEVCHENKO, E.V. (1989) [Mass non-nesting of Horned Larks in South-east Altai in 1988]. In: [*Ecological aspects of study, practical use and conservation of birds in the mountain ecosystems*], 108–109. Aspects of All-Union Symposium, Frunze, Russia.

SHISHKIN, V.S. (1982) [Peculiarities of breeding of larks in semi-deserts of the Northern Cis-Caspian Sea area]. *Ornithologiya*, 17: 83–90.

SHKEDY, Y. & SAFRIEL, U.N. (1991) Fat reserves of an opportunist and of a specialist species in the Negev Desert. *Auk*, 108: 556–561.

SHKEDY, Y. & SAFRIEL, U.N. (1992) Nest predation and nestling growth-rate of two lark species in the Negev Desert, Israel. *Ibis*, 134: 268–272.

SIBLEY, C.G. & MONROE, B.L. (1990) *Distribution and Taxonomy of Birds of the World*. Yale University Press, New Haven and London.

SIMMS, E. (1992) *Larks, Pipits and Wagtails*. HarperCollins, London.

SIRIWARDENA, G.M., BAILLIE, S.R., BUCKLAND, S.T., FEWSTER, R.M., MARCHANT, J.H. & WILSON, J.D. (1998) Trends in the abundance of farmland birds: a quantitative comparison of smoothed Common Birds Census indices. *Journal of Applied Ecology*, 35: 24–43.

SIRIWARDENA, G.M., WILSON, J.D., BAILLIE, S.R. & CRICK, H.Q.P. (2001) Can the historical CBC trend for skylark be 'recovered' using present-day agricultural habitat preferences and changes in agricultural land use? In: Donald, P.F. & Vickery, J.A. (eds) *The Ecology and Conservation of Skylarks* Alauda arvensis, 53–60. RSPB, Sandy.

SKEAD, D.M. (1975) Drinking habits of birds in the central Transvaal bushveld. *Ostrich*, 46: 139–146.

SMITH, C. (1869) *The Birds of Somersetshire*. Van Voorst: London

SNOW, D.W. (1955) The abnormal breeding of birds in the winter 1953/54. *British Birds*, 48: 120–126.

SOCIETY FOR THE PROTECTION OF BIRDS (1897) *Skylark*. Educational Series 22. SPB, London.

SODHI, N.S. & OLIPHANT, L.W. (1993) Prey selection by urban-breeding merlins. *Auk*, 110: 727–735.

SPAEPEN, J.F. (1991) Survival rates of some full-grown birds migrating through Belgium. *Le Gerfaut*, 81: 207–216.

SPAEPEN, J.F. (1995a) A study of the migration of the skylark *Alauda arvensis* based on European ringing data. *Le Gerfaut*, 85: 63–89.

SPAEPEN, J.F. (1995b) Estimating the size of migrator populations based on ringing data. Application to the skylark (*Alauda arvensis*). *Le Gerfaut*, 85: 91–93.

SPAEPEN, J.F. & VAN CAUTEREN, F. (1962) Migration of the skylark, *Alauda arvensis* L.. *Le Gerfaut*, 52: 275–297.

STEVENSON (1866) *The birds of Norfolk*. Van Voorst, London.

STEYN, P. (1988) Cooperative breeding in the spike-heeled lark. *Ostrich*, 59: 182.

STOATE, C. (1995) The changing face of lowland farming and wildlife. Part 1: 1845–1945. *British Wildlife*, 6: 341–350.

STOATE, C. (1996) The changing face of lowland farming and wildlife. Part 2: 1945–1995. *British Wildlife*, 7: 162–172.

STOATE, C., BOATMAN, N.D., BORRALHO, R.J., RIO CARVALHO, C., DE SNOO, G.R. & EDEN, P. (2001) Ecological impacts of arable intensification in Europe. *Journal of Environmental Management*, 63: 337–365.

STÖCKLI, S. (2002) *Territoriality, Nest Site Selection and Breeding Success of Skylarks (*Alauda arvensis*) in Territories with Different Crop Composition*. Unpublished MSc thesis, Department of Biology, ETH Zürich.

STOLT, B.-O. (1980) Directors of visible Skylark *Alauda arvensis* migration in east central Sweden. *Ornis Fennica*, 57: 71–76.

SUÁREZ, F. & MANRIQUE, J. (1992) Low breeding success in Mediterranean shrubsteppe passerines: Thekla Lark *Galerida theklae*, Lesser Short-toed Lark *Calandrella rufescens*, and Black-eared Wheatear *Oenanthe hispanica*. *Ornis Scandinavica*, 23: 24–28.

SUÁREZ, F., YANES, M., HARRANZ, J. & MANRIQUE, J. (1993). Nature reserves and the conservation of Iberian shrubsteppe passerines: the paradox of nest predation. *Biological Conservation*, 64: 77–81.

SUÁREZ, F., GARZA, V. & MORALES, M.B. (2002a) Habitat use of two sibling species, the Short-toed *Calandrella brachydactyla* and the Lesser Short-toed *C. rufescens* Larks, in mainland Spain. *Ardeola*, 49: 259–272.

SUÁREZ, F., GARZA, V. & MORALES, M.B. (2002b) The role of extensive cereal crops, dry pastures and shrub-steppe in determining skylark *Alauda arvensis* densities in the Iberian peninsula. *Agriculture, Ecosystems and Environment*, 95: 551–557.

SUFFERN, C. (1951) Skylarks making 'forms'. *British Birds*, 44: 387–388.

SUHONEN, J., NORRDAHL, K. & KORPIMÄKI, E. (1994) Avian predation risk modifies breeding bird community on a farmland area. *Ecology*, 75: 1626–1634.

SUZUKI, S., TANIOKA, K., UCHIMURA, S. & MARUMOTO, T. (1952) The hovering flight of skylarks. *Journal of Agricultural Meteorology of Japan*, 7: 149–151.

SWETNAM, R.D., WILSON, J.D., BRADBURY, R.B. & KREBS, J.R. (2001) Modelling the effects of agricultural change on skylark numbers using GIS. In: Donald, P.F. & Vickery, J.A. (eds) *The Ecology and Conservation of Skylarks* Alauda arvensis, 209–219. RSPB, Sandy.

TAYLOR, M.E. (1986) Skylark using human beings as a refuge. *British Birds*, 79: 592.

TELLERÍA, J.L., SUÁREZ, F. & SANTOS, T. (1988) Bird communities of the Iberian shrubsteppes. *Holarctic Ecology*, 11: 171–177.

THARME, A.P., GREEN, R.E., BAINES, D., BAINBRIDGE, I.P. & O'BRIEN, M. (2001) The effect of management for red grouse shooting on the population density of breeding birds on heather-dominated moorland. *Journal of Applied Ecology*, 38: 439–457.

THOMAS, M.R., GARTHWAITE, D.G. & BANHAM, A.R. (1997) *Arable Farm Crops in Great Britain, 1996.* Pesticides Usage Survey Report 141. Ministry of Agriculture, Fisheries and Food, London.

THOMAS, R.J. (1999) Two tests of a stochastic dynamic programming model of daily singing routines in birds. *Animal Behaviour*, 57: 277–284.

THOMPSON, F. (1939) *Lark Rise to Candleford.* Oxford University Press, Oxford.

THOMSEN, S. (2002) *The Ecology of the Skylark* Alauda arvensis *L. on the Canterbury Plains, New Zealand.* Unpublished PhD thesis, Lincoln University, Canterbury.

THOMSEN, S., WRATTEN, S.D. & FRAMPTON, C.M. (2001) Skylark *Alauda arvensis* winter densities and habitat associations in Canterbury, New Zealand. In: Donald, P.F. & Vickery, J.A. (eds) *The Ecology and Conservation of Skylarks* Alauda arvensis, 139–148. RSPB, Sandy.

THOMSON, D.L., GREEN, R.E., GREGORY, R.D. & BAILLIE, S.R. (1998a) The widespread declines of songbirds in rural Britain do not correlate with the spread of their avian predators. *Proceedings of the Royal Society of London (B)*, 265: 2057–2062.

THOMSON, D.L., MONAGHAN, P. & FURNESS, R.W. (1998b) The demands of incubation and avian clutch size. *Biological Review*, 73: 293–304.

THORBURN, N. (1954) Skylark's nest with two eggs in turnip field. *Field Naturalist* (1954): 4.

TICEHURST, C.B. (1932) *Birds of Suffolk.* Gurney & Jackson, London.

TIELEMAN, B.I. (2002) *Avian Adaptation Along an Aridity Gradient: Physiology, Behavior and Life History.* PhD thesis, University of Groningen.

TIELEMAN, B.I., WILLIAMS, J.B., MICHAELI, G. & PINSHOW, B. (1999) The role of the nasal passages in the water economy of crested larks and desert larks. *Physiological and Biochemical Zoology*, 72: 219–226.

TIELEMAN, B.I., WILLIAMS, J.B. & BUSCHUR, M.E. (2002) Physiological adjustments to arid and mesic environments in larks (Alaudidae). *Physiological and Biochemical Zoology*, 75: 305–313.

TOEPFER, S. & STUBBE, M. (2001) Territory density of the Skylark (*Alauda arvensis*) in relation to field vegetation in central Germany. *Journal für Ornithologie*, 142: 184–194.

TOMEK, T. (1990) Subfossil bird remains from Polish Tatra Mountains. *Przeglad Zoologiczny*, 33: 607–612.

TRYJANOWSKI, P. (1995a) [Autumn diet of the Skylark (*Alauda arvensis*)]. *Notatki Ornitologiczne*, 36: 176–178.

TRYJANOWSKI, P. (1995b) Gastrolith numbers in the Skylark *Alauda arvensis*. *International Studies of Sparrows*, 20–21: 41–42.

TRYJANOWSKI, P. (2000a) Ground song of the Skylark *Alauda arvensis*: frequency, temporal distribution and habitat dependence. *Vogelwelt*, 121: 49–50.

TRYJANOWSKI, P. (2000b) Changes in breeding populations of some farmland birds in W Poland in relation to changes in crop structure, weather conditions and number of predators. *Folia Zoologica*, 49: 305–315.

TRYJANOWSKI, P. (2001) Proximity of raven (*Corvus corax*) nest modifies breeding bird community in an intensively used farmland. *Annales Zoologici Fennici*, 38: 131–138.

TRYJANOWSKI, P., GOŁDYN, B. & SURMACKI, A. (2002a) Influence of the red fox (*Vulpes vulpes*, L. 1758) on the distribution and number of breeding birds in an intensively used farmland. *Ecological Research*, 17: 395–399.

TRYJANOWSKI, P., KUZNIAK, S. & SPARKS, T. (2002b) Earlier arrival of some farmland migrants in western Poland. *Ibis*, 144: 62–68.

TUCKER, G.M. (1997) Priorities for bird conservation in Europe: the importance of the farmed landscape. In: Pain, D.J. & Pienkowski, M.W. (eds) *Farming and Birds in Europe: the Common Agricultural Policy and its Implications for Bird Conservation*, 79–116. Academic Press, London.

TUCKER, G.M. & HEATH, M.F. (1994) *Birds in Europe: their conservation status.* BirdLife International, Cambridge.

VAUK, G. (1972) Welches Geschlecht haben in W-Deutschland überwintnde Feldlerchen (*Alauda arvensis*)? *Journal für Ornithologie*, 113: 105–106.

VERBEEK, N.A.M. (1988) Development of a stable body temperature and growth rates in nestlings of three ground nesting passerines in alpine tundra. *Journal für Ornithologie*, 129: 449–456.

VICKERY, J.A. & BUCKINGHAM, D.L. (2001) The value of set-aside for skylarks *Alauda arvensis* in Britain. In: Donald, P.F. & Vickery, J.A. (eds) *The Ecology and Conservation of Skylarks* Alauda arvensis, 161–175. RSPB, Sandy.

VICKERY, J.A, TALLOWIN, J.R., FEBER, R.E., ASTERAKI, E.J., ATKINSON, P.W., FULLER, R.J. & BROWN, V.K. (2001) The management of lowland neutral grasslands in Britain: effects of agricultural practices on birds and their food resources. *Journal of Applied Ecology*, 38: 647–664.

WAKEHAM-DAWSON, A. & AEBISCHER, N.J. (1998) Factors determining winter densities of birds on Environmentally Sensitive Area arable reversion grassland in southern England, with special reference to skylarks (*Alauda arvensis*). *Agriculture, Ecosystems and Environment*, 70: 189–201.

WAKEHAM-DAWSON, A. & AEBISCHER, N.J. (2001) Management of grassland for skylarks *Alauda arvensis* in downland Environmentally Sensitive Areas in southern England. In: Donald, P.F. & Vickery, J.A. (eds) *The ecology and conservation of skylarks* Alauda arvensis, 189–201. RSPB, Sandy.

WAKEHAM-DAWSON, A. & SMITH, K.W. (2000) Birds and lowland grassland management practices in the UK: an overview. In: Aebischer, N.J., Evans, A.D., Grice, P.V. & Vickery, J.A. (eds) *Ecology and Conservation of Lowland Farmland Birds*, 77–88. BOU, Tring.

WAKEHAM-DAWSON, A., SZOSZKIEWICZ, K., STERN, K. & AEBISCHER, N.J. (1998) Breeding skylarks *Alauda arvensis* on Environmentally Sensitive Area arable reversion grass in southern England: survey-based and experimental determination of density. *Journal of Applied Ecology*, 35: 635–648.

WALPOLE-BOND, J. (1938) *A History of Sussex Birds.* Witherby, London.

WALTERS, J. (1972) Double-yolked egg of skylark. *British Birds*, 65: 400.

WATKINSON, A.R., FRECKLETON, R.P., ROBINSON, R.A. & SUTHERLAND, W.J. (2000) Predictions of biodiversity response to genetically modified herbicide-tolerant crops. *Science*, 289: 1554–1557.

WEIBEL, U.M. (1998) Habitat use of foraging skylarks (*Alauda arvensis* L.) in an arable landscape with wild flower strips. *Bulletin of the Geobotanical Institute ETH*, 64: 37–45.

WEIBEL, U.M. (1999) *Effects of Wildflower Strips in an Intensively Used Arable Area on Skylarks* (Alauda arvensis). Unpublished PhD thesis, Swiss Federal Institute of Technology, Zurich.

WEIBEL, U.M., JENNY, M., ZBINDEN, N. & EDWARDS, P.J. (2001) Territory size of skylarks *Alauda arvensis* on arable farmland in Switzerland in relation to habitat quality and management. In: Donald, P.F. & Vickery, J.A. (eds) *The Ecology and Conservation of Skylarks* Alauda arvensis, 177–187. RSPB, Sandy.

WERNHAM, C.V., TOMS, M.P., MARCHANT, J.H., CLARK, J.A., SIRIWARDENA, G.M. & BAILLIE, S.R. (EDS) (2002) *The Migration Atlas: Movements of the Birds of Britain and Ireland.* T. & A.D. Poyser, London.

WHITE, G. (1789) *The Natural History and Antiquities of Selborne.* B. White & Son, London.

WHITTINGHAM, M.J., WILSON, J.D. & DONALD, P.F. (2003) Do habitat association models have any generality? Predicting skylark *Alauda arvensis* abundance in different regions of southern England. *Ecography*, 26: 521–531.

WILLIAMS, J.B. (1999) Heat production and evaporative water loss of Dune Larks from the Namib Desert. *Condor*, 101: 432–438.

WILLIAMS, J.B. (2001) Energy expenditure and water flux of free-living Dune Larks in the Namib: a test of the reallocation hypothesis on a desert bird. *Functional Ecology*, 15: 175–185.

WILLIAMS, J.B., TIELEMAN, B.I. & SHOBRAK, M. (1999) Lizard burrows provide thermal refugia for larks in the Arabian Desert. *Condor*, 101: 714–717.

WILLOUGHBY, E.J. (1971) Biology of larks (Aves: Alaudidae) in the central Namib desert. *Zoologica Africana*, 6: 133–176.

WILSON, J.D. (2001) Foraging habitat selection by skylarks *Alauda arvensis* on lowland farmland during the nestling period. In: Donald, P.F. & Vickery, J.A. (eds) *The Ecology and Conservation of Skylarks* Alauda arvensis, 91–101. RSPB, Sandy.

WILSON, J.D. & FULLER, R.J. (1992) Set-aside: potential and management for wildlife. *Ecos*, 13: 24–29.

WILSON, J.D., TAYLOR, R. & MUIRHEAD, L.B. (1996) Field use by farmland birds in winter: an analysis of field type preferences using resampling methods. *Bird Study*, 43: 320–332.

WILSON, J.D., EVANS, J., BROWNE, S.J. & KING, J.R. (1997) Territory distribution and breeding success of skylarks *Alauda arvensis* on organic and intensive farmland in southern England. *Journal of Applied Ecology*, 34: 1462–1478.

WILSON, J.D., MORRIS, A.J., ARROYO, B.E., CLARK, S.C. & BRADBURY, R.B. (1999) A review of the abundance and diversity of invertebrate and plant foods of granivorous birds in northern Europe in relation to agricultural change. *Agriculture, Ecosystems and Environment*, 75: 13–30.

WITH, K.A. & WEBB, D.R. (1993) Microclimate of ground nests: the relative importance of radiative cover and wind breaks for three grassland species. *Condor*, 95: 401–413.

WOLFENDEN, I.H & PEACH, W.J. (2001) Annual survival rates of skylarks on a coastal dune system. In: Donald, P.F. & Vickery, J.A. (eds) *The Ecology and Conservation of Skylarks* Alauda arvensis, 79–89. RSPB, Sandy.

WOODS, H.E. (1950) Skylarks' nests with 'doorsteps'. *British Birds*, 43: 371.

YANES, M. & SUÁREZ, F. (1996a) Incidental nest predation and lark conservation in an Iberian semiarid shrubsteppe. *Conservation Biology*, 10: 881–887.

YANES, M. & SUÁREZ, F. (1996b) Nest mortality and lark population viability. Ardeola, 43: 57–68.

YANES, M. & SUÁREZ, F. (1997) Nest predation and reproductive traits in small passerines: a comparative approach. *Acta Oecologica*, 18: 413–426.

YANES, M., SUÁREZ, F. & MANRIQUE, J. (1991) Snail-smashing by Thekla Lark *Galerida theklae* on *Otala lactea*: foraging behaviour and prey selection. *Ardeola*, 38: 297–303.

YANES, M., HERRANZ, J. & SUÁREZ, F. (1996a) Nest microhabitat selection in larks from a European semi-arid shrubsteppe: the role of sunlight and predation. *Journal of Arid Environments*, 32: 469–478.

YANES, M., HERRANZ, J. & SUÁREZ, F. (1996b) Facultative nest-parasitism among Iberian shrubsteppe passerines. *Bird Study*, 43: 119–123.

YANES, M., HERRANZ, J., MANRIQUE, J., DEL MORAL, J.C. & SUÁREZ, F. (1997) [Nest orientation of steppe passerines]. *Doñana, Acta Vertebrata*, 24: 210–216.

YARRELL, W. (1861) *A History of British Birds*. Van Voorst, London.

YOM-TOV, Y. (2001) Global warming and body mass decline in Israeli passerine birds. *Proceedings of the Royal Society of London (B)*, 268: 947–952.

YORK, D.L., CUMMINGS, J.L., ENGEMAN, R.M. & DAVIS, J.E. (2000) Evaluation of Flight Control™ and Mesurol® as repellents to reduce horned lark (*Eremophila alpestris*) damage to lettuce seedlings. *Crop Protection*, 19: 201–203.

# Index

*Scientific equivalents to English names of plants and animals, including the world's larks, are given in Appendices 1–2*

Aardvark   25
Acclimatisation societies   207–8, 209
Adaptive radiation   16
Afghanistan   49, 54
Aggression posture   95–6
Agincourt, Battle of   179
Agricultural intensification   69, 94, 99, 103, 123, 130, 134, 135, 153, 171–201, 198–9, 226
Agri-environment schemes   200, 201
Agrochemicals *see* Fertilisers; Herbicides *and* Pesticides
Alaska   16, 37, 49, 54
Albania   68
Albinism   57
Altai region   41, 54
Altitude   64, 143, 151
Andes   18, 37
Angola   23, 26
Ants   26, 44
Aphids   177
Arabian Peninsula   45, 49
Armenia   54, 64
Australia   18, 19, 22, 49, 77, 99, 139, 207, 208–9
Austria   68
Azores   49, 138

Barley   153, 193, 201
Basal metabolic rate (BMR)   45
Bathing   47
Bear Island   49
Beetles   122, 123, 124
Belarus   67, 68
Belgium   68, 138, 147, 212, 216
Bill
   size   39
   structure   20, 36, 38, 40
Blackcaps   73

Blyton, Enid   205
Bobolink   81
Body condition   46, 81, 118, 119, 124, 160, 190, 195
Body temperature   114
Borneo   49
Botswana   26
Bowing   90
Boyle, Robert   203
Brassicas   60
Breathing rate   75
Breeding 98
   co-operative breeding   26
Breeding season   41, 98–9
Brighton   144, 216
British Trust for Ornithology (BTO)   60, 67, 107, 130, 154, 188
Bronze Age   178
Brood patch   109
Brooding   114, 124
Brown Hare   183
Bulgaria   67, 68, 169
Buntings   20, 71, 77, 148, 178, 200
Burma (Myanmar)   49, 54
Bushlark, Red-winged   22

Caecum   158
Cagebird industry   76, 77, 203, 204, 216–17, 220–1
California   49, 54
Calls
   alarm   103, 111, 114
   chick location   125, 126
   flight   56
   flock contact   159
   nest departure   116
   spectrogram   160
Calorific intake   158, 178
Camouflage   41, 114, 129

Canada   49, 107, 109, 207, 208
Cape Verde Islands   19, 28, 36, 43, 49,
    51, 84
Carrington, Edith   218
Caspian   19, 41, 54, 62
Celtic   73
Cereals   60, 62, 100, 105, 130, 134, 152,
    154, 178–86, 187
  grain   123, 153, 154, 156, 158
  yields   177, 179, 180
Chasing   89–90, 148
Chick carrying   120
Chick provisioning   114, 117, 124
Chicks   113–14
  development   43, 114–16, 118, 124, 129
  diet   38, 122–4
  dispersal   125
  growth rates   43, 46, 118, 119, 124
  weight   115–16
China   49, 54, 56, 139
Cirl Bunting   200
Cisticola warblers   20–1, 79
Clap-nets   144, 168, 212
Clare, John   97, 206–7
Climate change   107, 139, 155
Clutch
  replacement   134
  size   42, 46, 103, 104–8, 111, 129,
    188, 195
Coastal habitats   59, 62, 66, 105, 129, 130,
    134, 135, 143, 152, 154–5, 163, 189
Cold weather   41, 110, 120, 165; see also
    Winter
Collective nouns   205
Collisions with aircraft and cars   164
Common Agricultural Policy (CAP)   175,
    187, 191, 199, 200
Competition   16
Conifer plantations   35
Conservation   198–201, 210, 218, 224
Copulation   90–1
Corn Bunting   71, 77, 148, 178
Corvids   65, 130, 131
Courtship   90
Cowbirds   109
Cranes   210
Crest   36
Croatia   68
Crops
  damage   197–8, 209, 222, 224
  diversity   65, 190–2
  structure   191

  see also Genetically Modified (GM)
    crops; Root crops; Spring cereals;
    Winter cereals and under named crops
Cuckoos   107, 138
Czech Republic   67, 68, 138


Dairy farming   187
Darwin's finches   94
Dawn chorus   85
DDT   192
Defensive territory   95
Dehesas   176
Delius, Juan   75, 81, 83, 84, 87, 91,
    92–3, 95, 98, 99, 102, 103, 104, 105,
    107, 109, 111, 116, 129, 130, 134–5,
    143, 163, 169
Denmark   67, 68, 76, 84, 86, 87, 95, 122,
    123, 138, 143, 146, 147, 182, 195
Density dependence   95
Deserts   15, 18, 41, 44–7
Didsbury   218
Dieppe   217
Diet   38, 44, 156–8
Digging   32, 36, 38, 39
Display
  courtship   89–90
  distraction   110, 117
Distribution   16–19, 48–51, 59, 64–6, 172
Disturbance   102, 117–8, 126
DNA-DNA hybridisation   20
Downland   216, 217
Drainage   171
Drinking   39, 44
Droppings   156, 158, 160
Drought   44–7, 51
Dunes   84, 91, 92, 95, 98, 129, 130, 134,
    135, 143, 155, 163
Dunstable Downs   217
Duration of song   82–4, 87
Dust bathing   41, 47, 160


Egg dumping   107
Egg laying   98, 99, 103
Egg rolling   109–10
Egg theft penalties   216
Eggs   216
  abnormality   104
  colouration   42, 97, 103
  size   103–4, 112
  weight   103

Egypt   32
Electricity pylons   65
Endemism   16, 18, 19, 43
Energetics
   of incubation   111
   of song-flight   81–3, 84
English Civil War   144
Estonia   68, 108, 139
Ethiopia   16, 19, 20, 24
European Economic Community (EEC) 175
European Swallow   111, 138
European Union (EU)   169, 175, 187, 199
   Birds Directive   168
Evolution   19–21
   of song-flight   80
Extra-pair paternity   92

Faecal sacs   125
Falconry   165
Farmland   59–63, 64–6, 69, 105–7, 119,
      121, 122, 123, 125, 130, 151–5, 163,
      173, 176, 198–201
Faroe Islands   53, 68
Feathers
   growth   82
   number   52
   *see also* Plumage *and* Primaries
Feeding
   of chicks   120–6
   during incubation   110
   methods   38, 39, 156
   rates   156
Fertile Crescent   178
Fertilisers   158, 180, 189
Fidelity   92–3
Fields
   boundary structure   65
   size   65, 155, 191
Finches   20, 80
Finland   64, 68, 108, 138, 139, 143
Fledging   116–17
Flight   110, 159
   courtship   90
   foraging   121–2, 124
   migration   146–8
   song   82–3
   speed of   146, 147
Flock size   147, 148
Flocking   44, 58, 148, 150, 159, 165–6,
      197–8
Flooding   120, 129

Folklore   216, 223
Foraging
   for chicks   95, 120–5, 188
   flights   121–2, 124
   techniques   38, 47
   winter   197–8
France   53, 61–2, 67, 68, 74, 78, 99,
      108, 138, 139, 143, 146, 147, 159,
      165, 168, 169, 175, 179, 184, 188,
      212, 215, 216

Gait   29, 45, 56
Gamekeepers   131, 132, 133
Gape   114
Gastroliths   156
Geckoes   43
Geese   158
Genetically Modified (GM) crops   196–7
Gerbils   47
Germany   66, 67, 68, 69, 84, 93, 94, 95,
      99, 108, 122, 129, 136, 138, 140,
      142, 148, 163, 166, 171–3, 175, 179,
      210, 223, 224
Gibraltar   53, 138, 139
Gondwanaland   19
Grass leys   192
Grasshoppers   123–4
Grassland   19, 59, 60, 61, 63, 105, 123,
      129, 133, 134, 151, 154, 157,
      188–90
Grazing   60, 61, 62, 129, 152, 158,
      189–90
Great Bustard   210
Great Grey Shrike   65, 167
Greece   68, 168, 169
Greenfinch   80
Grey Partridge   193
Ground song   75, 86
Guernsey   68

Habitats   16, 18–19, 59–63, 176
   diversity   95, 191
   preferences   47, 151–6, 191
   structure   122
Hard weather *see* Cold weather *and* Winter
Harrods   223
Harvesting of crops   179
Hatching   111
   failure   111
Hawaii   49, 53, 207, 208

Head scratching behaviour   20
Heathland   59
Hedgerows   190–2
Height of crops/vegetation *see* Vegetation
    height
Height of flight
    migration flight   146
    song flight   82–3
Heligoland   137, 140–1, 142, 148
Hen Harrier   158, 166
Herbicides   153, 193, 196
Hind claw   24, 26, 40, 52–3
Hobby   165, 166, 212–13
Hoopoe-Lark   28, 38, 45
Hoopoe-Lark, Lesser   28
Hopping   90
Hudson, William Henry   218
Hungary   68, 169
Hunting   71, 139, 149, 162, 164, 165,
    167–70, 210–15, 216

Iceland   49, 59
Identification   55–7
Incubation   27, 109, 111
    breaks from   110
    period of   87, 109
    self-incubation   42
India   27, 28, 34, 49, 54, 139
Indonesia   22
Infidelity   91, 92
Introduced populations   207–10
Iran   49, 54
Iraq   178, 198
Ireland   53, 54, 68, 143, 147
Isle of Man   68
Israel   46, 47, 54
Italy   39, 53, 67, 68, 69, 138, 139, 146,
    148, 149, 162, 168–9, 175, 214, 216,
    222
Ivory Coast   23

Japan   49, 54, 56, 83, 153
Jersey   68
Jordan   178

Kalahari   41, 42
Karoo   16, 41, 44
Kazakhstan   54
Kenya   16

Kestrel   64
Kleptoparasitism   38
Korea   49, 54, 56
Kurile Islands   49, 54
Kuwait   139

Lake Baikal   18, 62, 70, 139
Lammergier   28
Lapwing   80
Lark, Archer's   19, 24
Lark, Ash's   19
Lark, Barlow's   21
Lark, Bar-tailed   27
Lark, Beesley's   26
Lark, Bimaculated   30
Lark, Black   29, 30, 39
Lark, Botha's   19
Lark, Calandra   30, 198
Lark, Cape Long-billed   25
Lark, Clapper   23
Lark, Crested   34, 46, 47, 64
Lark, Degodi   19
Lark, Desert   27, 41, 42, 44, 47
Lark, Dune   18, 25, 41, 42–3, 44, 46, 111
Lark, Dunn's   32, 45
Lark, Dupont's   32, 33
Lark, Dusky   23
Lark, Flappet   23, 77, 79
Lark, Gray's   27, 28, 44
Lark, Greater Short-toed   30, 31, 47
Lark, Horned   16, 18, 37, 41, 42, 59,
    165, 198
Lark, Karoo   21
Lark, Large-billed   34
Lark, Lesser Short-toed   47
Lark, Malabar   34
Lark, Masked   31
Lark, Melodious   22–3
Lark, Obbia   31
Lark, Raso   16, 19, 35, 36, 39, 43, 46,
    49, 51, 57, 84, 94
Lark, Red   40
Lark, Red-Capped   30
Lark, Rudds   19, 24
Lark, Rufous-naped   22
Lark, Rufous-rumped   23
Lark, Rufous-tailed   27
Lark, Sclater's   42
Lark, Short-Tailed   34
Lark, Sidamo   24
Lark, Somali Short-toed   31

Lark, Spike-heeled   25, 26
Lark, Stark's   32
Lark, Sun   34
Lark, Tawny   34
Lark, Temminck's Horned   37
Lark, Thekla   33, 34, 64
Lark, Thick-billed   29
Lark, Tibetan   30
Lark mirror (lark glass)   213–15
Lark Star   212
Latin names   21, 73
Latvia   67, 68, 70
Lavender   61
Laverock   121, 204
Laying   98, 99, 103
Leaving the nest   116–17
Legal protection   169, 216, 218, 225
Legumes   60
Leipzig   210, 224
Liechenstein   68
Lighthouses   140–1, 143, 144, 161
Linseed   61–2
Lithuania   67, 68
Local movements   93, 143
Local names   121
London Markets   51, 216–22
Longevity   163, 164, 167
Low-belling   211
Lucerne   62, 153
Luxembourg   68

Madagascar   18, 22
Madeira   49, 138
Mali   31
Marsh warbler   73
Mate abandonment   120
Mate guarding   84, 92
Mauritania   138
Mayhew, Henry   221
Merlin   78–9, 162, 165, 166, 168, 170
Metabolic water   45, 46
Midway Atoll   49
Migration   39, 44, 93, 137–40, 169, 213
Migratory flight   146–8
Mimicry   22–3, 76–7
Minimum power speed   83
Miocene   20
Mixed farming   201
Moldova   68
Mongolia   139
Moon   147

Moorland   59, 61, 62, 105, 133
Morocco   32
Mortality   162–70
Moult   20, 82, 86–7
Movements   138, 140–6
Mowing of grass   129, 187, 190, 194, 201

Namib Desert   27, 41, 47, 111
Namibia   16, 26
Natal philapatry   93
Nature reserves   43, 131
Navigation   147
Negev   47
Nepal   49
Nesting   98–9
   number of attempts   133–6, 186, 188, 190
Nests   97, 101
   building   41–2, 100–3
   failure   41, 128, 184
   orientation   42
   parasitism   107
   predation/predators   42–3, 51, 183–4, 190
   productivity   104, 127, 133–6, 190
   rampart   42, 102
   scrape   101–2; *see also* 'Skylark scrapes'
   sites   43, 66, 182–5
   structure   66
   survival rates   46, 129, 131, 133, 185
Netherlands   66, 68, 104, 108, 138, 143, 148, 161, 166
New Zealand   18, 49, 53, 62, 99, 129, 139, 153, 199, 207–8, 209–10
Nightingale   73
Noise pollution   66
Nomadism   44, 144, 148, 159, 161
Norfolk   51, 84, 103, 124, 131, 133, 154, 155, 191, 225
North America   16, 18
North Atlantic Oscillation (NAO)   140
Norway   68, 139, 140, 143

Oats   100, 153, 158
Oilseed rape   152
Organic farming   122, 189, 194–5, 201

Pakistan   54
Parachuting   83

Parasites  47, 120
Parental care  117–18
Paris  216
Peregrine  79, 165, 166
Persecution  210–15
Pessulus  20
Pesticides  112, 119, 123, 130, 167, 177,
    178, 187, 192–6, 199, 201
Philippines  49, 54
Pipits  95, 107, 114
Pleistocene  20
Pliocene  20
Ploughing  179
Plumage  28
  colouration  41, 55, 56–7, 73
  dimorphism  29, 38–9
  maintenance  47
  variation  35, 41, 53–4
Poetry  72, 96, 203, 204, 205–7, 220–1,
    225
Poland  64–5, 67, 68, 70, 75, 86, 129,
    139, 166, 179
Politics  174–5
Population  67–71
  declines  58, 69–71, 107, 128, 135,
    142, 151, 167, 173–4, 190, 193
  density  64
  estimates  67–8
  recovery  176
  trends  67–71, 128
Portugal  53, 67, 68, 143
Post-natal dispersal  93
Postural behaviour  90, 95–6
Predation  128–33
Predators  43, 64–5, 127, 165–7
  avoidance of  43, 64–5, 78–9, 116,
    155, 166
  control of  131–2
Preening  109, 110
Primaries
  length  21, 39
  projection  51, 55, 56
Productivity  127–36
Provisioning rates  114, 124
Pusztas  176

Qatar  49
Quail  107

Rabbit  43
Races  53–5

Rainfall  41, 46, 102, 119, 120, 124
Raven  65
Red Fox  64, 129, 167
Replacement clutches  134
Resource partitioning  149
Return rates  93
Rice  153, 178
Ringing recoveries  93, 138, 143, 147,
    163, 164, 165
Rival conflicts  95–6
Roads  66, 122
Roman Conquest  178, 204
Romania  67, 68, 142, 169
Roosting  160
Root crops  60, 197, 198
Royal Society for the Protection of Birds
    (RSPB)  13, 70, 98, 99, 100, 103,
    107, 109, 116, 121, 129, 131, 133,
    159, 181, 218, 221, 222, 223, 224,
    225, 226
Rushes  141
Russia  49, 54, 56, 64, 67, 68, 76, 103,
    107, 108, 123, 138, 139, 146, 156
Ryukyu Islands  49

Sage  61
Sahel  23
Saltmarshes  59, 62, 66, 152, 154–5, 189
Sassoon, Siegfried  205
Savannah  18
Scutes  20
Seasonal variation in song  86–7
Seeds  44, 45, 47, 153, 178
Self-incubation  42
Selfridges  223
Senegal  138
Set-aside  59, 60, 62, 86, 103, 105, 106,
    122, 123, 130, 131, 133, 134, 157,
    187–8, 195, 200, 201
Sex identification  51, 55
Sex ratio  94, 148–9
Sexual dimorphism  29, 38–9
Shade  42, 45
Shakespeare, William  205
Siberia  18, 49, 53, 54, 62, 70, 77, 125,
    139
Sibling competition  118
Silage  189, 194, 201
*Silent Spring*  176, 192, 226
Site fidelity  92–4
Skylark  35–7, 48–9, 51–7

Skylark, Japanese  35, 49, 56–7, 85, 120
Skylark, Oriental  35, 36, 49, 54, 55–6
'Skylark scrapes'  201
Slovakia  68
Slovenia  68, 169
Snails  38
Snow  103, 138, 144, 145, 150, 151,
   160, 161
Social organisation  26
Society for the Protection of Birds (SPB)
   202, 218, 219, 221, 224
Soil moisture  64
Soil type  64
Somalia  16, 19, 24, 28, 32
Song
   dialects  77
   duel  96
   duration of  82–3, 87
   flight  56, 72–3, 75, 79–88, 170
   ground  75, 86
   nocturnal  33
   recognition  78
   seasonal variation  86–7
   spectrogram  74
   structure of  73–6
   subsong  75, 76
   territorial  75, 80, 85
   timing of  84–7
Song Thrush  38
South Africa  16, 19, 21, 24, 26, 40
Sowing  179
Spain  32, 43, 47, 53, 64, 67, 68, 131, 138
Sparrowhawk  165, 166, 167
Sparrow-lark, Grey-backed  26, 41
Sparrow-larks  27, 38, 43
Species richness  16
Spectrograms  74, 160
Spring cereals  179, 180, 181, 183, 184,
   186, 193, 200–1
Sri Lanka  49, 54
Starvation  116, 120, 124, 126, 128, 164
Steppes  18, 20, 59, 62, 64
Sternum  81
Stubbles  58, 131, 152, 153–4, 155, 157,
   158, 179, 184, 187, 192, 201
Subsong  75, 76
Subspecies  21, 26, 53–5
Sudan  23
Sugar beet  196, 198
Sunning  47
Survival  15, 44–7, 123, 151, 162
Survival rates  125, 163

Sweden  67, 68, 69, 84, 138, 139, 143,
   147
Switzerland  64, 68, 77, 93, 95, 98, 103,
   107, 108, 111, 112, 119, 120, 122,
   123, 124, 125, 129, 130, 134, 136,
   138, 163, 190, 191
Syllables  75
Syria  178
Syrinx  20

Taiga  49
Tanzania  23, 26
Tarsus  20
Tasmania  139, 198
Taxonomy  19–21
Temperature
   and chick growth  119
   and egg-laying  99, 103
   and incubation  110
   and song flight  83, 84
   *see also* Body temperature; Climate
     change; Cold weather *and* Deserts
Termites  24, 26, 44
Territoriality  44, 94–5
   and song  75, 80, 85
Territory
   density  59–63, 66, 131, 133, 134,
     178, 180–2, 188, 189, 190, 191, 194
   size  95
Theocritus  205
Thermoregulation  45, 116
Threatened species  19, 24, 26
Tibet  54
Tilled fields  152, 154, 157
Timing
   of migration  139–40
   of song  84–7
Tramlines  122, 180, 182, 183, 184, 185,
   192
Trammel-nets  211
Trampling  129, 190
Trapping  51–2, 132, 164, 211–13
Treaty of Rome  175
Tree Sparrow  69
Tundra  18
Turkestan  49
Turkey  54, 68, 148, 178

Ukraine  67, 68, 142, 146
Undersowing of cereals  192

Unpaired males   84
Uplands   143


Vagrants   49, 138, 139
Vancouver Island   16, 49, 53, 208, 210
Vegetation height   63, 100, 101, 181–2,
   187, 189
Vigilance   92


Water balance   44–6
Water resources   39; *see also* Rainfall
Weather, effect of
   on chick feeding   123, 124
   on productivity   196
   on song flight   85
   *see also* Cold weather *and* Winter
Weeds   192, 193
   leaves   156
   seeds   158, 196, 198
Weight   51, 115–16, 161

Wheat   123, 154
Wind speed   83, 84, 146
Wing-shivering   90
Wings
   beat rate   23
   length   51, 52, 146
   loading   39, 81–2, 96, 146, 149
   shape   39
Winter   38, 51, 58, 69, 77, 79, 93, 138,
   143, 144–6, 148, 150–61, 197–8,
   210, 217
Winter cereals   152, 157, 179, 180,
   181, 183, 184, 185, 186, 192, 193,
   201
Woodland   59, 66, 80, 178
Woodlark   18, 21, 35, 45, 66, 217
World War I   86, 224
World War II   174, 214
Worshipful Company of Poulters   210


Yellowhammer   160